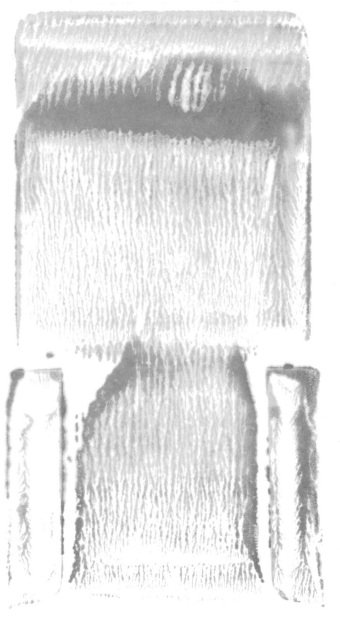

A HISTORY OF

MACHINE TOOLS
1700-1910

A HISTORY OF
MACHINE TOOLS
1700-1910

W. STEEDS

OXFORD
AT THE CLARENDON PRESS
1969

Oxford University Press, Ely House, London W. 1

GLASGOW NEW YORK TORONTO MELBOURNE WELLINGTON
CAPE TOWN SALISBURY IBADAN NAIROBI LUSAKA ADDIS ABABA
BOMBAY CALCUTTA MADRAS KARACHI LAHORE DACCA
KUALA LUMPUR SINGAPORE HONG KONG TOKYO

PRINTED IN GREAT BRITAIN
AT THE UNIVERSITY PRESS, OXFORD
BY VIVIAN RIDLER
PRINTER TO THE UNIVERSITY

FOR MY WIFE

PREFACE

This book is concerned with the development of machine tools over the period 1700 to 1910, a period that saw the machine-tool industry grow from virtually nothing to a state of maturity. I have chosen 1700 as a starting point chiefly because little material relating to earlier times is available; and the choice of 1910 as the ending date was made because, although the field then widened greatly, subsequent developments were largely matters of detail and these became too extensive for single-handed consideration. I hope, however, that this later period will be dealt with by others—perhaps a small team would be needed—since I believe that future generations will not think very highly of us if we fail to preserve for them not only records of current practice but also examples of current designs.

I have dealt only with metal-working machine tools and have excluded machines such as presses, which make use mainly of the plastic properties of the materials on which they work but are frequently regarded as being machine tools.

The whole period has been divided into manageable portions, within which I have discussed the basic types of machine tool separately. Each of the six chapters therefore covers a portion of the whole period, and in each of them there are sections covering lathes; drilling and boring machines; planers, slotters, and shapers; milling machines; gear-cutting machines; grinding machines; and miscellaneous machines.

I have, wherever possible, given references to the original sources.

I acknowledge with gratitude the help I have received from the organizations whose names occur in the text and in particular the service I have received over many years from the Librarian and library staff of the Institution of Mechanical Engineers. It will also be apparent to the reader that this book could not have been produced if I had not been able to make use of the illustrations that appeared in the pages of *The Engineer* and of *Engineering* during the last sixty years of the period covered.

CONTENTS

LIST OF PLATES

(AT END)

INTRODUCTION

THE elephant is said to be difficult to define but easy to recognize, once seen; the machine tool is difficult in both respects. To say that a machine tool is a combination of a machine and a tool is not very helpful, since the definitions of these terms are either so wide as to include many things that most mechanical engineers would say were not machine tools or so narrow as to exclude many that they would admit. It is necessary, however, to give some indication of what this book is about; put as briefly as possible, it deals with contrivances in which a cutting tool is used to bring a piece of metal to the shape, size, and degree of finish desired by the operator and which to some degree reduce the manipulative skill and physical strength he needs to achieve his object. This excludes such things as rolling-mills, coining presses, and sheet-metal working tools, in which changes of shape and size are produced by means of plastic flow in the material being formed. It is also taken to exclude such things as portable electric drills, but to admit machine tools such as simple lathes in which the tool is held and guided by the operator and in which a high degree of skill may be required of him. It also excludes all wood-working machines.

The terms used to describe machine tools and their components vary from place to place even in Britain, and they also differ between Britain and America. Some terms have also changed their meanings over the years. Thus 'broach' would, a century or so ago, have meant a tool for boring a gun, whereas now it means a tool that is pulled through a hole in order to change the shape of it— a tool that in earlier times would have been called a 'drift'. Similarly the machine now commonly called a 'vertical lathe' has, in the past, been called a 'circular planer', a 'turning and boring mill', and even a 'horizontal lathe'— the last because its work table was horizontal. The term 'capstan lathe' has a fairly definite meaning in Britain but is not used in America, where 'screw machine' is used to describe the same thing. In Britain the terms 'capstan lathe' and 'turret lathe' denote different things but they are often confused; in this book 'turret lathe' is held to include the capstan lathe unless it is essential to distinguish between them. Again, the words 'planing' and 'shaping' have often been used very loosely in connection with machine tools; in general 'planing' connotes a machine in which the cutting action is obtained by moving the work-piece past the stationary tool, whereas in 'shaping' the tool moves and the work stands still. But it has in the past been common to use the terms 'wall planer' and 'side planer' for machines in which the tools moved; and similarly gear-cutting machines in which the tools moved have been called 'gear planers'. In this book the commonly accepted modern usage has been adhered to as far as possible but the descriptions used by the makers have, in general, been retained.

The assignment of dates for the first appearance of the various types and models of machine tools is often very difficult, and quite commonly when dates are ascribed there is disagreement between different writers. The dates quoted in this book must not, therefore, be taken too literally. Nor must too much weight be attached to the names quoted as the inventors of new types of machine tool, since it is often as difficult to say who invented something as to say when it was invented. Furthermore, the same invention has frequently been made by more than one person in places widely separated and at different times, but still quite independently.

As far as possible the illustrations have been taken from sources current at the time of the production of the machine described, since this, in itself, is an indication of the date when the machine was made. This has sometimes meant that the quality of the reproduction is not as high as might be desired, despite the considerable efforts of the publishers towards achieving a better result. It has, however, been thought better to give these contemporary pictures rather than modern reconstructions of them. This difficulty is generally greater for the period 1890–1910 than for the earlier periods, since before 1890 the illustrations in journals and books are chiefly woodcuts or engravings, which generally reproduce very well, whereas from 1890 onwards they are half-tones, which are much more difficult to reproduce. The sources and dates of publication of the illustrations are quoted wherever possible.

1

The Period up to 1700

IT is not known when the first machine tool was made, but objects that appear to have been machined in a lathe have been dated by archaeologists as early as 1500 B.C.; and there are wall paintings and sculptured friezes which show that implements, such as the bow-drill and a whole range of hand tools, were in use some hundreds of years before the Christian era.

The earliest known illustration of a lathe is in a book written in A.D. 1395;[1] this shows a *pole lathe* similar to but more primitive than that shown in Plate 3, which is said to have been made about 1800. In the earlier illustration the driving cord is shown encircling the work at its right-hand end, and it is also shown in that position in some of the illustrations given by Le P. C. Plumier in his book *L'art de tourner en perfection*, published in 1701.

Primitive pole lathes are said to be still in use in parts of Asia and did not disappear in Europe until the nineteenth century. Improvements such as treadle and crank operation were, however, introduced. Machines depicted in some of Leonardo da Vinci's drawings show that the principles underlying the cutting of screw threads were understood at the end of the fifteenth century. But it is not known whether Leonardo's illustrations depict machines that were actually made or whether they are simply examples of his own inventive genius.

Hardly any actual machine tools that were made before the beginning of the eighteenth century have survived but one is shown in Plate 1a. This is a clock-wheel cutting machine and is now in the Science Museum, South Kensington. It is said to have been made about 1672. However, in Plumier's book there are many illustrations that show the state to which the lathe had been brought in 1700.

The lathe

One of the most important advances was the introduction of screw-cutting in the lathe. The method used up to the middle of the eighteenth century employed a master screw, which originally was made by hand and was copied in a form of lathe known as a *mandrel lathe*. A good idea of this is given by Plate 2, which reproduces one of Plumier's illustrations. A mandrel B is supported at its ends in the members A and C so that it can rotate about its axis. For ordinary turning the mandrel is prevented from moving axially by the member shown *in situ* at a and enlarged at M. This member is engaged with the groove 2 of the mandrel H; a similar member engages the bearing 3 and the two members are then dropped into recesses formed in the faces of the supports A and C. The workpiece is screwed to the overhanging end of the mandrel. The tools used in such lathes were fitted with long wooden handles and were supported at the cutting end by a simple rest such as is seen at D. For screw-cutting the member M was removed and one of the pieces b, which are similar in form to M but whose recesses have threads formed in them, was engaged with the appropriate screwed portion of the end of the mandrel. The lathe therefore merely copied an existing thread just as present-day lathes do. Only short lengths of thread could be cut and the accuracy achieved would undoubtedly be of a low order. Plumier does not indicate in this illustration the method of driving the work; for turning, a cord that encircled the mandrel may have been used, as in the pole lathe; a bow might have been used for screw-cutting.

The mandrel lathe does not originate a screw thread but only enables an existing one to be copied. One of the first machines for originating a thread was that of La Lievre. In this the tool was held in a holder that could slide parallel to the axis of the spindle of the machine; this motion was produced by what would nowadays be called a 'sine-bar'. The latter took the form of a plate that could move perpendicular to the spindle axis and whose edge was inclined at an angle suitable to the pitch of the thread being cut. The plate had a rack attached to it and this engaged a spur gear carried by the spindle. Since the length of the sine-bar that could be used was limited, only short screws could be cut by this method. An improved version of this machine was made by Gideon Duval about 1763.[2] In the early years of the nineteenth century Maudslay was much interested in the problem of originating screw threads and devised some ingenious methods of doing this.

It is obvious that considerable skill is necessary to achieve any satisfactory result in such a primitive machine as that illustrated in Plate 2, but some of the illustrations given by Plumier show most complex and intricate pieces. The material worked in these machines was usually wood or ivory, but Plumier specifically mentions the turning of iron and illustrates a form of tool and tool rest suitable for it.

The bulk of the components of the lathes themselves were made of wood and it was not until the end of the eighteenth century that metal construction became common.

One of the chief drawbacks of the pole-and-cord method of driving the work in the lathe was that only the motion in one direction could be used; the return motion was idle. This drawback was eliminated by the use of a treadle-and-crank drive, a method that was known to Leonardo da Vinci and became common during the eighteenth century. Another solution was to use a driving wheel that is separate from the lathe, as is shown in the background at the right in Plate 4. (In this position it could be used instead of the cord-and-pole drive to drive the lathe seen in the foreground.) A heavy fly-wheel is carried in bearings in a frame and is rotated by an assistant (or sometimes two) by means of a crank handle; the fly-wheel has a pulley attached to it and a cord runs from this to a pulley fixed to the spindle of the lathe or, when the work was carried on centres, runs round a cylindrical part of the work itself. The use of a separately mounted fly-wheel drive to a lathe is, however, mentioned in a book published in 1568.³ The arrangement shown in Diderot's illustration (Plate 4) was capable also of giving an alternating forwards and backwards motion to the work for screw-cutting.

An elegant type of drive is illustrated by Plumier. In this the fly-wheel and pulley were carried in a frame placed near the ceiling of the work-room and pivoted on bearings fixed to the wall behind the operator. The other end of the frame rested on a second frame. This second frame could slide vertically in guideways formed in two uprights at the rear of the lathe and could be moved up and down by a jack screw working in a fixed nut so that the tension of the driving cord could be adjusted. The overhead shaft projected through its bearing at one end and was furnished with a crank arm to which a cord was attached. By pulling intermittently on the cord the shaft and work could be given a continuous rotation. The lower end of the cord attached to the crank may have been attached to a treadle as in a pole lathe, but this is not shown in Plumier's illustration.

Gun-boring machines

Little information is available about the gun-boring machines used before 1700, if indeed there were any. The method adopted was to mount a cutter head on the end of a long bar that was rotated, sometimes by hand and sometimes by animal or water power, so as to clean up the rough bore left by the casting process. The longitudinal feed was given to the gun, which was secured to a carriage or sledge that could be hauled along a primitive bed or track by means of blocks and tackle. It does not seem to have been practicable with this method to bore a gun from the solid; in any case, a sounder casting could probably be obtained when a core was used. The earliest reliable information on improved

3

methods and machines relates to the first half of the eighteenth century and is therefore considered in the next chapter.

Although it seems probable that some form of drilling machine had been produced before 1700, none has survived and there are no illustrations of any. The planing machine also was not thought of but the germ of the idea was, perhaps, not far off. One indication of this is a machine described by Plumier that is the earliest example of a machine tool employing a linear motion for the cutting action. It therefore merits some consideration.

La machine à manche

This is the name given to the machine by Plumier, who says that it was invented by an Englishman for the purpose of machining diamond- and lozenge-shaped patterns on handles and similarly shaped articles. It is shown in Plate 5. It consists essentially of an upper frame (V in Fig. 2 of Plumier's Plate 44), along the side members of which a carriage can be moved by means of a screw, and of a lower frame (X in Fig. 3 of Plate 44) that carries the workpiece being operated upon. This workpiece is supported at its right-hand end on an adjustable dead centre and is secured at its left-hand end to a shaft that is free to rotate in bearings in the central and left-hand cross-pieces of the frame X. A weight S applied to a crank R tends to rotate this shaft and the workpiece, but this rotation is controlled by a template such as can be seen at a, C, and D, which is secured at its right-hand end to the carriage. When the carriage is moved along by the screw the projections aa of the template bear against one of the spokes of the capstan wheel F (shown in perspective at P). The carriage supports a cutting tool that can be adjusted by means of a captive thumb-nut in a direction perpendicular to the side members of the frame V. It will thus be seen that as the carriage is moved along so the work will be rotated to and fro and thus the tool will cut a zigzag groove in the workpiece. By reversing the template so that it faces the other way and by reversing the crank arm R a second groove can be cut so as to form, in conjunction with the first groove, a series of diamonds or lozenges. By indexing the work round, using another spoke of the member P, the pattern can be continued round the entire surface of the workpiece. Since the upper frame is hinged at its left-hand end and can be adjusted so that it is at an angle to the axis of the work, the work can be either cylindrical or conical.

2

1700 to 1800

THE eighteenth century saw great advances in many engineering fields and some considerable advances were made in machine tools. It seems probable, however, that the latter were mainly due to the former, whereas a century later it could be said that the opposite was true. During the decade preceding 1712 Thomas Newcomen brought his steam-engine to a satisfactory working state and from then onwards Newcomen engines were being installed in many parts of England and also abroad. In the first half of the century certain parts of these engines could be produced only with great difficulty and a large part of the work had perforce to be done by hand. The same limitation applied to the spinning and weaving machines that were then being developed, but since these could be made almost entirely of wood the lack of machine tools was not such a drawback.

The greatest and perhaps the earliest improvements in the machine-tool field during the century were made in gun-boring machines and these will be considered first.

Gun-boring machines

A gun-boring machine was installed in the Royal Arsenal at Woolwich around 1715[1] by Andrew Schalch, who was employed there and who, in 1718, became Master Founder. No details of this machine have been preserved, but it seems to have had some kind of a screw-feed since it is recorded that 'fine copper mixed with other gun-metal was issued to Mr. Schalch for the female of the great-screw of the boring engine at the Royal Foundry'. Andrew Schalch came to England from Holland, which seems to have been ahead of other countries in regard to gun-boring machines during the early years of the century. In 1713 a vertical gun-boring machine is said to have been invented by a Swiss named Maritz,[2] who later worked at the Netherlands State Gun Foundry at The Hague. Plate 6, which reproduces one of the illustrations given by Diderot in his encyclopedia, is thought to represent Maritz's machine or one made to his design. It will be seen that the cutter bar is rotated by animal power and that a downwards feed motion is given to the gun. The frame of the machine is made almost entirely of wood and forms part of the structure housing it. This use of the structure of a building to form part of a machine tool continued well into the second half of the nineteenth century.

The first boring machine in which the gun was rotated and the feed motion was given to the boring tool appears to have been produced about 1758 by another Dutchman, Jan Verbruggen, in collaboration with another Swiss, Jacob Ziegler. This machine, in which the axis of rotation of the gun was horizontal, was of massive construction and is regarded by some people as the first example of a machine tool for engineering, as distinct from ornamental and artistic, use. A replica is on show in the Dutch Military Museum at Leiden.[3]

Boring machines were in use at the famous Coalbrookdale works in 1723 and others were installed there in 1734 and 1740[4] but there is no information about their construction. They were probably similar to gun-boring machines, although initially they were used for other purposes and only some time later for boring guns.

The chief source of information on gun-boring machines during the eighteenth century is undoubtedly Gaspard Monge's *L'art de fabriquer les canons*. Monge produced his book at the instigation of the Committee of Public Safety of the French Revolution and it was published in 1794. It is a comprehensive review of the methods and equipment available for the making of guns and it covers all aspects of their manufacture. The machine tools illustrated and described in this book were almost certainly designed and built many years prior to the date of publication but definite dates cannot, unfortunately, be assigned to them. As the book seems to have been produced in order to stimulate the production of guns throughout France, it is possible that some of the drawings given in it are only intended to illustrate possible arrangements and adaptations of existing installations. As will be seen from the machines described below, considerable emphasis is placed on the production of guns in large numbers.

A four-station gun-boring machine

The machine shown in Plate 7 is similar to that of Maritz in many respects but differs fundamentally in that the guns are rotated and not the cutter bars. The gun castings are held in some form of chuck at their muzzle ends and are driven from their upper ends, where they are bolted up to gear wheels driven from a central pinion. This pinion is carried on the upper end of the central shaft of the machine, at the lower end of which arrangements are provided to harness the animals that turn the shaft. The feed motion was given to the boring bar through a lever by means of a dead weight, which acted through a rope and pulleys. The fulcrum of the lever had to be moved upwards as boring proceeded and the free end of the rope had to be hauled up at intervals in order to keep the weight in position. A capstan was provided for this purpose. The feed motions for the four stations were independent.

A two-station horizontal machine

Boring machines in which the work axis was horizontal were more popular for gun-boring than those in which the axis was vertical and eventually displaced them altogether. An example given by Monge is shown in Plate 8. The machine is double-ended and the guns are rotated by means of a horse gin through gearing. The drawing shows a lantern-gear meshing with an inserted tooth-spur wheel on the left-hand side and bevel gears, presumably cast, on the right-hand side, but it is not likely that different forms of gearing were used in any one machine and the two forms are probably shown as alternatives, the most convenient form being used in any particular installation. The feed motion is now imparted to the sliding head, which carries the outer end of the boring bar, by means of a rack and pinion. The pinion is still operated either by a dead weight on the lines of the previous machine or by means of a large capstan mounted directly on the end of the pinion shaft.

Monge also describes a four-station horizontal machine in which the guns are driven by a water-wheel whose shaft carries a pinion situated at the middle of a train of five gears (including the pinion). This resulted in the rotation of the guns on the outer stations being contrary to that of the inner guns and left- and right-handed cutters were therefore required.

Gun-boring tools

The cutters used in these gun-boring machines are described by both Diderot and Monge and are of some interest. One of Monge's plates is reproduced as Plate 9. The cutter, shown in the two elevations and the end view at the left, is suitable for initiating a hole in the solid and consists essentially of a combination of a spade drill with two boring cutters. The other cutters shown are only suitable for enlarging and cleaning up an existing hole, that shown in the two views at the right being used for cleaning up the blind end of the bore. It is of some interest to note that the actual cutting portions are separate renewable bits.

Before leaving the gun-boring machines it is convenient to consider two other machines used in the manufacture of guns which are also described by Monge.

7

These are shown in Plates 10*a* and 10*b*. The first is for drilling the touch hole and shows that late in the eighteenth century the bow-drill was still regarded as a suitable form of drill. The second shows a hand-operated device for cleaning up the trunnions of the gun. It employs a hollow facing cutter shown in detail in Fig. 4 of the illustration.

Cylinder-boring machines

The gun-boring machines of the eighteenth century could cope with the small-diameter cylinders required for pumps and with similar work and they produced cylinders sufficiently accurate for the Newcomen engines being built in increasing numbers during the middle years of the century. They could not, however, meet the demands for the greater accuracy that Watt required for his engines. The early machines employed a cutter head secured to the end of a bar that was rotated, usually by water power, while the cylinder casting was secured to a sledge that could be hauled along rails. Because of the great weight of the cutter head and the impracticability of supporting it by means of rubbing pads it was virtually impossible to produce accurate results. An improvement was made, about 1770, by Smeaton, who supported the greater part of the weight of the cutter head by means of a dead weight on the end of a lever mounted on a small wheeled carriage; but as the carriage ran on the unmachined surface of the cylinder this was no great improvement. The accuracy required by Watt and others for the improved forms of steam-engines was not attained until John Wilkinson built his famous boring mill at the Bersham Ironworks in 1775.

The general arrangement of this mill is shown in Fig. 1, taken from a paper given by E. A. Forward to the Newcomen Society in 1924 and copied by him from an original made by one Jno. Gilpin at some time before 1795; the original is now in the Watt Collection in the museum at Birmingham. The machine has four stations, the one at the bottom of the drawing on the right being a primitive lathe with a wooden bed, the second, on the opposite side and also at the bottom, is another lathe, probably for facing and turning large disc-like articles, while the remaining two stations are boring machines employing Wilkinson's new boring bar. The great feature of this was that it was supported in bearings at both ends. The cutter head travelled along the bar and was connected by a lug passing through a slot in the bar, which was hollow, to an inside member that was free to rotate on the end of a bar. Rotation of the bar was prevented by the cross head seen resting on the supports beyond the end of the cylinder. The bar was coupled to a rack, which meshed with a pinion, and the automatic feed was provided by a lever and weight which would have had to be frequently adjusted.

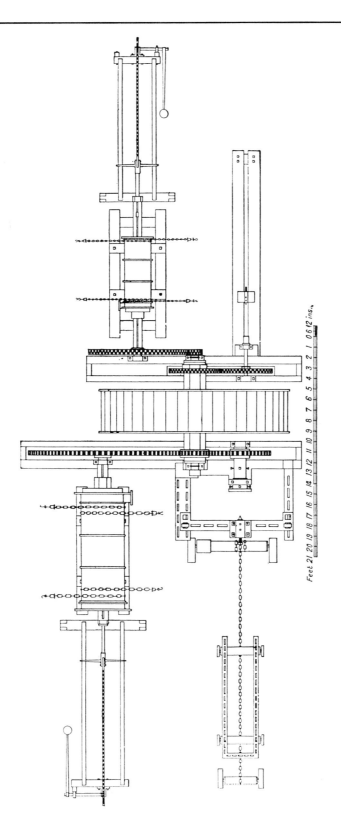

FIG. 1. Bersham boring mill *c.* 1775. *Trans. Newcomen Soc.*, vol. 5, 1924–5

The Wilkinson principle was quickly adopted by others and soon became common. Mr. Forward records that mills built on Wilkinson's plan were being installed at Coalbrookdale in 1780, by Banks & Onions at Birmingham in 1781, by Hornblowers in 1782, and by the Eagle Foundry at Birmingham in 1792. William Murdock is supposed to have built a horizontal cylinder-boring machine at the Soho Foundry in 1799.

Matthew Murray was also a builder of cylinder-boring machines and one that Forward thought might have been made in 1795, or shortly afterwards, is shown in Fig. 2. It is thought to be the first example of a cylinder-boring machine (as

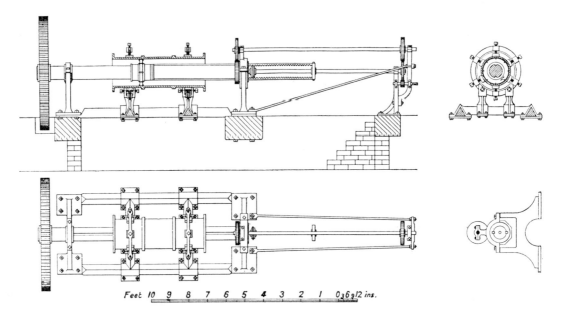

Feet 10 9 8 7 6 5 4 3 2 1 0 3 6 9 12 ins.

FIG. 2. Matthew Murray's boring machine 1817. *Trans. Newcomen Soc.*, vol. 5, 1924–5

distinct from a gun-boring lathe) that was fitted with a continuously acting feed mechanism. This was obtained by means of the two racks, which really constitute portions of a very long nut and are fixed to the cutter head. A short length of a screw, that functions as a worm, engages the teeth of the racks and is driven by the gearing, so that the difference between the speeds of the bar and the screw provides a suitable feed rate.

Lathes

At the beginning of the eighteenth century the lathe was made almost entirely of wood; it had no slide-rest and no self-acting feeds and only short screw threads could be cut on it; the accuracy attainable was poor and considerable skill was required to obtain any satisfactory results. At the end of the century

10

wood was becoming an anachronism as a material for components of lathes, the slide-rest had become almost an indispensable fitment, and lead-screws were the established method of screw-cutting.

This progress did not, however, occur uniformly throughout the century. Major improvements occurred only during the second half, improvements made in the first half being confined to the realm of what may, for convenience, be called the *ornamental* type of lathe. This term covers the lathes whose main purpose was to produce ornamental line patterns on the surfaces of objects, to turn intricate shapes in wood, ivory, and other materials, and to produce copies, sometimes to a different scale, of medallions and similar sculptured pieces.

Ornamental lathes

A few ornamental lathes will be described in order to show the progress made between Plumier's time and the middle of the eighteenth century.

The machine shown in Plate 1*b* is one that has been preserved and is now in the museum of the Conservatoire National des Arts et Métiers in Paris. In the catalogue of the museum it is described as a *Tour à portrait*. It was made by a Russian craftsman named Andréa Konstantinovich Nartov and was given by Peter the Great, in 1717, to a Frenchman with whom he had stayed during his sojourn in France.

The main frame of the machine is still made of wood but all the working parts are of metal and both the design and the workmanship are of a high standard. The horizontal spindle is carried in bearings at the top of an H-shaped sub-frame, which is pivoted at the bottom to the main frame so that the spindle can move to and fro in a direction perpendicular to its axis. It is also free to move axially in its bearings and is driven by means of a hand crank through the crossed belt that is clearly visible. The object being copied, which it will be convenient to call the medallion, is secured to a faceplate at the right-hand end of the spindle, and the workpiece or blank is secured to the left-hand end. A tracer is carried in a slide at the right-hand end of the machine so that the point of the tracer can be moved outwards radially relative to the spindle; the tool is carried in a similar slide at the other end. Both slides are drawn outwards by chains, which are attached to them and embrace pulleys mounted on a shaft lying at the back of the machine with its axis parallel to that of the spindle. This back shaft is given a slow-feed motion from the crank handle through reduction gearing, some of which can be seen in the lower part of the machine. By making the pulleys of different sizes the motion of the tool can be made to have any desired ratio to that of the tracer.

When copying the face of the medallion the H frame is locked in position and the tracer and tool are brought to the centre position where they are coincident with the spindle axis. The crank hand is then rotated so that the spindle rotates and the tracer and tool are gradually drawn outwards radially. The spindle is urged to the right by a spring carried in the small drum seen in the middle foreground, and as the medallion moves past the tracer the spindle is moved to and fro axially. The tool thus copies the medallion but produces a counterpart and not a replica of it, since a projection on the medallion will move the spindle to the left and the tool will produce a depression on the workpiece. It will also be seen that the ratio between the dimensions of the medallion and those of the workpiece in the axial direction will always be 1 to 1. A considerable number of cuts would have to be taken in this way in order to bring the work to a finished state.

For reproducing the features on the edge of the medallion a second tracer and a second tool are arranged in slides that are perpendicular to the spindle axis. The slides can be seen at the top in the illustration. They are actuated by chains and pulleys, the latter being carried on short shafts lying at right angles to the back shaft from which they are driven. Again the ratio between the motions can be varied by varying the sizes of the pulleys. When the peripheries are being copied the H frame must be unlocked so that it is free to rock, and the spindle must be prevented from moving axially. It will be seen that although the axial dimensions on the periphery can be reproduced at any desired ratio the radial dimensions will always be 1 to 1.

Another ornamental lathe

A second example of the ornamental type of lathe is shown in Plate 11*a*. It is now in the Science Museum and is thought to have been made in France about 1740. The bed of the lathe is made of metal and consists of two rectangular bars, fixed together and to the wooden supporting bench by brass castings. The spindle of the lathe is free to slide in white metal bearings in a massive metal headstock, which can rock about an axis parallel to that of the spindle and lying between the bars of the bed. Means are provided for locking the headstock in its central position, and the spindle is normally held to the left by a spring.

The spindle has three threaded portions at its left-hand end and these can be engaged by half-nuts formed on levers placed below. Thus threads can be cut as in a mandrel lathe. At its centre the spindle carries a number of rosettes or cam-discs; these can be brought into contact with tracer fingers carried in a casting secured to the front of the headstock. A spring keeps the rosettes up against the tracers, which can be adjusted for height. At the right-hand end of

12

the machine a compound tool-slide is mounted on the bed, its height being adjustable. The tool can thus be moved both axially and transversely. The work-piece is carried in a chuck that can be offset so that the axis of the work can be placed eccentrically in relation to the spindle axis. By placing a faceplate at the left-hand end of the spindle to carry a pattern plate, and by arranging a tracer finger to bear on it, patterns may be turned on the face of a disc. The spindle is driven by hand by means of a cord, and the fly-wheel and driving-pulley assembly is adjustable on the bracket carrying it, which itself is fixed to the supporting bench.

J. A. Schega's lathe

Most of the existing examples of ornamental lathes are of French origin, but the one about to be described was made in Vienna about 1767 and is now preserved in the Deutsches Museum in Munich.

The spindle of the machine (Plate 11*b*) is again able to rock to and fro perpendicular to its axis, but this freedom is now provided by carrying its bearings in blocks that can slide in arcual guides formed in the fixed headstock. For simple turning operations this freedom must, of course, have been elimi-nated but no means for doing this are to be seen on the machine. For simple turning the spindle is driven by a crossed belt from the treadle motion but for ornamental turning a slow-speed hand drive is provided. The crank handle seen at the front of the headstock is on the end of a transverse shaft that carries two worms, one of which can mesh with the gear seen on the spindle while the other can mesh with a wheel carried on a shaft at the back. This back shaft is carried in bearings arranged at the top of two levers, which are pivoted to the base structure at their lower ends. The levers are coupled by short connecting rods to the spindle-bearing blocks. The rosettes or cams for ornamental turning are carried on the back shaft and a tracer finger is mounted on the top face of a simple rest carried by the base. The means whereby the rosettes are kept up against the tracer finger are not apparent. At the left-hand end of the machine there is a bell-crank, which is pivoted on a vertical pillar and carries a roller that could bear on a disc fixed to the end of the spindle. The second arm of the bell-crank is coupled to one end of a connecting rod by means of a primitive form of universal joint. The other end of the connecting rod is formed into an eye, which embraces a journal on the back shaft. The purpose of this arrange-ment is not known but it would seem that the rocking motion of the back shaft given by the rosettes could be converted to an axial oscillation of the spindle to enable patterns to be formed on the faces of discs. The universal joint men-tioned above is necessary to allow for the fact that the end of the bell-crank lever moves in a horizontal plane in the arc of a circle whilst the end of the connecting rod moves in a vertical plane.

There is also an indication that an index plate could be fixed to the left-hand end of the spindle.

Screw-cutting on this lathe is by the mandrel-lathe principle, the spindle being provided with three threaded portions that can engage levers pivoted in the headstock.

Considering the complexity of the headstock and spindle assembly it is somewhat surprising that only a simple hand-rest is provided for the tools. An interesting feature is that many of the nuts used in the construction of the machine are cylindrical in form and have axial holes for a pin spanner.

Before passing on to other types of lathe mention may be made of what is perhaps the most elaborate example of the ornamental lathe. It was made about 1780 by I. T. Mercklein, who seems to have been a native of Saxony, and it is now in the Musée des Arts et Métiers in Paris. In addition to the usual features of the ornamental lathe this one was provided with fly cutters whose speed bore a definite relation to that of the workpiece, so that epicycloidal and similar patterns could be cut.

Tool and slide rests

The practice of using cutting tools that were held by hand on a simple rest continued throughout most of the eighteenth century and is still current today in woodworking lathes, but the use of a rest, in which the tool was secured and which provided some adjustment for the position of the tool, had become common by the end of the century and originated much earlier. An illustration in a manuscript dated 1480 shows a tool rest consisting of a lower member that can be fixed to the bed of the lathe and is provided with a dovetail in its upper surface in which a second member, carrying the tool, can be moved in and out by means of a screw.[5]

In Diderot's encyclopedia there are several illustrations of tool rests for lathes. One of them, which was used on a lathe for turning patterns on gold and silver plate-ware, is shown in Plate 12. The uppermost slide carries the tool and also a roller follower, which is kept up against the template being copied by means of a calliper-type spring. It moves in a dovetail formed in the middle member of the rest. This middle member moves axially in relation to the work and is screw operated. Another dovetail slide between the middle and the base member is also screw operated and is situated radially. The whole rest can be adjusted along a slot formed in the bed of the lathe and can be secured in place by a bolt whose head fits in the square dovetail seen in the bottom of the base member.

14

The template is formed on the inside of an annular member placed at the outside of the faceplate to which the work is fixed, and so the work is turned to a shape that is a direct copy, on a slightly smaller scale, of the template.

All the slides are dovetailed and the female part is formed with a loose piece at one side that can be adjusted so as to take up any backlash; screws control this adjustment and other screws lock the loose piece in place.

This tool rest was probably made before the middle of the eighteenth century and the lathe on which it is shown (in another plate) looks as if it might have been made a century earlier.

A slide rest, perhaps the first to be made in England, is shown in Fig. 3, which is taken from Robertson Buchanan's *Practical essays on mill work and other machinery* where the design is attributed to Joseph Bramah. The rest may have been made by Bramah but is thought by some people to have been the work of Henry Maudslay, in 1794. The body of the rest incorporates the dead centre and thus the assembly forms the tailstock as well as the tool rest of the lathe. The tool is secured in the end of a square-sectioned bar that can slide axially in holes formed in the upright portions of a bracket. This bracket can be swivelled on a member that can slide in the body of the assembly in a radial direction. A screw placed underneath the tool bar carries a nut that can be fixed to the bar by means of a clamp. The tool can therefore be set to turn either parallel or tapered work, and can also be adjusted radially.

Screw-cutting

The mandrel lathe, which has been mentioned as one of the earliest machines on which screw threads could be cut, had serious limitations; the length of thread that could be cut was quite small and only a limited number of pitches could be cut. A method of cutting threads in which the length of the screw could be much greater than in the mandrel lathe is shown in the foreground at the left of Diderot's illustration, Plate 4. This could, perhaps, be described as a mandrel lathe but this term generally connotes a machine in which the work was carried on the end of the mandrel and was not supported at its outer end. Thiout was responsible for an improvement to the mandrel lathe, as indicated in Fig. 4, which is self-explanatory; the date of this improvement is uncertain but must have been about 1740–50. It is perhaps worth pointing out that the arrangement of levers introduces errors into the pitch of the screw being cut, but these would be negligible in the short screws normally produced on such a machine.

The limitations mentioned above are not present when a lead-screw driven by gearing from the lathe spindle is employed, and this innovation consequently marks the beginning of a new era in lathe work. Unfortunately it is not known

15

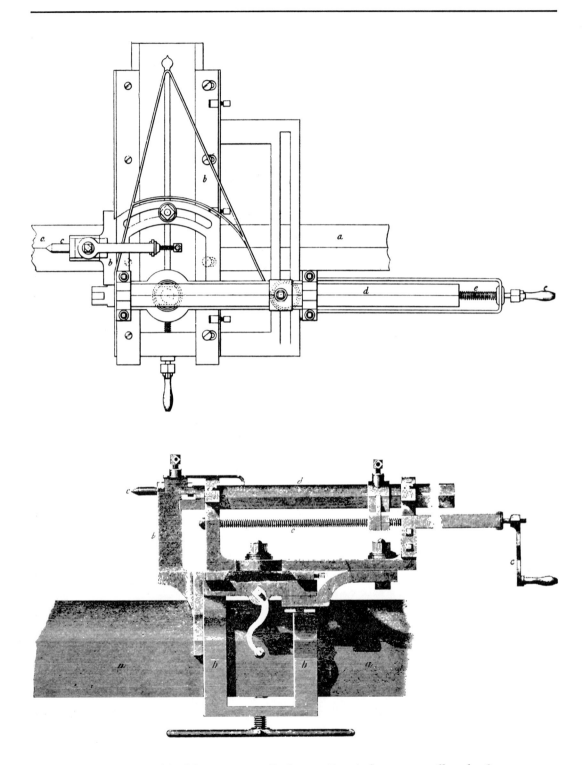

Fɪɢ. 3. Bramah's slide rest *c.* 1794. Buchanan, *Practical essays on mill work,* 1841

who made this advance or when it occurred. Leonardo da Vinci seems to have been fully aware of the principle involved and sketches a machine in which the principle was applied, but it is doubtful whether this machine was ever built. The earliest reference to the use of a geared lead-screw appears in a paper presented to the Royal Society by John Smeaton.[6] In this paper Smeaton says he 'first met Henry Hindley, the clockmaker and mechanician', in 1741 and then saw his screw-cutting lathe; he goes on '. . . [he] also showed me how, by means of the single screw on his lathe he could cut, by means of wheel-work, screws of every necessary degree of fineness (and, by taking out a wheel, could cut a left-handed screw of the very same degree of fineness).'

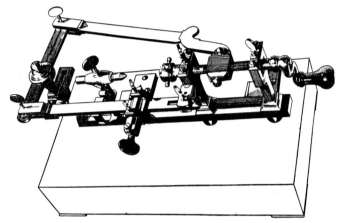

FIG. 4. Thiout's screw-cutting lathe *c.* 1740. Singer, *A history of technology*, vol. 3

There is a footnote to Smeaton's paper that appears to have been written by Smeaton himself and says that 'A machine for cutting the endless screw of Mr. Ramsden's dividing engine on principles exactly similar is fully and accurately set forth in his [Ramsden's] description of his dividing engine above mentioned'. It is a pity that no more is known about Hindley's lathes since he would seem to have possessed some machines that were out of the ordinary for his period. In a letter written by Hindley to Smeaton in 1741–2 he describes how he made and divided a brass circle that was over 2 ft 6 inches in diameter by soldering a 1-inch-wide strip of brass together at its ends and then 'turned it of equal thickness, on a block of smooth-grained wood on my great-lathe in the air' (that is, on the end of a mandrel). A lathe that would swing a piece over 2 ft 6 inches in diameter was much larger than any of the lathes preserved from that time.

Fusee-cutting machines

The fusee was invented for maintaining the torque exerted by a clock spring as the spring unwound, and the difficulties of making it in the lathes of that time stimulated the invention of several machines for the purpose. Some of these are described by Thiout in his *Treatise on Horology* and two are illustrated in Plates 13*a* and 13*b*. The first is attributed to Regnaud de Chaalon but the name of the inventor of the second is not given. The actions are fairly clear from the drawings but a few observations may be useful. The lever system of the first machine can be adjusted so as to produce a pitch on the fusee thread that is different from the thread on the mandrel, and by pivoting the lever *e* at either *P* or *R* the hand of the thread can be changed. The tool bar *H* is kept in contact with the rest *F* by a weight attached to the eye 7; the tool can be adjusted axially by means of the thumb nut *N* and locked by the thumbscrew *M*. The second machine is rather more elaborate. The thread on the mandrel moves the nut *H*, which is guided by a tongue that engages a slot cut in the frame member, and a pin at the rear end of it moves the lever *K* about a pivot at its upper end. A slot in the lever engages a block pivoted on a pin carried by the member *M*, and thus moves the sliding member *P* along. The position of the block *M*, and thus of the block that engages the slot in the lever *K*, can be adjusted by the screw *Q* and is indicated on a scale by the pointer *T*. The cutter is held in the end of the calliper member *YVZ* and is supported sideways by the member *u*. The calliper is pivoted on centres carried by the sliding member *P* and its lower arm *Z* bears on the former *W*, thereby causing the tool to follow the shape of the fusee as it moves along axially.

Ramsden's screw-cutting machines

Jesse Ramsden was one of the finest instrument-makers of the eighteenth century and made many improvements to mathematical and astronomical instruments. At some time before 1777 he designed and made an 'engine' for dividing the circular graduated scales of astronomical instruments. This engine incorporates many novel design-features and is evidence of a very high standard of workmanship. The main wheel of the engine was 45 inches in diameter and was cast in bell metal. In the account of this engine that Ramsden gave to the Commissioners of Longitude (who published it in 1777)[7] he describes how he turned this wheel on his lathe. Here again is evidence of the existence of a lathe very much larger than any of that period that have survived to the present day or of which written accounts are available. Judging from the appearance of Ramsden's instrument his lathe was certainly capable of producing excellent results.

The main wheel of the dividing engine had teeth cut on its circumference and these engaged the threads of an endless screw or worm. In order to produce this worm with the requisite degree of accuracy Ramsden designed and made a machine for the purpose; it is shown in Plate 14, which is reproduced from the paper mentioned above.

18

A triangular bar *A*, which was presumably mounted on some kind of base or bench, forms the bed of the machine and upon this the saddle *P* can slide. The saddle bears on the bed only at its ends and it is held down by clamp pieces *g*. These can be adjusted by the screws *n*. At one end of the bed a bracket *C* is fixed, while a second bracket *B* can be fixed at any desired point along the bed. These brackets provide bearings for the shaft *E* on which the worm thread is to be cut, and for the lead-screw *N*. The centre *M* forms one bearing of the lead-screw and the other is a plain journal in the bracket *C*. Both the bearings on the shaft *E* are of the double cone-type as used in the dividing engine. The shaft *E* is rotated directly by the crank handle and the lead-screw is driven through the gears *Q*, *R*, and *L*. A nut *N* embraces the lead-screw and is split so that any shake can be eliminated by tightening the screws *oo*. In order to eliminate any ill effects that might arise from misalignment of the lead-screw and the bed-way, the nut is connected to the saddle by means of two steel strips *SS*, which are pivoted at one end to the nut on pins held in the lugs *T* and at the other end are pivoted on pins *aa* of the universal joint *W* (this is shown in the scrap view *X*). The ring member of the universal joint surrounds the lead-screw and its trunnions are pivoted in holes formed in the bracket *b*. The means whereby the nut *N* is prevented from rotating on the lead-screw are not shown or described; the strips *SS* would not be effective for that purpose. The tool holder *K* is a bar of triangular section that fits in a V-groove formed on the top of the saddle, being secured by clamps *G*. Because the worm had to be hardened and tempered before the thread was cut (so as to avoid distortion in hardening) the cutting tool is a diamond secured to the end of the holder.

Ramsden's second machine

A short time after producing his circular dividing engine Ramsden designed and produced a linear one and this was also described in a paper published by the Commissioners of Longitude in 1779. In his description of the instrument Ramsden explains that a worm of greater accuracy was required for the linear than for the circular engine, and so he designed an improved machine for producing it. The general arrangement of this machine is shown in Plate 15, which is reproduced from Ramsden's paper. The bed *G* and saddle *O* of the machine are similar to those of the earlier one. The bed is fixed to the frame of the machine (not shown in the drawing) at *H* and *I* (the letter *I* is omitted from the drawing but was presumably at the right-hand end of the bed). Brackets *M* and *N* are fixed to the bed and provide bearings for the shaft *K* on which the worm is to be cut and on the end of which the gear *L* is secured. This wheel meshes with the bevel pinion *a* on the shaft *E*, and this shaft is supported in double cone-type bearings in brackets carried by the frame of the machine, which also provides the bearings for the shaft C on the upper end of which the wheel A is secured. The shaft C is 2 ft long and has a centre-point bearing at its lower end and a conical journal bearing at the upper end, close to the wheel A. The latter has a pulley fixed to it and this pulley is coupled to the saddle by a flexible steel strip t. Hence, as the crank X is turned the saddle is drawn along the bed and the shaft K is rotated. The required ratio between the rotation of the shaft and the translation of the saddle is obtained by selecting appropriate numbers of teeth for the wheels A, a, and L and a suitable diameter for the pulley B; the proper size for the pulley was determined by an experiment in order to allow for the effect of the thickness of the connecting strip. The graduated disc F, which could be locked to the shaft E when required, was needed in this experiment. The cutting tool was again a diamond, mounted on the end of a triangular bar that rested in a V-groove formed in the saddle. The depth of cut can now be adjusted by a screw S and the clamp screw V then secures the tool in place.

Vaucanson's lathe

Jacques de Vaucanson (1709–82) was a French engineer who achieved fame in several fields of engineering and made some notable advances in machine-tool design and construction, although this does not seem to have been his principal field. His lathe, shown in Plate 16a and now in the museum of the Conservatoire National des Arts et Métiers, was made during the decade 1770–80 and marks the transition from the older wooden-bed and ornamental lathe to the all-metal 'engineering' type. It could take workpieces up to 300 mm (12 in) in diameter and 1 m in length.

The bed of the machine is built up of square-section iron bars bolted together. The bed-ways, also of square section, are placed with their surfaces at $45°$ to the horizontal, so that the ways are of the V-form as used by Ramsden and later by Bramah and Maudslay. The saddle is a brass casting and is provided with a screw-operated cross slide. The work was supported on dead centres at both ends and only a small amount of adjustment was provided. The vertical plane containing the line of centres is situated some distance behind the bed-ways. There being no headstock or spindle, it seems that the work must have been driven by means of a belt or cord passing round a pulley that was secured in some way to the work and was operated by an external wheel. The saddle is traversed along the bed-ways by means of a lead-screw but this could be operated only by hand. This, however, is the first example of a tool rest that could be traversed along the whole length of the bed-ways; in previous lathes the extent of the traverse was limited to that provided by the tool slide of the slide rest and this was always quite small. The lead-screw is also notable because it has a square, and not a V-shaped, thread.

Vaucanson's lathe is something of an enigma; it is very advanced in its construction for its period and yet lacks many features that would have enhanced its usefulness considerably and had been used some years earlier in other lathes. It would seem to be a difficult lathe to operate, particularly if the work to be turned was of widely varying diameter and length. But if it was designed for a particular job it may have been very well adapted for its purpose and, in view of the other fields in which Vaucanson was active, this explanation has met with some support.

Holtzapffel's lathe

In 1785 Holtzapffel produced a mandrel-type screw-cutting lathe that has been called an 'industrial' lathe. It hardly seems to merit that title although it was clearly not designed for 'ornamental' turning. The spindle had ten threaded portions and also carried a three-step driving pulley. The operation was by treadle and the lathe had a wooden bed, a wooden tailstock, and only a simple hand tool rest. Compared with Vaucanson's lathe that of Holtzapffel seems to belong to an earlier epoch.

Senot's lathe

The screw-cutting lathe made by the Frenchman Senot in 1795 now rests in Paris alongside that of Vaucanson, over which it shows some important improvements. It is shown in Plate 16*b*, a view from the rear of the lathe. There is now a spindle, which is provided with a chuck and is carried in bearings in two brackets that are fixed to the bed. The spindle does not have a cone pulley and the method of driving the work is not apparent. It could have been by means of a crank handle fixed to the overhanging end of the spindle. A dead centre supports the right-hand end of the work and this is held in a poppet that is also supported in two brackets fixed to the bed. The right-hand (outer) bracket has a plain journal-bearing and the left-hand one has a threaded hole, the inner end of the poppet being threaded. This provides the adjustment for the centre; no means of locking are visible. The bed-ways are formed of rectangular bars, screwed to the upper surfaces of square-section members so as to form a T-shaped assembly, and the saddle can traverse the whole length of the bed, being moved by a lead-screw placed below it and between the bed-ways. Change gears couple the spindle to the lead-screw, which is notable for its size; it is nearly 2 inches in diameter and over 4 ft long and has an excellent finish; at the time of its production it must have been a great advance over any other lead-screw except that of Vaucanson. Two fixed steady rests are provided to support the work and the saddle carries a travelling rest; all these rests are adjustable. It seems possible that this lathe also was produced for a particular purpose perhaps, in this case, for finishing screwed work that had been roughed out in some other lathe; it does not seem to have been intended for the general run of turning operations. It is sometimes claimed that Senot's lathe is the first example of the use of change wheels in connection with screw-cutting but, as has been mentioned above, it seems fairly certain that Hindley had produced one some fifty-five years earlier.

David Wilkinson's lathe

In 1798 David Wilkinson, who was one of a family of American engineers, was granted an American patent for an improved screw-cutting lathe and he is said to have built and put into operation, in 1796, a machine that incorporated his ideas.[8] This machine has not survived and the patent papers and some references in books and papers published some time later give the only information about it. The drawing accompanying the patent shows a bed on which a headstock and a tailstock support the work and, at the rear, a similar headstock and tailstock support a lead-screw. The headstock spindles carry gears on their inner ends and these mesh with a central driving-gear, which is carried on a spindle in a bracket fixed to the bed. This spindle is shown being driven from a water-wheel. Both the work and the lead-screw are supported on centres and are driven by driving plates and carriers. A travelling carriage supported on three rollers moves on top of the bed; it is provided with a screw-adjusted tool rest at the front and supports a split nut at the rear. The method of guiding this carriage seems somewhat inadequate but appears to have consisted of a rib on the bottom that fitted in a groove in the bed; in the patent drawing, however, a considerable clearance is shown between the rib and the groove. The machine as built must have differed in many respects from the one outlined in the patent specification, since it is said that with slight modifications it was subsequently in considerable use for industrial work and that in 1848 over 200 were in use in government arsenals in America.

Maudslay's first screw-cutting lathe

This famous machine, which is probably more widely known than any other early machine tool, is thought to have been made in 1798 and is now in the Science Museum, South Kensington. It is shown in Plate 17a. The bed consists of two triangular bars supported at their ends by cast brass feet. The headstock and tailstock are carried on the rear bar and the headstock is at the right of the machine. This is somewhat unusual since one has to go back to Plumier, or forward to about 1850, to find other examples. The headstock spindle is geared to a short shaft carried in a bracket bolted to the foot casting. The inner end of this shaft has a coupling that connects it to the lead-screw lying between the bars of the bed. At its left-hand end the lead-screw is supported on a dead centre in a bracket carried by the front bar of the bed. This has led to the supposition that the lead-screw could be easily changed for another having a different pitch, so that the gearing was not the sole method of allowing for varying pitches in the work. The saddle is supported by both the bars of the bed and is a gun-metal casting. On its upper surface there is a dovetail slide that incorporates the tool holder and is moved in and out by a screw fitted with a handle and a graduated disc. This lathe is clearly much better adapted for the general run of turning work than those of Vaucanson and Senot.

Maudslay's second screw-cutting lathe

Maudslay was greatly concerned with the attainment of accuracy in the work he produced, particularly with the production of accurate screw threads for machines, and in 1800 or thereabouts he produced a machine specially adapted for the production of accurate screws. This also can be seen in the Science Museum and is shown in Plate 17b. The bed-ways are now flat and the work-piece is rotated manually by means of a capstan wheel. The lead-screw is again placed centrally between the ways of the bed and is coupled to the spindle by the gearing seen in the illustration. The intermediate wheels of this gear train are carried on a swinging arm; this enables wheels of different sizes to be meshed, as has been common practice since Maudslay's time. The saddle has a simple screw-operated cross slide that incorporates the tool holder. The screw of the cross slide has a graduated disc and a steady rest is provided for the work. The machine can be justly classed as a tool-room specimen, whereas the earlier one might be called a shop machine; but it must be remembered that the earlier machine has seen more arduous service than the later one. They both show the high standard that Maudslay set.

Other eighteenth-century machine tools

Except for lathes and boring machines very few machine tools have survived from the eighteenth century, nor is there much information to be got from written records. It seems unlikely that the only drilling machines then available could have been the bow-drill types shown in Plate 10a, but the only other example is a small machine made by Vaucanson. In this the bed is similar to that of his lathe and carries the saddle or base of the drill-head assembly; a screw placed between the bars of the bed serves to traverse the saddle along the bed-ways. Two vertical columns are fixed in the saddle and are joined by a bridge piece at the top, which serves as one of the bearings for the screw that moves the drill head up and down. The drill spindle is provided with a pulley having a V-grooved rim. The two screws of this machine are provided with graduated discs and verniers are fitted. The machine seems to have been made for some special purpose since it does not seem well-adapted for performing the drilling operations arising in general engineering or instrument work. The date of manufacture is not known definitely but must have been before 1782 when Vaucanson died.

A list of the tools installed at the Soho Foundry of Boulton and Watt at the end of the eighteenth century is extant. It mentions two drills, one described as 'large' and the other as 'small', both being 'upright', but no details of these machines are available.

Although there are some references to planing machines which relate to the eighteenth century these are all of doubtful authority and none of them gives any details from which the form of the machine in question can be ascertained. A machine for 'planing cast iron' is mentioned in the *Transactions of the Society of Arts* in 1783 but was not described because 'it could best be understood by viewing it in the repository'. There is a reference in *The Engineer* of 2 May 1862 in which it is stated that '. . . the first planing machine appears to have been made in 1794 at Horrocks, Miller and Co.'s works at Preston where it was used for planing mule tracks. This Ancient Briton was 5 ft long, had a cross beam with a tool head upon it and was worked by hand through a drum and chain', but no further information relating to this machine has come to light. An engraving in Buchanan's *Mill work and other machinery* shows a planing machine that was invented by a Frenchman named Nicolas Forq in 1751 for the purpose of planing parts of the pump barrels to be used at the Marly Water Works near Paris and was erected at Mauberge. This machine is referred to in the catalogue of the Musée des Arts et Métiers.

Matthew Murray has been credited with the building of a planing machine for machining the D-slide valves that he invented, but this story depends solely on the recollections of one of his workmen many years later and no details of the machine have been disclosed.

About 1788 Joseph Bramah designed a metal-cutting saw for producing one of the components of the lock he had invented. This machine has survived and is now in the museum at South Kensington. It is shown in Plate 18. The saw is held in the end pieces of an open rectangular metal frame that can be moved to and fro by a long hand lever and is guided in two metal guide bars. The hand lever is coupled to the frame by a V-shaped connecting link, which is pivoted to the lever at its apex and bolted to the saw frame at the other end, where it

24

would seem that the slackness of fit of the bolts and clevises is relied on to absorb the slight angular movement of the connecting link due to the apex moving in a circular arc. The workpiece is held in the fixture seen in the middle of the saw frame, and can be rotated about a horizontal axis, so that slots can be cut in various angular positions. The hinged cross lever seen in its raised position can be lowered and held in place by the latch seen at the left; it then provides a guide to steady the saw.

Machines employing rotating cutters could perhaps legitimately be classed as milling machines, but probably no one would use this title for a lathe that employed a fly cutter, and many would not apply it to machines in which the cutter was more like a burr or a rotary file than a milling cutter in the modern sense. The eighteenth-century machines using rotary cutters are not therefore strictly milling machines. Those used for cutting gear wheels can be put into the class of gear cutters but it is difficult to see where some others can be put if they are not included with milling machines.

Plate 19 is a reproduction of a machine, described in Diderot's encyclopedia, which uses a rotating cutter to shape the octagonal exteriors of musket barrels. The barrel is clamped in a frame that can be moved to and fro by hand in ways formed in the body of the machine. Underneath is a cutter that is rotated by the large fly-wheel seen on the right. There is an adjustment to enable the cutter to be moved towards the work to regulate the cut. The barrel is held between centres, but the right-hand one can be indexed to eight positions and the centre itself is serrated so as to grip the barrel. Except for small components this machine is made of wood. The date when this machine was made is not stated by Diderot but it was probably about 1750–60 or, perhaps, earlier.

The hand-operated gear-cutting machines that were used by eighteenth-century clockmakers mostly employed rotary cutters and would seem to have been fairly common although few have survived. One, which is now in the Science Museum, is shown in Plate 20a. It is attributed to a Spaniard named Manuel Gutierrez, and is thought to have been made in Madrid about 1789. The blank is fixed to the upper end of a spindle, which carries a dividing plate at its lower end, and the cutter is carried in a bracket that can swing so as to cause the teeth of the cutter to pass through the blank. The bracket itself is carried in another bracket that can be rotated about a horizontal axis on a pivot in the main frame. This would enable oblique teeth to be machined. The depth of cut and the adjustment for wheels of different sizes can be regulated by moving the whole cutter head along the frame number, a screw being provided for this purpose. No wood is used in the construction of this machine.

3

1800 to 1830

THE remarkable progress in design and workmanship that was made during the latter half of this period overshadows the developments of the first half, which were concerned with refinements to the chief existing type of machine tool, the lathe, rather than with the development of new types of machine tool that distinguishes the second half of the period.

Lathes

The use of wood for the basic structures of lathes still survived, and many machines built during the period did not incorporate improvements that had been made during the last quarter of the eighteenth century. This, however, is to be expected, since even today it takes some time for knowledge to spread and 150 or so years ago communications were comparatively poor. But even when wood was used there were definite improvements to be seen, as, for example, in the lathe shown in Plate 20b. This was built by Georg von Reichenbach in 1800 and is now in the Deutsches Museum, Munich. The workmanship shown in this lathe is excellent. The spindle is carried in bronze bearing blocks mounted directly on the tops of the heavy uprights of the bed structure; it carries a three-step cone pulley and has two threaded portions. A somewhat curious method of driving the spindle is adopted. The treadle pulls on the end of a cord, which passes over an idler pulley (which can just be seen in the picture) and is attached to a crank pin carried by the driving pulley; this pulley is on a shaft which carries a heavy fly-wheel at its other end. The threaded portions of the spindle can be engaged by levers, as in most mandrel lathes, to enable screw threads to be cut. A simple thrust-bearing is arranged at the left-hand end of the spindle for use during ordinary turning operations, and a chuck can be mounted at the right-hand end. The slide-rest provides both axial and transverse movements and the whole assembly can be swivelled so that tapers can be turned. A rest for hand tools is provided and there is a steady for supporting the outer ends of long work that had to be threaded.

26

The lathe shown in Plate 21*a* is also housed in the Deutsches Museum but is quite a different affair. The name of the maker is unknown but the lathe is thought to have been made in 1810, in England, from whence it was brought to Oberzell, near Würzburg, in 1818. It is a large lathe, capable of doing heavy turning work, and is virtually made in two separate parts. The illustration shows the rear view of the machine; on the right there is the driving assembly and on the left the lathe proper. The former consists of two shafts placed at right angles and supported in plummer blocks mounted on a heavy wooden frame. One shaft carries a four-step cone pulley by means of which it can be driven and also a bevel gear that can be moved axially in its bearings, the shaft having a sliding coupling to permit this. The second shaft carries a pair of bevels, also in plummer blocks, and it can be moved axially so as to mesh either of the bevels with the central driving gear. This provides a forward and a backward drive to the spindle of the lathe. The output shaft of the bevel assembly has a spur gear fixed to its end and this meshes with a gear mounted on the lathe spindle. It appears that the driving member of this pair of gears could be changed for one of a different size and that for this purpose the whole of the bevel assembly could be moved in or out.

The spindle of the lathe carries a faceplate at one end and a gear at the other, by means of which a lead-screw placed centrally below the work can be driven. The gear on the lead-screw also meshes with an idler gear carried by a swinging arm, and the idler meshes with a gear on a square shaft mounted at the front of the bed of the machine. At the other end of this square shaft a crank handle can be mounted and it seems that this was to enable the lathe to be operated manually if necessary.

The bed-ways are flat and carry the tailstock and the saddle. The poppet of the tailstock is adjusted by means of a jack screw carried by a bracket that is bolted up to the main casting, an eye-bolt being provided to lock the poppet in place. The saddle has two tool slides at both front and rear and the tools used seem to have been about 1 × 1 inch in section. They are held in brass castings; these have eye-bolts at the top and are secured to steel bases that can slide in dovetails formed in the upper surface of pedestals. The slides are provided with adjusting screws and the pedestals can be swivelled on the saddle.

All the gearing of the machine appears to have been cast with integral teeth that do not seem to have been machined.

If this lathe was, in fact, built in 1810, it provides a notable example of the progress that had been made during the first decade of the century, since it is clearly capable of machining quite large castings and forgings.

Two lathes of unknown date

The dates of manufacture of the machines shown in Plates 21*b* and 22*a* are unknown, but it is almost certain that the second was made by Maudslay and must therefore come within the period now being considered; the writer has ventured to put the first one into this period as well. This machine is now preserved in the Bridewell Museum in Norwich. It looks as if it might have been built for use in connection with large clockmaking work, since it is provided with a very large index plate and with a fitting that could have carried a fly cutter. It would thus have been well adapted to produce large toothed wheels of comparatively light weight, such as those used in tower clocks. The bed consists of three heavy triangular bars. Two of these lie in the same horizontal plane and are secured to pedestal members at their ends; the third lies midway between, but at a higher level than, the others, from which it is supported by heavy brackets. There is a rest for hand tools but also a tool slide, which carries a spindle for a fly cutter and can be moved along a slide that can be swivelled on the base of the rest. This base can be traversed along a sub-bed parallel to the ways of the main bed. The whole of this tool-rest assembly may have been added after the machine had been built and looks somewhat flimsy in comparison with the rest of the machine. The museum authorities now attribute this lathe to Johnson Jex, a blacksmith and clockmaker of Letheringsett.

The second machine was still in the works of Maudslay, Sons & Field when they were closed down in 1900. It was described by W. A. S. Benson in articles that appeared in *Engineering* on 18 and 25 January 1901, from which this illustration is derived. The bed is again made of two heavy triangular bars, supported in pedestals that are bolted to the foundations. The bar seen in the foreground lies in the same vertical plane as the axis of the spindle, while the other bar is placed out at the edge of the faceplate. The headstock is arranged on a separate entablature of cast iron. The spindle carries the faceplate, to the rear of which a large toothed ring is bolted; this can be driven from a pinion mounted on a shaft at the front of the entablature and is itself driven from a pulley (not visible in the picture) through a spur reduction. This provides the slowest speed. Three other speeds are obtained from the large belt pulley, seen at the right of the machine, which drives three gears fixed to the spindle. In addition the spindle carries three V-grooved pulleys for direct drive by a cord. The heavy saddle and tool slide are clearly seen. There is no self-acting feed motion. Benson says that this machine was constructed in Maudslay's lifetime, that is, before 1831. He also says that there was a much larger one in the works at the time when they were closed and that this appeared to date from the same period.

This may have been the lathe referred to by Maudslay's grandson in his contribution to the discussion of the paper given to the Institution of Civil Engineers in 1885 by W. W. Hulse. Mr. Henry Maudslay then said that his grandfather designed a lathe that had a faceplate 9 ft in diameter but was provided with a pit 20 ft deep, measured from the axis of the spindle, so that it could handle very large jobs. In this discussion a Mr. Cowper mentioned a lathe he had built in 1845 for turning the roller paths of bridges. It could swing jobs up to 36 ft in diameter and 30 tons in weight and had a spindle of $9\frac{1}{2}$ inches in diameter.

Maudslay's 1810 lathe

This machine is said to have been manufactured for sale rather than for Maudslay's own use and the price is said to have been £200. An example of it is preserved in the Science Museum and is shown in Plate 23. The bed is a triangular bar, supported at one end in the headstock casting and at other points on short pedestals or feet, by which it is mounted on the top of a work cabinet. The headstock spindle is carried in a plain bearing at its right-hand end and on an adjustable centre at the other end; it carries a five-step cone pulley and, on the outer, or chuck, side of the right-hand bearing there is a bronze gear for driving the lead-screw when screws are being cut. A swinging arm is provided to carry the intermediate gears. The tool-slide assembly is mounted on the bed for ordinary turning operations; it then has its long lower slide perpendicular to the spindle axis while the upper and shorter slide is parallel to that axis. For screw-cutting this assembly is removed from the main bed and, after being turned through a right angle, is mounted on the triangular extension of a bracket secured to the main bed, as shown in the illustration. The axis of the long slide is then parallel to the spindle axis and the end of its screw can be coupled by a shaft to the last wheel of the change-gear train. The tailstock has a separate jack screw to adjust the poppet and this is carried in a bronze bracket bolted to the end of the main tailstock casting. The spindle is driven from a treadle indirectly through an overhead countershaft, which is carried by a swinging frame that maintains the belt tension. The upper slide of the tool rest, on which the tool is secured, is provided with stop screws. Accessories such as a two-jaw chuck, a work steady, and a plate for supporting work that is to be drilled, are provided.

About this time Maudslay wanted to cut, on one of his lathes, a screw whose pitch was about 0·1 per cent smaller than that of the lead-screw of the lathe. He considered doing this by gearing the lathe spindle to the lead-screw in the proper ratio but found that it was impracticable to arrange gears with the required numbers of teeth. He therefore devised a mechanism,[1] which he

29

attached to his lathe, to enable him to cut the screw. A supplementary slide was placed on top of the saddle of the lathe so that the tool could be given a small motion, relative to the saddle, parallel to the bed-ways of the lathe, and this motion could be subtracted from the main motion of the tool. He produced the supplementary component motion by means of a bell-crank, or bent, lever whose arms were in the ratio 1 to 10. The lever was pivoted on a vertical pin carried by the saddle. The long arm of the lever was pivoted at its end to a block that could slide along a triangular bar arranged in a horizontal plane in front of the lathe bed and placed at a small angle to the bed-ways. The short arm of the lever engaged the supplementary slide. Thus as the saddle was moved along the bed by the lead-screw the block moved along the triangular bar and caused the end of the lever to move outwards. This gave the supplementary slide a small motion in the opposite direction to the motion of the saddle and thereby produced the required reduction in the pitch of the screw being cut. By inclining the triangular bar the other way a screw having an increased pitch could be cut. This mechanism, regarded as a correcting device, could correct only uniform errors along the whole length of the lead-screw. But in 1826 Bryan Donkin, a Fellow of the Royal Society, used the principle of Maudslay's device in a dividing engine he designed; he placed his correction bar in a vertical plane below the saddle of the machine and let the long end of the bent lever merely bear on the upper edge of the bar by gravity only. He was thus able to give the upper surface of the bar an irregular wavy profile, which he established by experiment, and to correct irregular errors in the main screw of his engine.

Holtzapffel's 1815 lathe

This is an ornamental lathe and is included because it is a good example of the standard of workmanship that had been attained at the time of its manufacture. It is shown in Plate 22*b*. The basic structure is wooden, but a metal bed is provided to carry the headstock, tailstock, and slide-rest assembly. The spindle is carried in two plain bearings and has a five-step cone pulley for a treadle drive. The cone pulley has two gears fixed to it, either of which can drive a shaft at the back of the lathe through a train of several gears, these being carried on an arm on which their positions are adjustable. The back shaft is carried in brackets supported by a separate bed similar to the main bed, and at its end cams can be mounted so as to impart an oscillating motion to the tool slide. (In earlier ornamental lathes the oscillating motions were given to the lathe spindle.) The face of the large end of the cone pulley is engraved and enables angular settings to be made against an index carried by an arm hinged to the headstock casting.

30

Richard Roberts's lathes

After spending about two years with Maudslay, Richard Roberts (1789–1864) went to Manchester and started on his own. He then built several machines for his own use and amongst them was the lathe shown in Plate 24*a*; this was subsequently used in the works of Beyer, Peacock & Co. until it was presented to the Science Museum where it now rests. In some respects it marks a definite advance in lathe design. The bed is a casting which has three ways formed on it as shown in Fig. 5*a*. The flat way in the middle is in line with the spindle axis, and the headstock and tailstock are carried on this and the rear, inverted V, way. The saddle is carried on the front of the bed and there is a gib at the

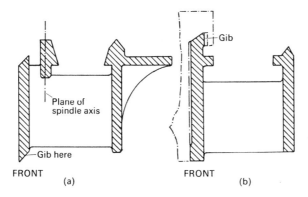

FIG. 5. Roberts's 1817 and 1820 lathe beds.

bottom; the saddle can therefore traverse to some extent past both the head-stock and the tailstock. The headstock spindle is carried in parallel bearings and the thrust is taken by a screw, which bears against the left-hand end. The spindle carries a four-step cone pulley and the arrangement of the back gear is similar to that still in common use. It was originated by Roberts and differs from the later designs only in the manner in which it is brought into action. This is done by sliding it along, together with its bearings and in a direction perpendicular to its axis, in short slide-ways formed in brackets attached to the rear of the headstock. Cams are provided to do this. For the direct drive the cone pulley is locked to the large gear on the right, which is keyed to the spindle, and the pinion on the left, which drives the backshaft, is fixed to the cone pulley which is free on the spindle. The saddle can be traversed by means of a screw, lying along the face of the bed and driven from the spindle through a change gear. The latter consists of a pinion that is free to slide along the rear end of the spindle on a feather and so can be made to mesh with any one of seven rings of teeth formed by pins inserted into the face of a disc that turns in bearings about an axis perpendicular to the spindle axis. The pin-wheel shaft carries a bevel gear at its lower end and this can engage either of two bevels that can slide to the left or right on the lead-screw; this provides a forward or reverse motion, or a disconnection, of the power traverse. The nut embracing the lead-screw is carried in bearings in the saddle and is coupled by two gears to a shaft carrying a ratchet wheel; when the power traverse is wanted the ratchet wheel is prevented from rotating by means of a pawl, but when the pawl is released the nut can rotate freely or be rotated by a hand lever to give a manual traverse. The poppet barrel is screwed internally and does not rotate; it is moved by a hand-wheel and screw, which are carried by a bridge piece supported by pillars extending from the tailstock casting.

Another lathe built by Roberts, about 1820, for the special purpose of cutting screw threads, is shown in Plate 24b. The bed-ways are seen in Fig. 5b and are somewhat different from those of the sliding lathe described above, but the tailstock is still carried on one V and one flat surface. The saddle is supported entirely on the front shear of the bed but there is no gib at the bottom. The spindle is driven indirectly through gears from the large driving pulley and is provided with a means of indexing the workpiece when multiple threads are being cut. Changes of pitch can be obtained by altering the gearing between the lead-screw and the spindle but the lead-screw could also be easily changed for another of different pitch. The tool slide is fitted with a quick withdrawal mechanism independent of the screw for the adjustment of the cut. The nut of the adjusting screw is left free to move in and out slightly and was controlled by a forked lever that could be operated from the front of the lathe, the motion being determined by stops. The tool box also had a simple means of varying the angle of the tool to suit the helix angle of the thread being cut.

James Fox's lathes

Another pioneer in the development of machine tools who was active as early as the first decade of the nineteenth century was James Fox the elder. He founded a works in Derby where he made machinery for the textile industry as well as making machine tools, some of which appear to have been built especially for that industry.

In the catalogue of the Musée des Arts et Métiers three drawings of a lathe by Fox are listed as having been received by the museum in 1818. Fig. 6 has been prepared from copies of these drawings. The lathe shown embodies some of the features that are also found in a lathe made by Fox which has survived and in others about which information is available.

The bed is a box casting, open at the bottom and having a slot down the

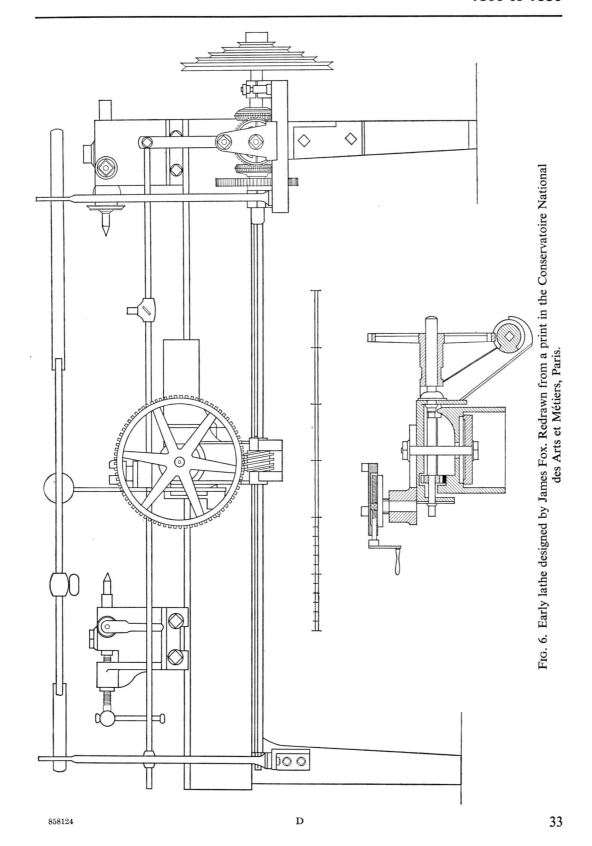

FIG. 6. Early lathe designed by James Fox. Redrawn from a print in the Conservatoire National des Arts et Métiers, Paris.

middle of its upper surface; the bed-ways comprise a flat at the front and an inverted V at the rear. The headstock has no cone pulley and the only drive to the spindle seems to be a small pulley, suitable for a flat belt, situated on the inner end of the spindle just behind the live centre. The spindle projects at the other end, however, and another driving pulley may have been carried there. The saddle is provided with extensions giving a long engagement with the bed-ways and these extensions can pass to the front and rear of the headstock, so that the tool rest can be brought close up to the live centre. A bridge piece, inside the bed and bearing on flat edges on the under sides of the bed-ways, keeps the saddle from lifting. The tool-rest assembly consists of a casting, bolted to the upper surface of the saddle and provided with a pillar to carry the tool slide.

The saddle can be traversed along the bed by means of a pinion and rack, either by hand or by power—a feature that Fox is generally regarded as having initiated. The rack in this machine is, however, at the front of the bed, whereas in the other machines of his that are described below the rack is at the back. The power traverse is provided by a worm and wheel mounted at the rear of the saddle, the worm being on a square shaft carried in bearings at the back of the bed. This shaft is driven from a five-step V-grooved pulley through a spur reduction gear, and a bevel-gear cluster provides a forward and a backward motion. The change is effected by sliding a dog-clutch member, situated between the bevels and operated from the saddle position by a rod which carries dogs giving an automatic disengagement of the traverse at any desired position. The rod itself is supported at one end in a stanchion bolted to the bracket carrying the feed shaft and at the other end by the rocking lever that moves the dog-clutch.

Two large stanchions, one at each end of the bed, carry a sliding bar that was used for shifting the driving belt.

The lathe mentioned as having survived is now in the Birmingham Museum and is shown in Plates 25a and 25b. Its resemblance to the lathe described above will be noticed. The headstock spindle is now driven from a six-step cone pulley suitable for a flat belt and this is carried at the rear of the headstock, the drive to the spindle passing through one of the two pairs of gears providing a high and a low ratio. The outer end of the cone-pulley shaft is supported in a separate pedestal bolted to the foundations. The general arrangement of the power traverse is the same as in the machine described above but the rack is now placed at the rear of the bed. The four-step cone pulley driving the power traverse is itself driven from a cone pulley, mounted on the overhanging end of a short shaft placed at the front of the headstock and driven from the spindle through a pair of gears. The bed-ways are again a flat and a V and the saddle can again traverse past the headstock. The tool-slide assembly is very much as before but heavier, since the lathe is larger, and there is now a second, lower, slide at right angles to the upper one. The casting that carries the tailstock poppet is bolted to an intermediate member that can be traversed in a dovetail slide across the bottom member. The latter has long bearings on the bed-ways. The tailstock of the previous lathe could also be adjusted transversely by a very small amount, just sufficient to enable any slight misalignment of the line of centres to be remedied. The lever and rod seen at the front of the machine operate the dog-clutch for reversing the traverse.

The date of manufacture of this lathe is doubtful; it has been placed as early as 1817 but the writer is inclined to put it some five to ten years later.

In the Musée des Arts et Métiers there is also a model of a lathe said to have been made by Fox about 1830. This lathe, which is shown in Plate 26a, is also very similar to the two just described although there are differences. The bed-ways do not extend past the headstock and the saddle is somewhat different; it may have been specially made so that when the tool-rest assembly had been removed the lathe could be used as a boring machine. There is now a multiplicity of drives to the headstock spindle; two of these are direct drives by flat belts, a third is through gears from the pulley seen at the rear, while three more are given by the pulley seen at the left in the front. This pulley drives the shaft seen carrying a three-gear cluster and this shaft and the pulley shaft are mounted in a frame that can rock on the short shaft seen below. This enables any one of the gears of the cluster to be meshed with the large gear on the lathe spindle, the rocking of the frame accommodating the changes in the centre distance. The principle utilized here is the same as that of the drive to the spindle of the Brainard–Lincoln-type milling machine described in Chapter 5 and that used in the Norton change-gear box mentioned in Chapter 6.

Joseph Clement's lathes

Joseph Clement (1779–1844) worked for both Bramah and Maudslay, Sons & Field before setting up for himself, and about 1820 he built a machine that is virtually two separate lathes having a common bed. It is now in the Science Museum and is shown in Plate 26b. Clement's most remarkable lathe, however, is undoubtedly the gap-bed facing-lathe, which he must have built about 1825. It is fully described in a paper given to the Society of Arts in 1828. Plates 27 and 28 are taken from this paper and show the general construction very clearly. Incidentally the drawings, which were done by Clement himself, are an example of the draughtsmanship for which he had a reputation. The headstock assembly is separate from the bed structure but is tied to it by struts, whereas in the heavy

Maudslay lathe described above there is no connection. The headstock is shown in detail in Plate 27. The spindle carries a two-step cone that can be driven from an overhead shaft, and there is also a large gear-wheel that meshes with a pinion carried by a shaft at the rear and driven by a separate pulley. A short worm-gear fixed to the spindle can be meshed with any one of four worm-wheels (33, 34, 35, and 36 in Plate 27), which can be moved along the shaft 30 for that purpose. To accommodate the variation in centre distance this shaft can be rocked about the axis 26 and then be held in place by locking the arcual member 31 by means of set screws. This arrangement provides the drive to the cross slide of the tool rest for the facing operations for which the lathe is particularly suited and during which the cutting speed can automatically be maintained at a constant value. This result is attained by coupling the screw that gives the cross feed to the tool to the mechanism that moves the crossed belt of the variable speed drive, seen on the right, along the two tapered pulleys (seen in Plate 28). To obtain the desired cutting speed two 'fusee' pulleys (P and Q) are used and Clement made a mathematical analysis of the system in order to obtain the best results. Although the machine is primarily adapted for facing work held in the chuck, a tailstock is provided so that work can be turned between centres using the top traverse of the slide rest. The bed-ways of the lathe have a somewhat peculiar cross-section and it would almost seem as if they had been made so in order to reduce the labour involved in finishing them, which almost certainly had to be done manually since Clement at that time did not have a planing machine.

An interesting lathe for its period is that shown in Plate 29a. This was made about 1830 by Henry Gambey (1787–1847) who was an instrument maker in Paris. He had a reputation for accuracy in his work and is said to have used in his shops only machine tools made by himself. The basic structure of this machine is wooden, but metal ways are provided to carry the headstock and the slide-rest assembly; one of these ways is flat and the other is an inverted V. The spindle of the lathe is robust and carries a belt pulley, which also serves as a dividing plate and a faceplate, or chuck, for the work. No tailstock is provided as the lathe was intended solely for chuck work. The slide-rest assembly is beautifully made and both the upper and the lower slides can be swivelled, graduated arcs being provided for setting them. Their screws are fitted with graduated discs and the operating handles are geared down to them. The upper slide is fitted with spring-loaded rollers to eliminate play without increasing friction and it carries an independently driven drilling spindle.

A lathe that is somewhat heavier than those described above is shown in Plates 29b and 30a. It is now in the Deutsches Museum, Munich, and is said to have been built about 1830. The headstock consists of two end castings; these carry the bearings for the spindle and are united by a central casting. The end castings are bolted to cast-iron rail members, which form the bed of the lathe and have integral cross members. The gears of the double reduction drive to the spindle are cast and show no signs of having been machined. The arrangement for taking the thrust on the spindle is somewhat peculiar; the gear of the second reduction pair is fixed to a sleeve, which is keyed to the spindle and at the left bears against the flange that can be seen in Plate 30a. Two set screws are carried by this flange and bear against the left-hand upright of the headstock; these contacts are all that prevent the flange from rotating.

The tool-slide assembly is bolted to the rails of the bed but can be moved along when necessary by means of a rack and pinion. The cross-sliding member that carries the tool bar slides on a cylindrical member held in the front and rear castings of the assembly. Rotation of the cross slide about this cylindrical member is prevented by a support, which can be seen at the right-hand side, and by the adjusting screw seen at the left. The latter engages a half-nut formed on the underside of the cross-slide casting. The casting that carries the tool bar can be swivelled on a lower casting so that tapers can be machined. A wide rest for hand tools is also provided. The faceplate of this lathe is about 6 ft in diameter.

Boring machines

In 1795 Peter Ewart designed a vertical boring mill which was intended for installation in the Soho Foundry then under construction. A drawing of this machine is given in the paper by Forward mentioned in the previous chapter. It was not, apparently, ever built, but Forward says that Michael Billingsley of Bowling Ironworks near Bradford patented and built, in 1802, a mill that was practically an exact copy of Ewart's but had iron instead of wooden framing. In 1828 this machine was seen working at Bowling by two French engineers who described it in their account of their travels. This account was published in the *Annales des Mines* for 1829. A machine by John Dixon, which is thought to have been built about 1808, employed a travelling cutter head, but the feed was obtained by a non-rotating screw concentric with the bar and embraced by an external nut that could be rotated by hand.

At this time, that is in 1808, Matthew Murray was building cylinder boring-machines for export, and Figs. 7 and 8, which are reproduced from Forward's paper, show one of Murray's machines that was installed in an engine works at Chaillot in about 1822. In this machine the cutter head is fixed to the bar that travels through the bearings in the supporting pedestals. The bar is driven by the large gear, seen on the left, which is a sliding fit and has a key that engages a key-way in the bar. The feed is obtained by means of the concentric screw seen at the right which rotates with the bar. The screw is engaged by a nut, carried by the outer bearing and driven at a speed slightly different from that of the bar by means of the gearing shown. The lower left-hand gear of this can slide along its square shaft.

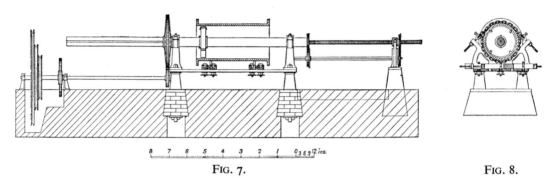

FIG. 7. FIG. 8.

FIG. 7. Murray's 'Chaillot' cylinder boring-machine *c.* 1822. Front view.
FIG. 8. End view.

A boring machine that may have been designed by William Murdock is shown in Plate 31, reproduced from *The Engineer* of October 1895. This machine was still in position in the Soho Foundry in 1895 when the works were dismantled and it employs the worm drive patented by Murdock in 1799. The left-hand pedestal can be moved out of the way on rollers in order to enable the cylinder to be got into position on the V blocks. The cutter head, which is not shown, travelled along the bar, and the feed was provided by a screw that was housed in the groove seen at the top of the bar and engaged a nut secured to the cutter head. The screw itself was rotated by means of the planetary gearing seen at the left. The opinion has been expressed by some writers that Murdock produced a boring bar and cutter head on these lines as early as 1800, but Forward says in his paper that he had been unable to find any evidence of this.

Drilling machines

This period is rather barren in respect of drilling machines, at least so far as examples that have survived or are described in authentic records are concerned. But no doubt progress was being made, since in the following period the drilling machine was brought out in the forms that are still used today.

Two machines that may possibly have been installed in the Soho Foundry during this period are shown in Plate 32. They were still in place in the Foundry in 1895 and were then described in *The Engineer*. It has been suggested that these machines were built before 1800 and also later than 1830, but it seems improbable that machines built into the shop structure, as these are, would have been built much later than 1830, since self-contained machines, which must have been much more convenient in operation, were then available. On the other hand, the Soho Foundry was not finished until 1796 and did not get into full operation until some time later and then did not make the smaller components of the Watt engines. A date before 1800 therefore seems unlikely. But the use of a worm drive similar to that which Murdock designed for the Soho boring mill suggests that he may have had a hand in the building of these drilling machines; this is not incompatible with a date after 1800. Murdock's patent on the worm drive was not taken out until 1799.

Planers

If the period is a poor one for drilling machines it is a vintage one for the planing machine. In 1817 Richard Roberts produced his small hand-operated machine which he claimed to be the first ever made; this is now in the Science Museum and is shown in Plate 30*b*. In its general features it is much the same as modern planers. The tool is carried in a clapper box and its slide can be swivelled on the saddle, which traverses on a cross-beam. The cross-beam elevates on two columns or standards, but these are not braced together at the top and the elevating screws have to be operated independently. The table is moved by the capstan wheel and a chain. There is no self-acting feed mechanism.

Roberts's claim to have originated the planer was hotly disputed in his lifetime by the grandsons of James Fox who asserted that their grandfather had produced a planer in 1814. The dispute was aired in the columns of *Engineering* in 1862 but the matter will probably never be settled and is not of great importance. James Fox almost certainly did produce a planing machine between 1810 and 1820 and subsequently produced them in large sizes, whereas Roberts did not.

The machine shown in Plate 33 is now in the Birmingham Museum. It came out of Milford Mill, Derbyshire, and its design and manufacture are attributed to James Fox. The table is driven from countershaft gear through an open and a crossed belt running on two loose pulleys with a fixed pulley between them. The latter drives the table through double reduction spur gearing and a pinion meshing with a rack on the underside of the table. The belts are shifted by strikers, operated by dogs clamped to the table, and they can be shifted by hand from either side of the machine. The work is secured to one or more of three sub-tables, which are carried on two V's on top of the main table. The latter slides on the main bed on one V and one flat way.

The tool is carried in a clapper box and can be swivelled for angular cuts. The tool head is moved across the beam by means of a square-threaded screw, which is given an intermittent motion by dogs clamped to the near side of the table and operating a vertical square bar to which short lengths of rack can be secured in any position to suit the height of the beam. The beam is clamped to the standards when the machine is in use but can be elevated by two screws. The two uprights and the cross piece at the top, which form the standards, are cast in one piece, and this is bolted to the bed and stayed by two inclined bars at the back.

The worm and wheel seen on the end of the bed enable a shaft, which runs from one end to the other, to be rotated. At the middle this shaft carries a pinion, which meshes with a short rack that can slide in a vertical guide in a pedestal that is bolted to the foundations. At the top, the rack has a shoe that can bear on the underside of the table rack. It has been suggested that this arrangement was used to lift the table when it had stuck after a spell of idleness.

The date when this machine was built is uncertain; it has been placed as early as 1817 but the writer thinks it probable that it was some years later.

Clement's planing machines

Clement was active in building planing machines during this period and is said to have had one working as early as 1820, but information about this machine is lacking. The machine that he designed and built about 1825, however, is a most remarkable effort and stands in the same class as his constant cutting-speed facing lathe described above. The Society of Arts took the unusual step of commissioning a Mr. Varley to produce a full description of this machine for publication in the transactions. This account appeared in 1832. Two of the drawings made by Mr. Varley are reproduced in Plates 34 and 35, and use is made in the following description of the reference numbers appearing in the plates.

The table moves on flanged wheels, some 2 ft in diameter, which are fixed on axles supported in plummer blocks on the massive foundations. End motion of the axles is eliminated by thrust screws at their ends and oil baths are provided for these. The use of wheels in this way was presumably to reduce friction, since the machine was manually operated, one man being usually sufficient but two being employed when 'it had to make long and full cuts both ways'. The machine can cut on both strokes and is undoubtedly the first machine to incorporate this feature.

The table drive is reversed by means of the bevel cluster (t, u, s, Fig. 1), the dog-clutch being operated by the long lever (6), which is moved by dogs (11, 12) secured to the side of the table. To avoid shock and to enable the momentum of the fly-wheel to assist in the reversal of the table, a slipping clutch is incorporated in the middle wheel of the bevel-gear cluster.

The double cutting is achieved by carrying the cross-beam in plummer blocks (*pp*), which can be raised or lowered on the standards by screws (23). The whole beam can therefore be tilted about a horizontal axis so that one tool can cut on one stroke and the other on the return. The tilting is done automatically by the reversing mechanism coupled to an arm (37, Fig. 1) attached to the beam. Stops are provided to position the beam in its two positions and these can be used to lock the beam when required. Clapper boxes on the tool heads are not required when double cutting in this manner. The tool heads can be swivelled in order to cut dovetails.

The self-acting feed is obtained from the motion of the reversing lever that operates the levers (39 and 54). These are coupled to the levers (37 and 52) that respectively tilt the beam or give an intermittent rotation to the cross screw by means of the pawl (52).

The reversal of the table is also assisted by the pre-loaded springs (20, Fig. 4) carried by the reversing lever (13). The pre-load is maintained by tying the ends of the springs to the lever, and the springs have to be further loaded before the table dogs can lift the pawls that lock the lever. The springs then produce a rapid and certain motion of the reversing linkage while also helping to bring the table to rest and accelerate it in the opposite direction. Mr. Varley reported that the reversing mechanism worked so smoothly that 'the bed (i.e. the table) goes to the end perfectly quiet, and returns so immediately as to remove all sense of its weight, and the man at the winch handle neither hears nor feels the return'.

When operating on side faces the beam is locked and single cutting is employed. The relief for the tool is then obtained by moving the tool head sideways; this can be done either manually or automatically, by locking the pawl (52) to the wheel (47) so that the wheel and the cross screw are given an oscillating motion by the reversing mechanism.

The work table can be fitted with brackets carrying centres to enable cylindrical work to have flats or key-ways planed on it.

To enable the teeth of racks to be cut a long screw can be passed through a hole (Plate 35, Figs. 1, 82) in the end of the table and a nut can be secured in this hole. The outer end of the screw can then be anchored in a pedestal bolted to the base of the machine. The screw is fitted with a micrometer dial and index to ensure accurate spacing. The cutting action is obtained by traversing the cutter head across the beam, and the relief for the tool is obtained by moving the cross beam up and down. Stops are again provided to ensure accurate return to the cutting position.

When using the cross motion of the tool to machine transverse faces the tool relief is obtained by moving the table slightly. For this purpose a short screw can be mounted in a nut carried by a bracket on one of the standards and can be coupled to a bracket fixed to the side of the table. Stops are again provided to ensure accurate positioning.

An extra wide non-tilting beam can also be fixed to the back plates of the plummer blocks to enable extra wide jobs to be machined by transverse cutting.

At the centre of the table a hole is machined to take a spindle on which large gear-wheels can be mounted so that the teeth can be machined, using the motion of the cross beam on the standards to give the cutting action and the to-and-fro motion of the table to give the relief. A large indexing plate is fixed to the spindle.

Milling machines

It has been mentioned that the machines using rotary cutters in the eighteenth century and earlier have been regarded by some writers as examples of filing machines rather than as milling machines, and if the latter are defined as machines capable of removing metal in the form of fairly large chips instead of a fine swarf it is probably true to say that the earlier machines were not milling machines. The appearance of the first milling machine in the restricted sense mentioned cannot be dated with certainty, but there is evidence that such machines were being made and used in the second decade of the nineteenth century. For example, Richard Roberts in a letter to *The Engineer* in 1862 says: '. . . the firm of Maudslay & Co. constructed a machine while I worked there in the year 1815 the object of which was to true a number of cast iron blocks to one size. The tool of the machine was a rotary cutter which soon lost its edge in removing the skin of the iron and which made such an intolerable noise that it had to be given up . . .' This machine, therefore, seems to have been unsuccessful, and the first successful one is in all probability one that Edward Parkhurst, in an article in the *American Machinist* of 8 March 1900, said had been shown to him in 1851 by Robert Johnson of Middletown, who told him that it was brought into use in 1818. Parkhurst says that Johnson did not claim to have built the machine, which, as can be seen from Fig. 9, was of a primitive nature; in particular, there was no vertical adjustment between the work and the cutter. Edwin A. Battison, in an article in the *Smithsonian Journal of History*,[2] discusses this matter at length and describes a lathe headstock acquired by the Smithsonian Museum of History and Technology in 1964 which he regards as being the basis of Johnson's machine. A much heavier but even more primitive machine, which is now in the possession of the New Haven Colony Historical Society, is said to have been made by Eli Whitney in 1818, but Battison shows that this claim is almost certainly erroneous and that the machine was probably made at least a decade later. The Whitney machine, like the Johnson one, had

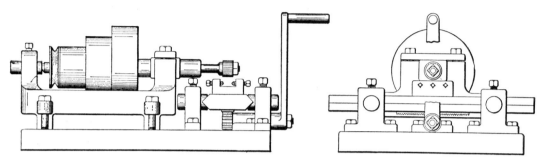

FIG. 9. The Middletown milling machine *c.* 1818. From *Am. Mach., Lond.* 8 May 1900.

no vertical adjustment but a self-acting feed was provided. This was derived from a belt, driven by the cutter spindle, and the drive was through a worm and wheel to the table screw. The worm shaft was carried at one end in a pivoted bearing so that the worm could be disengaged from the wheel. Both these machines seem to have been produced with a specific job in view and to have been used in the manufacture of firearms.

Nasmyth produced a milling machine in 1830 or thereabouts in order to machine the flats on a large number of small hexagon nuts that Maudslay required for a model of a steam engine. At a later date, when he had his own workshop, Nasmyth built an improved version of the machine which he says 'was eagerly adopted by mechanical engineers whom we abundantly supplied with this special machine'. The general appearance of the machine is shown in Fig. 10. The cutter used by Nasmyth was a side and end mill, cutting principally on the end; it rotated about a horizontal axis and the work table was fed past the cutter by a screw

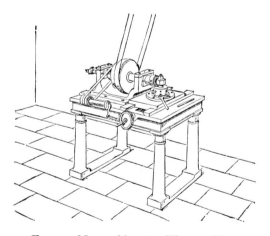

FIG. 10. Nasmyth's nut-milling machine.
Smiles, *James Nasmyth.*

actuated by a crank and a ratchet driven from the spindle. For milling the nuts an indexing work holder was used.

Gear-cutting machines

In his paper on spur-gearing, which he gave to the Institution of Mechanical Engineers in 1908, Thomas Humpage illustrates a gear-cutting machine that could, he says, at that time be seen working in Bristol. The picture has a caption '18th century wheel-cutting machines for clockmakers'. It is a robust machine and the cutter is now power driven. The cutter head can slide up and down the vertical face of a casting that can move along a horizontal slide in order to accommodate wheels of different size. The workpiece is carried on a vertical spindle which, at its lower end, carries a dividing plate as in earlier machines.

Humpage also illustrates some gear wheels that were cut on a machine said to have been made by J. G. Bodmer between 1820 and 1830. The machine itself is not illustrated but parts of the segmental cutters used in it are shown and these have teeth, which definitely put them into the class of milling cutters. Some examples of these cutters can be seen in the Science Museum and they are described in Bodmer's 1939 patent (mentioned in the next chapter). This, however, is not inconsistent with their having been used at the earlier date, since it seems to have been common practice to make and use inventions long before they were patented. Another illustration in Humpage's paper is reproduced in Plate 36a; this machine is believed to have been made by Richard Roberts, although Humpage says that some people thought it might have been made by Bodmer. Roberts certainly had a gear-cutting machine as early as 1821 because there is an advertisement in an issue of the *Manchester Guardian* in that year in which Roberts states that he 'has cutting engines at work on his new and improved principle which are so constructed as to be capable of producing any number of teeth required; they will cut Bevil, Spur & Worm Gear . . . and the teeth will not require fileing up'. In Roberts's machine the work axis is horizontal and can be raised or lowered in a sliding head to accommodate wheels of different sizes. The cutter rotates about a horizontal axis and can be fed parallel to the axis of the work so that wheels of considerable face width can be machined. The whole cutter slide can also be tilted on trunnions so that conical blanks can be machined, but it is doubtful whether Roberts could, in this way, produce bevel gear teeth that would run together satisfactorily without modification subsequent to machining.

Thomas Gill in his *Technological repository*, published in London in 1822, describes an inserted tooth cutter for machining the teeth of clock gears and attributes it to W. Hardy.

Two machines of unknown date

The machines shown in Plates 36*b* and 36*c* were amongst those present in the works of Maudslay, Sons & Field at the time of their closure. They are both bevel-gear cutting machines, and the second is clearly an improved version of the first. The writer has ventured to put the date of manufacture of the first of these machines into the period 1800–30; the second machine may well have been made during the following period. In both machines the profile of the tooth is copied from a template. A pin, carried by the arm on which the tool box reciprocates, bears on this template, so that as the tool is fed into the blank the arm is rotated about the axis of the bearing in which it is pivoted, the axis of this bearing being arranged to pass through the apex of the pitch cone of the gear being cut.

Miscellaneous machines

An engraving machine for producing reduced copies of medallions was invented by Hulot, a French mechanician, about 1800, and one of these is now preserved in the Science Museum. In the machine the original and the work are mounted on circular faceplates, which are rotated in unison about their fixed horizontal axes. In front of them there is a long bar, which carries a tracer and a cutting tool and is pivoted on a universal joint, the work being between the universal joint and the original that is being copied. The faceplates are rotated slowly, and the bar is moved very slowly, so that the tracer moves across the original from the circumference to the centre and the cutter moves across the work likewise. The displacement of the cutter along its arc is thus smaller than that of the tracer in the ratio of the distances of the axes of the faceplates from the centre of the universal joint. Similarly, the displacements perpendicular to the planes of the faceplates are reduced in the same ratio.

About 1822 a self-centring 'wire' chuck was made by a Mr. S. Mordan in connection with the manufacture of a pencil case that he had patented. This is described in the catalogue of the Science Museum as 'the precursor of many modern drill chucks'.

A lathe for machining cylindrical objects, in which a complete revolution was either unnecessary or impossible, was built about 1830. A model of it is now in the Science Museum.

4

1830 to 1860

AT the end of the previous period all the basic types of machine tool except the slotter, the shaper, and grinding machines had been produced, and some of them had reached a stage where their general form would not change fundamentally for some decades. During the present period developments of these basic machines occurred but these were in respect of size and capacity, the improvement of general performance, and in detail design. The rate at which machine tools developed as a whole was maintained during the period and the output of machines increased very considerably. The period was one of great activity in all fields of engineering, principally because of the advances made in prime movers and the boom in railway building. It is not thought necessary to deal in detail with the minor changes that were made and the machines described will illustrate the general progress made.

Lathes

In 1833 Joseph Whitworth started on his own in Manchester and began to design and produce machine tools that profoundly influenced other makers and brought him world-wide fame. In 1835 he produced a lathe that had a self-acting cross feed to the tool but, as has been seen, Clement had done this ten years earlier. Whitworth's design, however, was very much simpler. In 1839 Whitworth patented a sliding-bed lathe that subsequently became a popular form. In this the bed that carried the saddle and tailstock could be moved along the base on which the headstock was fixed, thereby giving a gap of variable width. This retained the advantages of the fixed-gap bed while eliminating the disadvantage of having a considerable overhang of the tools when short pieces were being turned.

In an engineering exhibition in London in 1907 the firm of C. Churchill & Co. showed a lathe that was reputed to have been built in 1837. It is illustrated in *Engineering* of 18 October 1907. As this firm was of American origin it is probable that this was an American design. There are separate ways for the saddle

and the tailstock, each having one V and one flat, and the headstock is positioned on the same ways as the tailstock. The saddle is a simple flat table, with
an upper member pivoted to it along its rear edge, and there is a set screw at the
front to raise and lower the tool rest. The saddle has a rack and pinion traverse
but the rack is situated well to the left of the saddle and lies in front of the
headstock. The tailstock has a cross motion. Rising tool rests of this type were
very popular in America during the middle and latter half of the nineteenth
century.

Bodmer's lathes

In 1839 and 1841 J. G. Bodmer took out two patents in which he described
several machines, including some lathes that are of considerable interest. One
of these was designed particularly for the turning of the crankshafts of steam
engines, and for other eccentric work. It had two headstocks, both of which
were fitted with spindles carrying large faceplates; these faced each other. The
left-hand one had a normal cone pulley and back gear and was fixed to the low,
wide bed, while the right-hand one did not have any cone pulley and was adjustable along the bed; it could be driven in synchronism with the left-hand one by
means of a shaft, between the bed-ways, which carried pinions that engaged
teeth on the peripheries of the faceplates. The left-hand pinion could be slid out
of engagement when the right-hand faceplate did not have to be driven. The
shaft carrying the pinions also extended beyond the end of the bed and could
be driven by a variable-speed gear, comprising a sun-and-annulus epicyclic
train and a double cone and shifting-belt drive. One of the cone pulleys was
fixed on the input shaft, which also carried the sun gear of the epicyclic; the
other cone pulley was geared to the annulus; while the planet carrier, which
was the driven member of the train, was coupled through a short shaft provided
with universal joints, of Bodmer's own design, to the pinion shaft driving the
faceplates. The latter had dovetailed slides formed in them and in these ways
V-shaped jaws could be moved to any desired position by means of screws;
scales were provided to enable settings to be made.

Bodmer's relieving lathe

This is, perhaps, one of his most important inventions and was devised by him
for the production of his patent 'convolute' taps. The threads of these taps were
given a spiral relief so that, in Bodmer's own words '. . . not only is the top of
the thread eased in a convolute form, as is usually done by hand, but likewise
the bottom thereof and the sides of the thread also are tapered or relieved in the

47

same proportion, so that the tap acts like an ordinary turning tool instead of making its way through the nut by pressure'.

The lathe is shown in Plate 37; it has a normal headstock, tailstock, saddle, cross slide, and lead-screw. The cross slide is, however, controlled by two screws, one of which (*l*) has a quick-pitch external thread and an internal thread that forms the nut for the second screw (*o*), which is free to turn in a bearing in the cross slide (*p*). This second screw provides the means of adjusting the cut of the tool and the quick-pitch screw provides the backing-off motion. For this purpose it carries a bevel pinion (*k*) that meshes with a wheel (*f*) carried in the saddle and free to slide along the key-wayed shaft (*d*) seen at the rear. This shaft receives an oscillatory rotational motion from the cam or former (*b*) through the lever (*c*), which is fixed to the shaft. An automatic adjustment of the cut was given on the return of the saddle to the starting position at the right, when the adjustable ramp (*u*) actuated the pawl-lever and thus turned the ratchet wheel on the end of the cross-slide screw. The lever (*c*) was held in contact with the cam by the weight (*m*) but could be lifted off by means of the lever (*w*), which also operated the reversing belt gear on the overhead countershaft.

Bodmer's 'circular planer'

It will be seen from Plates 38 and 39*a* that this machine is what would now be called a vertical lathe or vertical boring mill. The general arrangement will be clear from the drawing. The circular table was intended normally to be supported on the V-ways at its periphery but when high speeds were required, as for drilling operations, the centre spigot could be raised so that the V-ways were clear. The drive to the table was by teeth formed on its rim, through a pinion and gears from an overhead countershaft, and an oscillatory motion could be obtained by using open and crossed belts. The principal claim made for this design was that which is still made, namely, the ease of positioning work on the table.

Bodmer's differential slide lathe

The general arrangement of this machine is that of an ordinary lathe, but two lead-screws were employed and these meshed with the opposite sides of a worm-wheel placed between them and carried by the saddle on a vertical axis. The screws could be driven either separately or together, at the same speed or at different speeds, either from the headstock spindle or from pulleys and gears at the right-hand end of the bed. When both screws were driven at the same speed the worm-wheel did not rotate but acted as a nut to give a traverse to the saddle.

48

When the screws were driven at equal speeds in opposite directions the worm-wheel rotated but the saddle did not traverse. The rotation of the worm-wheel could be made to give either a cross-feed to the slide rest or a rotational feed to the tool rest, which was carried on a circular dovetail. This latter motion enabled spheres to be turned with a power feed. Bodmer also visualized the cutting of tapers by suitably adjusting the speeds of the screws so as to give the necessary combination of longitudinal and cross feeds.

An early American lathe

A lathe said to have been built in 1854 by an American named Baxter D. Whitney is described in the *American Machinist* of 14 March 1908 and has some unusual features. It is shown in Plate 39*b*. There are four ways on the top of the bed, three being inverted Vs and the fourth, at the front, a rib with a semi-circular top. The saddle bears on the latter and at the rear is supported on a jack screw, which bears on a shoe that slides on the rear V. The saddle and tool rest can therefore be tilted as in the lathe described earlier. The headstock, tailstock, and steady rest all stand on the inner Vs. The backgear of the headstock is placed below the spindle and the saddle is traversed by a rack that is secured to it at one end and can be seen projecting at the left of the machine. A transverse shaft underneath the headstock carries a pinion that meshes with the rack and at the front end this shaft carries a large wheel. The wheel is actually two worm-wheels made in one piece; its periphery is V-shaped and has teeth for a right-hand worm on one side and a left-hand worm on the other. The worms meshing with these teeth are carried in a bracket at the bottom, which can be rocked so as to bring either worm into mesh. The worms are geared together and are driven from the spindle by a belt, an idler being provided to enable this belt to clear the rack giving the longitudinal feed. The rod seen at the front of the bed carries a bevel gear at its left-hand end, and this gear meshes with a bevel gear on the worm-wheel shaft, thereby providing a hand traverse. The tailstock has a cross-traverse motion and the plain cylindrical poppet barrel has a lug at its outer end through which a jack screw passes. The lathe can take work up to 18 inches in diameter and about 6 ft long.

Two heavy lathes

The lathes shown in Plates 40*a*, 40*b*, and 41 were both working in the Soho Foundry up to the time when it was closed down. One of them is now preserved in the museum at Birmingham. The line drawings are reproduced from *The Engineer*, which had the foresight to send representatives to the works to describe and make drawings of the machines there before they were dispersed.

Both machines are facing lathes and both were probably built during the present period; there is, however, a possibility that the one shown in Plate 40*a* may have been built towards the end of the previous period. The worm and wheel drive of this machine is similar to that used on some other machines at Soho and the design, if not directly due to William Murdock, certainly derives from him. Murdock took out a patent for such drives in 1799 and is thought to have built a horizontal boring-machine for the Soho foundry which incorporated such a drive either a year or two before, or soon after, 1800. Apart from its massive proportions and its worm drive there is nothing very remarkable about this machine.

The machine shown in Plates 40*b* and 41 is said by the authorities of the Birmingham museum to have been built at the Soho Manufactory before 1850 and to have been moved to the Soho Foundry at some subsequent date. The spindle is driven indirectly from a cone pulley having seven steps and mounted on a shaft at the back. At the end of this shaft, close to the faceplate, there is a pinion that meshes with the internally toothed ring seen bolted to the back of the faceplate. Also on the cone-pulley shaft there are two gears that can mesh with two gears carried on the spindle. These provide a double reduction drive from the cone pulley back to the cone-pulley shaft and thence, via the pinion and internal gear, to the faceplate, and so give a very low speed. Alternatively, for the higher speeds the pinion can be disengaged and the drive go direct from the cone-pulley shaft to the spindle. The lathe was fitted with five tool slides, four of which were carried on pedestals that could be bolted to the bed plate in positions at the front and back, where they could machine the peripheries and faces of large wheels. The fifth tool slide is the massive assembly seen in front of the faceplate. The upper slide of this assembly can be rotated through an angle of about 25° on the cross-slide saddle. The cross-slide body slides along ways on the lower casting and the latter can be swivelled through a small angle on a bottom plate that is bolted to the base plate. For the latter purpose the bottom plate has an arc on which teeth are formed, and a pinion carried by the lower slide casting meshes with these teeth.

The feed gear seen at the front of Plate 41 is driven by the telescopic and universally jointed shaft from overhead gearing, which in turn is driven by belt from the headstock spindle; it provides two ratios that are obtained by fixing, by means of a taper pin, either the middle or the left-hand gear seen on the shaft at the rear. This shaft carries bevel gears at each end and these engage the two pairs of bevel gears seen in the picture. The left-hand pair provide the transverse feed and the right-hand pair the longitudinal feed; both can be reversed by sliding dog-tooth clutches situated between the bevel gears.

G. and J. Rennie's gun-barrel lathe

In 1841 the third edition of Robertson Buchanan's *Practical essays on mill work and other machinery* was published; it was revised by George Rennie and contained an appendix by James Nasmyth which is a valuable source of information on the machine tools of the period. It can be assumed that any machine described in this appendix must have been conceived, and almost certainly built, at some time before 1840. The book had a companion volume of plates, most of which were line drawings; they are beautifully drawn and add immensely to the value of the text. Some forty machines are described and considerable use has been made of this work in this chapter.

Rennie's lathe was designed to turn the outside of the barrels of muskets to a profile that was neither cylindrical nor conical although it was a surface of revolution. The tool had to be guided so that it produced the required profile, and the designers thought it necessary to support the barrel during the operation. The arrangement they arrived at is interesting. The general form of the lathe is conventional as regards the bed, headstock, tailstock, and the self-acting motion for the saddle. The latter, however, in place of a slide rest, carried a frame in which four 'dies' could slide radially along guide ways formed in its face. The dies could be moved in and out by means of a rotatable cam-plate in which four eccentric grooves were cut to receive ribs formed on the backs of the dies. These dies formed a travelling support for the work and one of them also carried the cutting tools, of which there were two, one for roughing and one for finishing. The dies were moved in and out by a curved former bar, which was fixed to the front of the bed and actuated a short vertical rack carried in the saddle frame. The teeth of this rack engaged teeth formed on the periphery of the cam-plate. The machine is said to have been capable of turning and finishing three barrels per hour and several are said to have been in use in the Royal Armoury at Enfield as well as at Constantinople and in Egypt. For some reason it was thought necessary to carry the barrel on a 'tightly fitting mandril'.

Nasmyth, Gaskell & Co.'s great boring lathe

This is described as being of 'large dimensions . . . capable of boring cylinders of great diameters . . . well adapted for turning locomotive wheels'. Apart from its size it had no very notable features. The headstock and the bed were separately secured to the foundations. A large faceplate fitted with adjustable clamping jaws was provided, and there was a compound slide-rest that could be moved along the bed and also transversely, but only by hand. The main feed-motion was provided by the tool slide. A variation of this machine was produced as a facing lathe in which the faceplate was driven by a pinion that engaged an internal gear fixed to the rear of the faceplate and was driven direct from the line-shafting of the shop; but other speeds could also be obtained from the headstock gearing. Nasmyth in his appendix also described a lathe made by F. Lewis of Manchester that was capable of swinging work up to 7 ft in diameter.

Two Whitworth lathes

Two of the few machines that have survived from the period now being considered are shown in Plates 42*a* and 42*b*. The first is now in the Science Museum and dates from 1843, while the second was made probably several years later and is now in the museum at Birmingham. Both machines incorporate some of the features covered by Whitworth's 1835 patent. The smaller lathe seems to have been designed for a treadle drive and its headstock incorporates a dividing plate, geared to the driven gear of the backgear. The latter employs the eccentric-shaft method of engagement that later became the conventional method. Both machines employ Whitworth's self-acting feed arrangement. In this the longitudinal feed is obtained from a lead-screw and a nut, which can be engaged by sliding it into mesh. The cross feed is also obtained from the lead-screw but by an indirect method. A short vertical shaft, carried in bearings in the saddle, has a bevel gear at the top and a worm gear at the bottom, and the latter engages the lead-screw threads. When the sliding nut is engaged to give the sliding motion the vertical shaft does not revolve, but if the nut is disengaged while the lead-screw continues to revolve then the worm-wheel and bevel gear are rotated. A short horizontal shaft carried in the saddle has a bevel gear at its front end and is driven from the vertical shaft, while at its rear it has a spur that can be slid into mesh with a gear on the back end of the cross-slide screw. An idler can be introduced to give a reverse motion. The bevel gear on the vertical shaft also engages a bevel gear on a second horizontal shaft that carries a handle at its front end and, when the lead-screw is at rest and the cross feed disengaged, this provides a hand feed to the saddle. The handle can be disengaged when the self-acting feed is in use.

Whitworth also patented and built lathes in which two slide rests were used, as shown in Fig. 11. Each of these rests could also hold two tools. The two rests could be moved radially and simultaneously by a cross screw with right- and left-handed threads, but could be independently adjusted by means of the top slides of the rests. One of the main objects sought was to reduce the deflection and vibration of long workpieces.

In 1840 Joseph Beattie, the engineer of the London & South-Western Railway works at Nine Elms, London, patented a double-ended lathe for turning the two wheels of railway-stock axles simultaneously. About this time several other forms of double-ended lathes and boring machines were also built, including one that became very well known as the Brymbo lathe. Some of these machines had a drive to both headstocks and could be used as two separate lathes, and one was actually made up of two lathes placed face to face on a common foundation. Others had one of the headstocks driven from the other through a shaft placed at the back and this drive could be disengaged if required. In some of these machines the two headstocks were fixed on the bed or foundation, while in others one of them could be moved along to accommodate axles of different lengths. Illustrations of models of some of

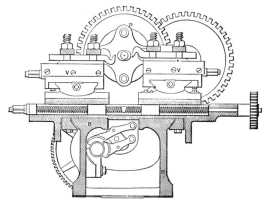

FIG. 11. Carriage of Whitworth's 'compound duplex lathe'. *Proc. Instn civ. Engrs*, vol. 17, 1857-8

these lathes can be seen in *The Engineer* of 10 July 1857. Several makers, including Whitworth, exhibited double-ended lathes in the 1851 exhibition. About 1850 Nasmyth patented and built a 'double or ambidexter' lathe, in which the headstock was placed at the centre of the bed and had a single spindle with a chuck or driving-plate at each end. There were two tailstocks and two saddles each with its own lead-screw.

In the turning lathe shown in Fig. 12, made during the second decade of this period by John Mason of Rochdale for machining large drums, the tool rests are carried on a bed mounted on ways provided at the front of the base plate. The whole assembly could therefore be moved in or out according to the diameter of the work. The tool rests could also be removed and replaced by a multiple-spindle drilling-head so that the work, after being turned, could also be drilled.

By the time of the 1851 exhibition lathes were being made in all sizes, from 7- to 8-ft wheel lathes down to small machines for amateurs, but in the report on the exhibition it is stated that there was no example of the 'colossal lathes which are employed for boring cylinders' being exhibited. A railway-wheel lathe shown by Sharp Brothers & Co. was a double-ended machine with two compound slide-rests, the headstocks being bolted to a T-slotted base-plate. Whitworth also showed a wheel lathe and two duplex lathes with beds 18 and 36 ft long respectively. The term 'duplex' here denoted that the lathes each had two saddles. Other firms showing large lathes were Smith, Beacock & Tannett;

Shepherd, Hill & Spink; and Parr, Curtis & Madely. The Lowell Machine Shop, an American firm, showed a 12 in centre lathe in which 'a lightness of construction carried to the extreme point consistent with strength and stiffness presents a singular contrast to the solid proportions adopted by our own engineers'.

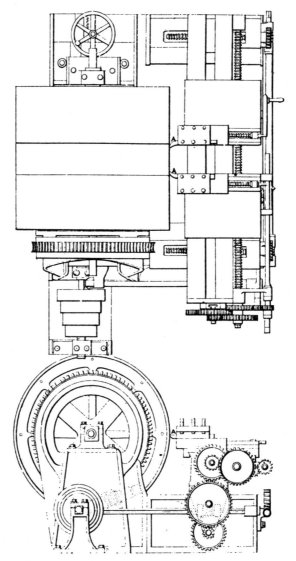

FIG. 12. Lathe by J. Mason c. 1850. *Proc. Instn civ. Engrs*, vol. 17, 1857–8

In 1852 W. B. Bement of Philadelphia designed a vertical 'boring engine', which is illustrated by a line drawing in the *Handbook for the artisan, mechanic and engineer* published by Oliver Byrne in 1853. In this machine the boring bar was carried by a member supported by three pillars, one at each side and one at the back, in the middle. It had a screw feed that could be disengaged by means of a half-nut, and a rack and pinion provided a rapid traverse. The weight of the bar was counterbalanced. The work table rotated in bearings in the base of the machine. It was driven by a cone pulley through bevel gears and a pinion that engaged an internal gear fixed to the table. Bement seems to have been very active at this time and several other machines of his are described in Byrne's book; some of these are mentioned in later sections of this chapter.

The turret lathe

It is no exaggeration to say that the invention of the turret lathe revolutionized machine-shop practice in regard to lathe work. This great step forward was made during the period now under discussion but, as with many inventions, there is some uncertainty as to whom the invention was due and exactly when it was made. In his book *English and American machine tool builders* J. W. Roe says that the turret lathe was built commercially by Robbins & Lawrence of Windsor, Vermont, in 1854. In an article in the *American Machinist* of 9 June 1900 E. G. Parkhurst says that F. W. Howe, who worked for Robbins & Lawrence, improved on plans made by J. D. Alvord for a 'turret-head screw machine', and that in 1860 he, Parkhurst, was shown one by Howe himself and that it bore the inscription 'Designed by F. W. Howe and manufactured by Robbins & Lawrence, Windsor, Vermont'. Later on Parkhurst says that Stephen Fitch, about 1843, contracted to produce 30 000 components for a percussion lock for which Henry Ashton of Middletown, Connecticut, had obtained a contract and that 'he [i.e. Fitch] afterwards made at his own expense a self-revolving turret-head screw machine which from 1845 to 1853 turned out excellent work'.

In an article in the *American Machinist* of 12 December 1908 E. A. Dixie gives an illustration that bears the caption 'First Turret Lathe in America', but he says 'who built it or when it was made no one knows but it was among the first tools in the Gay & Silver shop'. This firm originated in 1835 and became Gay & Silver in 1857; their works were situated in North Chelmsford. The turret of this lathe indexed about a vertical axis and was carried on a slide that moved in a sub-bed fixed to the main bed of the machine, so that it was what is now called, in England, a *capstan* lathe. The turret slide was moved by a pinion rotated by a four-armed 'pilot' wheel, and the pinion engaged a rack fixed to the turret slide. There were stops at the back of the machine for controlling the movement of the turret slide, and a locking bolt positioned the turret rotationally. A saddle carrying a cross slide was provided and there were tool-holders at both front and rear. The saddle had a nut that engaged a lead-screw at the front of the bed.

The headstock had a three-step cone pulley but it is not clear whether back gears were fitted. The spindle was hollow and carried a chuck at one end, while eight screws were provided at the other end to steady the stock. In his article Dixie also illustrated another turret lathe in which the turret was indexed about a horizontal axis and which was described as an 'Old Horizontal Turret Lathe'; no date was given for the year of its manufacture but the implication was that it was more or less contemporaneous with the one just described. In this second lathe the turret was carried in a saddle that moved directly on the bed of the machine and was actuated by a four-armed capstan; this capstan rotated a pinion that engaged a rack fixed to the bed. A saddle carrying a cross slide with two tool posts was again used and was actuated by a pinion which engaged a rack; the latter was fixed to the saddle at one end and passed below the headstock as in the Baxter D. Whitney lathe described earlier. The headstock had a four-step cone pulley but no back gear was fitted. The spindle again had a chuck at one end and steady screws at the other.

But in the U.S. Census report that Chas. H. Fitch wrote for the American Government in 1883 he says:

A form of horizontal chucking lathe is here illustrated (Fig. 27). In this the work revolves upon a spindle. A cluster of tools is turned by means of a small handle with a spring and ratchet movement and a hook rests in a groove at the back-end of the uppermost tool-holder making a connection with a rack in the same line and the tool is operated by being thus advanced or withdrawn by a gear on a spindle which, as shown, is turned by three handles or otherwise by a handwheel. If the movement of the tools is about a vertical spindle the machine is called a turret lathe.

And again:

The simple form of turret lathe, the tool stock chucking by hand, shown in the illustration (Fig. 28) is stated to be the earliest turret screw machine made for general sale. It was designed in 1858 by H. D. Stone of the Jones & Lamson Company of Windsor, Vt.

Fitch's illustrations are reproduced in Plates 43a and 43b. It would appear that the term 'chucking' is used by Fitch in the sense of 'indexing'. A machine, very similar to that shown in Plate 43a and also described as a 'chucking lathe', is illustrated in Roe's *English and American machine-tool builders* and Roe attributes the design to 'Mr. Root'.

It seems, therefore, that all that can be said with any degree of certainty is that the turret lathe originated in America between 1840 and 1850 and that while it seems that Stephen Fitch and F. W. Howe respectively invented the types shown in Plates 43a and 43b, others, whose achievements have not been recorded, made important improvements.

56

The use of the two positions mentioned above for the axis about which the turret was indexed has continued to the present day, although the vertical axis has become by far the commoner.

Whitworth's screw-cutting machine of 1835

In his patent, number 6850 of 1835, Whitworth describes an automatic machine for screwing such pieces as headed bolts, studs, etc. His specification embodies some elements that are found in the later automatic screw-machines of Spenser and others. The drawing accompanying the specification is reproduced in Fig. 13. The pieces to be screwed are loaded by hand into fingers on the end of the bar g (Fig. 17 of Whitworth's specification), which can slide axially and also vertically. The bar is then moved forward by the rotation of the cam p (Fig. 15) so that the workpiece is fed into the chuck through the opened dies of the head T. The chuck jaws are then closed by the cam ss (Fig. 15), lever cc, and cone k. The cam p then retracts the loading fingers and the cam v allows the weight f to close the dies. Meanwhile the rotation of the half-gear c (Fig. 15) rotates the spindle several times and the lead-screw at the end of the spindle L moves the latter forwards so that the work enters the dies and screwing is performed. The dies are then opened by the cam v. Meanwhile the extractor fingers on the bar h (Fig. 17) have been raised into alignment with the spindle L by the eccentricity of the cams pq and the medium of the levers kl (Fig. 15) which can rock on the rod nn. The groove in the cam q can then move the extractor fingers forwards and then backwards so as to remove the finished piece. Simultaneously the other half-gear c has rotated the spindle backwards so that it returns to the starting position and the cams pq have brought the loading fingers into position so that a fresh cycle can commence.

Boring and drilling machines

There were few notable developments in boring machines during this period; the introduction of lathes that were capable of boring large cylinders seems to have caused the vertical boring-machine to fall into disfavour. In a paper that Thomas Spencer Sawyer gave to the Institution of Civil Engineers in 1857, and in which he reviewed current machine-tool practice, he said 'Cylinder boring machines usually have horizontal boring bars carried between centres and the feed may be to either the boring head or to the work'. One reason that was advanced for the preference for the horizontal machine was that both faces of the cylinder could be machined at the same setting as the bore, which was not practicable with the vertical machine.

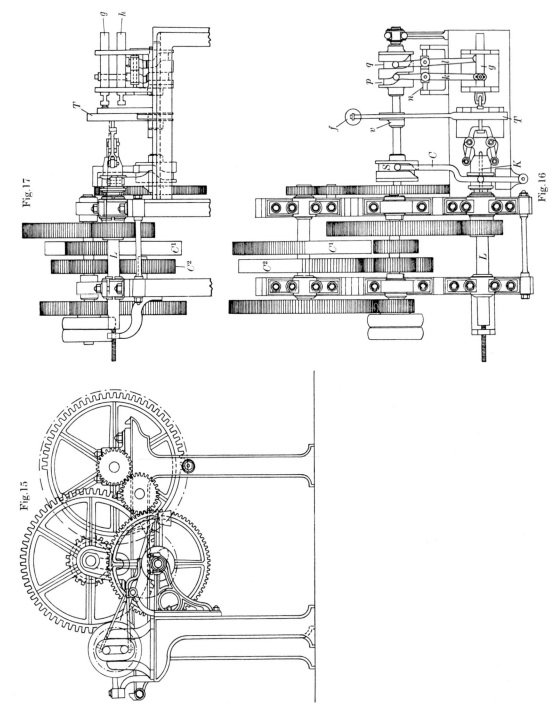

FIG. 13. Whitworth's bolt-screwing machine 1835. Patent No. 6850–1835

The machine shown in Fig. 14, which is from Sawyer's paper, may be taken as typical of the horizontal boring-machine of this period. It is virtually a lathe fitted with a boring bar that has a travelling head which differs from that of John Wilkinson only in that the feed is by means of a screw. A machine that was clearly built specially for boring and is not a lathe equipped with a boring bar is shown in Plate 44. The maker and date of manufacture of this machine are unknown and although it seems probable that it was made during the present period it may have been earlier. It is one of the machines that remained in the works of Maudslay, Sons & Field when they were closed down in 1900.

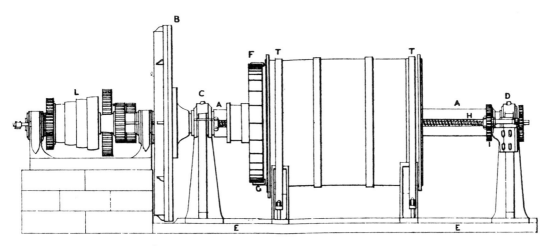

FIG. 14. Typical boring mill and lathe c. 1850. *Proc. Instn civ. Engrs*, vol. 17, 1857–8

The work is secured to a flat table that can move along V-ways in order to bring the axis of the hole into alignment with the axis of the boring spindle. The clamping arrangement for this table seems somewhat primitive but quite adequate. Alignment in the vertical plane is obtained by raising or lowering the whole spindle-head assembly, including the cone pulley. The latter is made to take a driving cord and was probably driven from a swinging countershaft of the type that Maudslay seems to have favoured. The screw feed to the spindle is belt-driven.

The firm of Nasmyth, Gaskell & Co. was one of the largest builders of machine tools during the middle of the nineteenth century and they built vertical boring-machines during the period now being considered. The one shown in Plate 45 is described by Nasmyth in his appendix to Buchanan's *Mill work and other machinery*. He prefaces his description by pointing out the advantages of the vertical arrangement—the absence of deflection in the cylinder being bored and in the boring bar itself being the most important ones, while a minor one was that the chips fell clear of the cutters. This machine utilizes the building in which it is installed to provide support for the upper bearing of the boring bar, and the driving gear is placed in a pit below ground level. A flat belt running on a cone pulley provides the drive, which is taken through change-speed gearing to a worm and wheel by which the boring bar is driven. The upper part of the bar is separate from the portion below ground so that it can be hoisted out of the way in order to get the work into position. The downward feed of the cutter head is by a screw and nut and, by means of 'a peculiar arrangement' of the nut, the cutter head can be drawn up without turning the screw. Nasmyth mentions that one of these machines could be seen in the 'erecting shops at Her Majesty's Dock Yard, Woolwich'. He also describes a similar machine that was made for the Great Western Steam Navigation Company for the purpose of boring the 10 ft diameter cylinders of the 'Mammoth' which, at the time he wrote, was being built at Bristol.

These machines of Nasmyth, Gaskell & Co. are very similar to one that was still in position in the Soho Foundry when it was closed down in 1895, but that shown in Plate 46, which was also there at that time, is very different. Perhaps the most remarkable feature is the use of belts running in a horizontal plane, a practice that millwrights have generally avoided. The machine was said to have been used for boring engine beds and had several separate work tables that could be moved along the very long bed.

A multiple-spindle boring and drilling machine

During this period John Mason, whose name has been mentioned earlier in this chapter, built the machine shown in Fig. 15. This has five spindles, each with a chuck at both ends, so that ten pieces of work can be operated on simultaneously. The drills or boring bars do not rotate but are given the feed motion; they are held in chucks carried by saddles at either side of the spindle head. These saddles have self-acting feeds but can be independently controlled.

Drilling machines

A pillar drill that embodied an interesting infinitely variable power-feed mechanism is described by Bodmer in his patent of 1839. A conical pulley on the drive shaft of the machine is coupled to a similar but inverted pulley by means of a belt, and inside this second pulley there is a double-sun-type planetary gear, the compound planet of which is carried by a pin mounted in the pulley. One part of the planet meshes with a sun gear that is also driven from the main driving-shaft, and the other part meshes with a second sun gear that is coupled to the screw of the feed mechanism. When the belt of the variable-speed drive is adjusted so as to make the speed of the driven pulley equal to that of the driving shaft, the epicyclic gear imparts no motion to the feed screw, but as the belt is adjusted, by means of a treadle, so as to alter the speed of the driven conical pulley, so the epicyclic gear imparts a motion to the driven sun and to the feed screw.

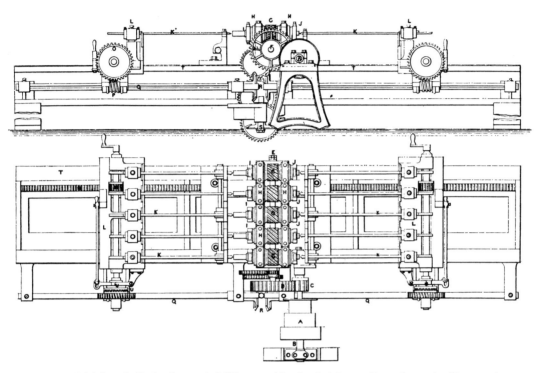

FIG. 15. Multiple-spindle boring and drilling machine by J. Mason. *Proc. Instn civ. Engrs*, vol. 17, 1857–8

An example of the pillar drilling-machines being made by Whitworth towards the end of this period and now exhibited in the Birmingham museum is shown in Plate 47a. In this the work table is mounted on a slide on a knee bracket that can pivot on the saddle; this enables several holes to be drilled without having to unclamp the workpiece. Some variations in design are shown in Plates 47b and 47c. In these the drill spindles slide through the bosses of the bevel gears that drive them and which rotate in the fixed boss of the column casting. The overhang of the drill thus increases as the drill is fed downwards. In the first example there is only one adjustment for the position of the workpiece, while in the second a compound slide provides motion in two directions. Another variation in design is shown in Plate 48a where the work table is borne on a cylindrical pillar carried by the column casting. This enables the table to be swung out of the way when necessary, as can be done in the Whitworth machine, but provides a more rigid support.

In 1848 Richard Roberts patented a machine for drilling a large number of holes in the frameplates of clocks and watches. The positions of the holes were controlled by a 'standard template'. This is an example of a drilling jig, but such jigs were being used many years earlier in France and also in America.

Towards the end of this period the Hungerford bridge across the Thames at Charing Cross was under construction and for the purpose of drilling the rivet holes in the plates used for the main girders the machine shown in Fig. 16 was built by John Cochrane. There are eighty drills of 1 in diameter, the spindles

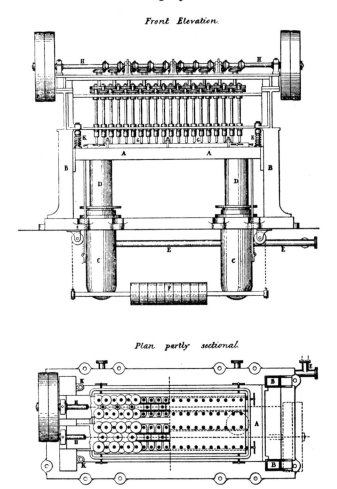

Front Elevation.

Plan partly sectional.

Scale ¼₀ᵗʰ.

Ins.12   6   0   1   2   3   4   5   6   7   8   9   *10 Feet.*

(Proceedings Inst. M.E.1860. Page 201.)

FIG. 16. Cochrane's multi-spindle drilling machine.
Proc. Instn mech. Engrs, 1860

are driven by bevel gears, and the feed was obtained by moving the work table upwards by means of two hydraulic rams capable of exerting a total force of 20 tons.

Radial drilling machines

The period under discussion saw the introduction of the radial type of drilling machine, a development in which several engineers played a part. One of the earliest examples of this type of machine is shown in Plate 48*b*. This was made by Benjamin Hick & Son at some time before 1840. The method of raising the arm is somewhat peculiar and did not survive, although it was used many years later in some American milling machines. In some respects, such as the use of a square shaft and bevel gears for the drive to the spindle, the design is in advance of its contemporaries.

A form of radial drill that became very popular and continued to be built well into the twentieth century is shown in Plate 49*a*. The arm that carries the spindle head is an inverted L-shaped member with trunnions at the top and bottom of the vertical limb; these are held in bearings in a saddle that can slide up and down the vertical face of the column casting. The drive to the spindle is taken from a horizontal shaft carrying the belt pulleys through bevel gears to a vertical shaft co-axial with the trunnions, and thence through a second pair of bevels to a horizontal shaft running along the arm, and finally through bevel gears to the spindle itself. Key-ways provide for the sliding of the gears along the shafts, an improvement on the square shaft. The main advantage claimed for the design was greater rigidity; a slight disadvantage was that the arm could be swung only through an angle of rather less than 180°.

A wall-mounted radial drilling-machine made by Sharp, Roberts & Co. of Manchester about the middle of this period is shown in Fig. 17. The use of the wall to replace the column presumably reduced the cost of manufacture but has some obvious drawbacks.

Planing, slotting, and shaping machines

During this period planers of the conventional form did not change much except in details, but they were built in larger sizes. Some new forms were, however, produced, notably the wall, or side, planer and the travelling tool-machine. James Fox, Roberts, and Whitworth were the principal builders but many other firms entered the field during the period.

A machine built by Fox is shown in Plate 49*b*. This now stands in the Musée des Arts et Métiers and is said in the catalogue to have been built in 1833. The table ways are similar to those used by Fox in his lathes, one being a V and the other a flat; the drive to the table is by pinion and rack, and reversal is by means of a bevel-gear cluster and a dog-tooth clutch. The work table is made in two parts, the upper one being pivoted on a transverse axis on the lower so

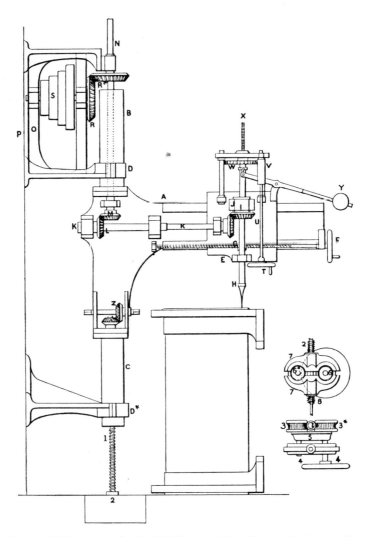

FIG. 17. Wall-mounted radial drilling machine, Sharp, Roberts & Co.
Proc. Instn civ. Engrs, vol. 17, 1857–8

that wedge-shaped pieces can be machined easily. The cross-beam is set at a fixed height and the only vertical adjustment for the tool is by the extra long tool-slide; there does not seem to be any provision for tilting the tool for the machining of dovetails or similar angled surfaces. All these features indicate that this machine was made for some particular purpose, probably in connection with some of the textile machines that Fox was manufacturing. The machine is not described in the catalogue of the museum as a model but its size seems to imply that it is.

The first planing machine in which the cutting motion was given to the tool while the work remained stationary seems to have been built by an eminent French engineer named La Morinière about the year 1854. He is said to have subsequently built many machines of this type, which is known in France as the 'French' form, whereas the type in which the work moves and the tool is stationary is known there as the 'English' type. Plate 50*a* shows a model of one of La Morinière's machines. The work is clamped to a fixed bed, while the cross beam that carries the tool heads can slide along V-ways provided on the side frames of the machine and placed so that they lie approximately in the plane of the cutting edge of the tool. One of the tool heads is arranged to cut on the forward stroke and the other on the return. The tool heads can be tilted but, as in Fox's machine just described, the only vertical adjustment is that provided by the tool-head slide. This would seem to limit the size of the work that could be handled, which seems somewhat contradictory, since one of the principal claims made for this type of machine is that the tool-head assembly is lighter and easier to move than is the table and work of the conventional machine.

In 1835 Whitworth patented a planing machine in which the tool-head assembly travelled over the fixed work, but in this machine the assembly travelled on four wheels. Plate 51 reproduces the drawing accompanying the specification and it will be seen that the V-ways on which the wheels run are placed well below the cutting plane. Two screws are used to give the motion, one at each side, and instead of nuts, small pulleys whose flanges engage the flanks of the screw threads are used. Reversal of the motion is by means of a bevel-gear cluster and a dog-clutch. The machine is fitted with the double-cutting tool-head that was used on Whitworth's later machines. A single tool is used and is carried in a cylindrical member that can be rotated about its axis through 180°, so that the tool can face both ways. The rotation is brought about by the over-run of the travelling carriage through the medium of cords. The arrangement is more clearly seen in Plate 52, which shows a machine of the conventional type built by Whitworth in 1842 and now in the Science Museum. The work table of this later machine is moved by a single central screw on the end of which there is a bevel gear that engages two bevel wheels, each of which is coupled to a belt pulley; a loose pulley lies between these two pulleys and reversal is by shifting the single belt across from one outer pulley to the other. This, of course, gave the same speed for both strokes, which was what was required.

Roberts, in his patent of 1838, shows a similar reversing mechanism, but it is placed at the side of the machine and drives the table through a double-spur pinion and a stepped-tooth rack. He did not claim this drive as a novelty. His machine also incorporated a double-cutting tool box but in this two tools placed back to back were used and each was brought into action when required by tilting the tool box about an axis perpendicular to the table axis, rather as Clement tilted the cross-beam of his machine.

At some time prior to 1840 Benjamin Hick & Sons of Bolton built a machine similar to that of Morinière but employing steel belts instead of the chains used by Morinière. This machine had a capacity of 30 ft × 9 ft 6 in and is illustrated in Buchanan's *Mill work and other machinery*.

J. G. Bodmer also invented a double-cutting tool box for planing machines and this is described in his patent of 1839. Two tools are used, each carried in a holder that can slide up and down in the tool head; they are actuated by a short lever pivoted on its centre and engaging slots in the sides of the tool holders. This lever is operated by the reversal mechanism of the table drive. In the same patent Bodmer also described the machine shown in Plates 53 and 54. This might well be the first example of an open-side planer. The tool head is carried at the end of a ram that can move horizontally in ways in a saddle. The saddle can move up and down the pillar on which it is mounted and the pillar can be rotated about a vertical axis on its base. The base carrying the pillar can be traversed on ways perpendicular to the table ways. The latter are on two levels in order to accommodate the L-shaped work table, to which work could be bolted on either the horizontal or the vertical face. A gib is provided below the higher way in order to prevent any lift from occurring. An auxiliary table is provided to support large jobs that overhang the main table and this can be moved to any convenient distance from, and is driven from the same shaft as, the main table. Provision is made to enable the upper end of the tool-head pillar to be braced to any convenient point of the structure in which the machine is housed.

A planer that was built in America during the first decade of the period under discussion is described in the *American Machinist* of 31 October 1908. The work table was 39 in wide and 12 ft long and it moved on shallow cast-iron ways supported on a granite base. One of the ways was an inverted V and the other was flat, and it is stated that they were finished by chipping and filing. The work table was operated by a chain that passed over sprockets placed at the centres of transverse shafts at the ends of the bed. The rear shaft was driven from overhead pulleys through two pairs of bevel gears and a vertical shaft. An open and a crossed belt gave the reversal but it is uncertain whether this was part of the original machine.

Several makers exhibited planing machines in the 1851 exhibition and amongst them there was a diminutive machine made by Shanks & Co. 'for the use of opticians'. Whitworth also showed a small planing machine in which the work table was driven by the crank and slotted-lever mechanism that later became the most popular method of operating the rams of shaping machines. One of these machines is now preserved in the Birmingham museum. At some point during this period Batho & Bauer built an almost identical machine and this is shown in the line drawing of Fig. 18. It is not known whether Whitworth, Batho &

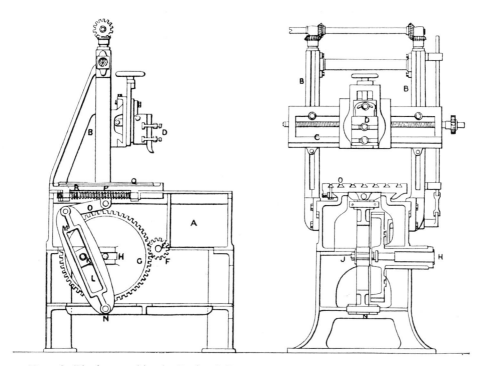

FIG. 18. Planing machine by Batho & Bauer. *Proc. Instn civ. Engrs*, vol. 17, 1857–8

Bauer, or some other maker was the originator of the mechanism, but since it is a variation of the well-known Whitworth quick return motion it seems likely that he invented it, indeed, in the description of Whitworth's machine in the official catalogue of the 1851 exhibition, it seems to be implied that it was Whitworth's invention. However, Rose, in his *Modern machine shop practice*, published before 1887, describes the two mechanisms as the '*Whitworth quick-return* and the *vibrating link*' types and says that the former is the commoner.

About 1866 Wm. Sellers & Co. built a planing machine in which the standards structure travelled over the fixed work. Each standard at its foot had an inwards projection formed into an inverted V at the top and a V at the bottom; these Vs engaged corresponding ways provided at the sides of the bed. The standards were traversed by means of pinions at each side; these were carried on the ends of vertical shafts and engaged racks fixed to the bed. At their upper ends the shafts were driven by a belt through toothed gearing, the arrangement being indicated in Fig. 19. Reversal was controlled by stops on a screwed shaft driven from one of the pinion shafts. The stops could be adjusted to vary the stroke by the operator who travelled with the standards on a platform provided for him.

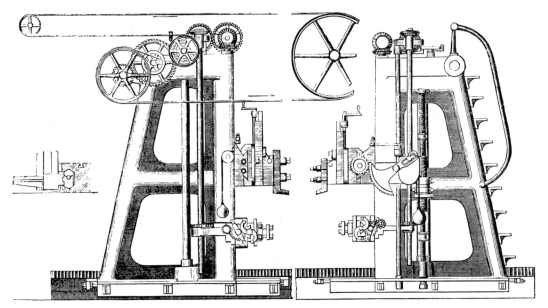

FIG. 19. Wm. Sellers's travelling-standards planing machine c. 1860. *Engineering*, *Lond.* 22 June 1866

Wall planers

The general arrangement of this type of planer is shown by Plate 50*b*. The work is fixed on horizontal tables, and the cutting tool is carried in a head on a saddle that travels along ways formed on a casting that is supported by a wall of the building in which the machine is housed. The supports shown in the picture are for exhibition purposes only. This form of planer has some advantages over the conventional forms, particularly when heavy, large pieces of work are concerned. They are always called planers although it is the tool that travels. They have always been adapted to take cuts in a vertical direction as well as in the horizontal, the tool head then travelling up and down the ways on the front of the saddle. The date when the first such machine was built is unknown, but that shown is certainly the earliest one that has survived and, in all probability, was the first to be made. It is now in the Birmingham museum and is thought to have been installed in the Soho Factory about 1830 and to have been brought to the Soho Foundry at a later date. The machine needs no detailed description but one or two things about it may be of interest. The vertical surface of the saddle has been planed but its slots are un-machined and the surfaces of the work tables do not appear to have been planed. This appearance may, however, be due to wear and tear. The screw seen at the top of the wall casting is said to be the original one installed when the machine was made.

A similar but larger machine is illustrated in *The Engineer* of 27 September 1895 and was in the Soho Foundry at that time. This larger machine was almost certainly made at a later date, probably towards the end of the period under discussion.

Slotting machines

The slotting machine appears to have been invented during the early part of the present period and Richard Roberts has been credited with this innovation. It has also been suggested that the design was influenced by that of the morticing machine that Maudslay made for Brunel, but there is no definite information on these points. However, Buchanan, in his *Mill work and other machinery*, gives an illustration of a slotting machine made by Sharp & Roberts. This is reproduced in Fig. 20. The machine gives the impression of being rather flimsy but it has all the essential features of much later designs including a tilting table. Buchanan also illustrates a design by F. Lewis, a prominent Manchester machine-took builder of the period, and this is shown in Fig. 21. It also has a tilting work table but the frame, although much more robust than that of Roberts's machine, is still rather light. Probably the most important improvement that was made during the latter part of this period was the introduction of the box-like casting for the main frame members of almost all machine tools, an innovation that is

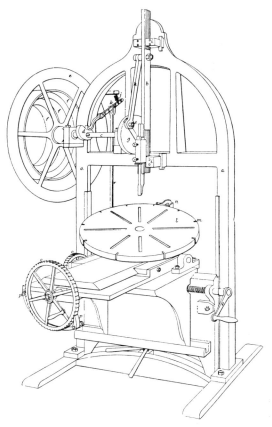

FIG. 20. Sharp, Roberts's slotting machine. Buchanan, *Practical essays on mill work*, 1841

69

generally attributed to Whitworth. An example of a large wall-mounted slotting machine is shown in Plate 55; this was installed in the Soho Foundry and was probably made towards the end of the first decade of this period.

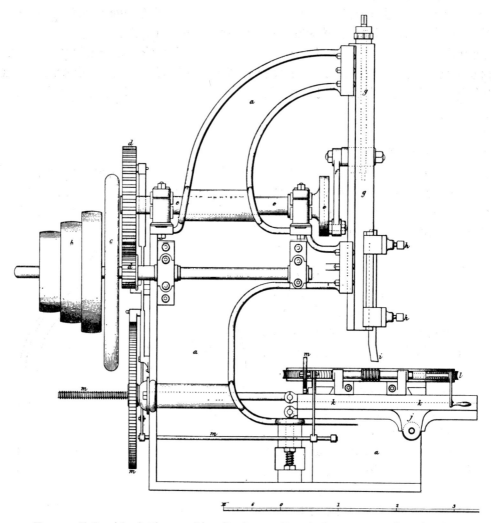

FIG. 21. F. Lewis's slotting machine. Buchanan, *Practical essays on mill work*, 1841

A design by Bodmer, which appeared in his patent of 1839, is shown in Plate 56. The slide in which the ram is carried can be rotated about a horizontal axis on the cross-member uniting the massive standards, so that the tool travel could be out of the vertical, a feature that did not become common until many years later. The work table is supported on two knee-castings that can be elevated on ways on the faces of the standards. The work table can be traversed in two directions at right angles and a circular table, which can be removed, is provided. The tool box is carried on a ball-and-socket joint at the bottom of the ram, and the connecting rod is used to cause the box to rock slightly so as to provide the relief for the tool on the return stroke.

Shaping machines

The claim that James Nasmyth invented the shaping machine is made by Smiles[1] and he is said to have done this in 1836. The machine is shown in Fig. 22, which is reproduced from Smiles's book; incidentally Nasmyth called his machine a *planing* machine. It incorporated most of the basic features of

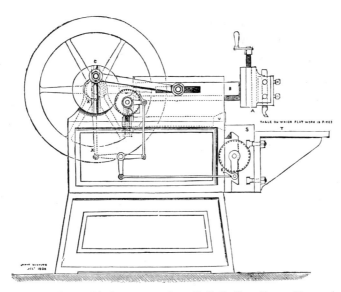

FIG. 22. Nasmyth's 'steam arm' *c.* 1836. Smiles, *James Nasmyth*

later productions but did not have a swivelling tool-slide and there was no quick return for the ram. An actual shaper, once owned by Nasmyth, is now in the Science Museum, but this is a bench machine and differs from that shown in Fig. 22 in having a Scotch yoke instead of a connecting rod.

However, when the Maudslay, Sons & Field works were closed down in 1900 a very old shaping machine was found in the plant and was illustrated in the article on the works that appeared in *Engineering* of 1 February 1901. The machine is certainly very primitive in comparison with that of Nasmyth and, as it seems unlikely that Maudslay would have built such a machine if a much better design had been available, it is possible that the Maudslay machine is the earlier. In it the tool was carried in a member that could slide along two cylindrical bars and was driven by a crank and connecting rod. The slide bars could be adjusted up and down on four screwed pillars provided with nuts, but no other vertical adjustment was provided except by loosening the tool in its holder. The work table was a flat plate carried on a dovetail slide placed at right angles to the slide bars and the feed motion was hand-operated.

Nasmyth's design became one of the commonest forms for the shaper, but during the decades following its invention the travelling-head type of machine was developed and by 1850 this also was an established form.

In America a pillar-type shaping machine was designed by W. B. Bement in 1851 and is described in Oliver Byrne's *Handbook for the artisan, mechanic and engineer*. It was called the *American Compound Planer* and the ram was operated by a screw, reversing being by open and crossed belts. The work table traversed on ways on the face of the pillar. In another similar machine, described by Byrne and also designed by Bement, the ram was actuated by a lever pivoted at its mid-point on a horizontal axis. The upper end of the lever was formed into a toothed quadrant, which engaged a rack fixed to the underside of the ram. The lower end was slotted and was oscillated by an adjustable crank and a sliding block. The machine was described as the *Improved Compound Planer* and was made by the firm of Marshall, Bement & Colby.

During the decade 1840–50 the travelling-head type of shaping machine was introduced, probably by Whitworth, who exhibited one in the 1851 exhibition. The appearance of this machine can be seen from Fig. 23, but this actually

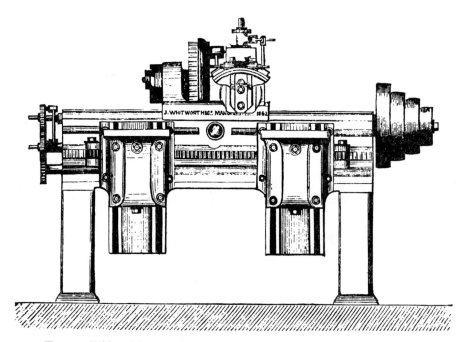

FIG. 23. Whitworth travelling-head shaping machine. Clark, *The exhibited machinery of 1862*, Pt. 3

shows the machine exhibited in 1862. The differences, however, are unimportant. The Whitworth quick-return motion was used and self-acting motions were provided for the longitudinal motion of the saddle, the vertical or angular motion of the tool slide and the rotation of the mandrel used for circular work. In the 1862 exhibition Whitworth also showed a slotting machine in which the head carrying the ram could travel along the top of the bed of the machine.

Milling machines

Very little is known regarding the development of the milling machine between about 1820, when the machine used by Robert Johnson at Middletown was made, and the early years of the present period. In those early years, however, great progress was made in the use of milling machines and important improvements were made in their design. An early advance was the introduction of a support for the outer end of the cutter spindle that had hitherto been overhung; this appears to have originated in the shops of Gay & Silver at North Chelmsford and a picture of one of the earliest of them is shown in Plate 57a. The power feed seen in this picture is said to have been added some time after the machine itself was made. Vertical adjustments between the cutter and the work are made by moving the spindle head up or down on the column.

One of the greatest improvements was the introduction of what has become known as the *Lincoln* type of milling machine because in the early days the firm of George S. Lincoln of the Phoenix Ironworks, Hartford, Conn. became the principal commercial makers of the machines. The design of this type of machine has been attributed to the American, Thomas Warner,[2] who was employed at the United States Armory at Springfield and is said to have built his machine in 1840; but F. W. Howe was undoubtedly one of the greatest influences on the development of the type and Elisha Root, Francis Platt, and others played an important part. It seems impossible to distinguish just which of the improvements was made by each of these engineers, but the result was a machine that became immensely popular and was built in large numbers by several different manufacturers and was exported to several European countries.

The general appearance of the Lincoln-type miller in its early days is shown by Plates 57b and 57c. The first of these is taken from the *American Machinist* of 28 June 1900, and the second from a report on machine tools made by F. R. Hutton[3] for the United States Government and published in 1885. In his introduction Hutton says that his report represents American practice down to the close of 1880. The first of these machines is said to have been made in 1854 and it differs only slightly from the other. The machines need little description but a somewhat surprising feature is that the cone-pulley shaft is carried on bearings fixed to brackets that are integral with the standards in which the spindle bearings slide up and down, so that as this is done the mesh between the gears coupling the cone pulley to the cutter spindle would vary. The mesh could be adjusted by moving the bearing blocks of the cone-pulley shaft on their brackets, but this would be inconvenient if it had to be done frequently. It thus seems that the machines were intended for long runs on particular jobs, and initially this was probably the case, because these machines were developed in shops that were engaged on contracts for large quantities of rifle components.

One of the improvements that Elisha Root is supposed to have made to the Lincoln miller is the use of an overarm that elevates with the spindle as in the Gay & Silver machine. An illustration of this is given in the issue of the *American Machinist* quoted above and is reproduced in Plate 57*d*.

An original form of milling machine that is said to have been designed by Frederick Howe and was called an *Index Miller* is shown in Plate 58*a*. This is taken from a publication of the Taylor & Fenn Company who, in 1907, became the owners of the Phoenix Iron Works of the George S. Lincoln Company where the machine was built in considerable quantities in the mid 1850s and later. The spindle is driven directly by the pulley but can slide axially through it and the spindle bearings, this motion being controlled by the hand lever seen at the rear on the right. The work is held in a fixture that can rotate about a vertical axis and be positioned by the index plate seen below it. The fixture can also be raised or lowered by means of a screw actuated by the hand-wheel seen at the front. Because the work could not be traversed the spindle head was made to slide along ways on the top of the bed, two lead-screws, one at the front and the other at the rear, being used for this. The central shaft carrying the hand-wheel seen in the picture was geared at its other end to these lead-screws. Machines almost identical with this one were still in use at the U.S. Armory at Springfield in 1900 and one is illustrated in the *American Machinist* of 7 April 1900. The only noticeable differences are that the hand-wheel actuating the elevating screw of the work-holding fixture is mounted directly on the top of the vertical shaft instead of being connected by bevel gears, and that a power feed to the spindle head is fitted. The latter seems to have been added subsequent to the building of the machine.

The vertical milling-machine is particularly adapted for the machining of irregular profiles by copying a former or template and machines expressly designed for this purpose were developed during the period. An early example, which may be the first of its kind, is shown in Plate 58*b*. According to C. H. Fitch, who wrote a report similar to that of Hutton, it was designed by F. W.

Howe for the firm of Robbins & Lawrence. The spindles are carried in two saddles that can be traversed across the face of the cross-beam by means of a rack and pinion, and the saddles have a vertical adjustment for the cutter height. The work table can also be traversed along the bed by means of a rack and pinion. The saddles are provided with lugs in which followers can be secured, and these are kept in contact with the former, or pattern, by one of the motions, whilst the other motion provides the feed. At a later date a weight acting through a chain was used for the first purpose.

In England the milling machine did not develop nearly so rapidly as in America, possibly because the demand was for large machines to deal with the components of locomotives and stationary steam-engines rather than with the large quantities of small components for which the early American machines were most suitable. But certain forms of machines using milling cutters that were produced in England during the period show a high standard of design.

The small milling machine made by Nasmyth when he was working for Maudslay has been mentioned. In 1847 he modified a drilling machine so as to make it suitable for cutting cotter holes and key-ways, using a special cutter that he invented; this was a simple form of end mill. He seems to have subsequently made similar machines in considerable numbers. Some years later several other firms were producing machines of this type and one, made by Sharp, Stewart & Co., is shown in Plate 59a. This machine is now in the Musée des Arts et Métiers in Paris and another is in the Science Museum. In 1855 Stewart & Furnival took out a patent for a similar kind of machine; the design is shown in Fig. 24, which is taken from a paper given by Thomas Forsyte to the Institution of Mechanical Engineers in 1856. According to Forsyte the firm were making these machines in 1848. The crank that provided the to-and-fro motions of the cutter heads was driven through elliptical gears in order to make the motion more uniform. Similar double spindle-head machines were also made by Batho & Bauer and are described in Sawyer's paper to the Institution of Civil Engineers in 1857. A heavier machine by Sharp Stewart, which was described as a 'marine slotting drill', is shown in Plate 59b.

The development of the milling machine was dependent to some extent on the development of the cutters. Bodmer's segmental cutters have been mentioned. Whitworth was using formed cutters in a gear-cutting machine during the fourth decade of the nineteenth century and in his worm-wheel cutting machine used a hob. According to Charles H. Fitch, an American named Elham Allan was using formed milling cutters in 1830, but he does not say how these cutters were backed-off. According to Bodmer, screw taps were backed-off by hand prior to

75

his invention of his backing-off lathe in 1839, and presumably formed milling cutters were also relieved by hand or, perhaps, by means of a straight-cut relief; but the latter would not retain the shape of the cutter after grinding. The introduction of the formed relieved milling cutters commercially did not, however, come until the next period.

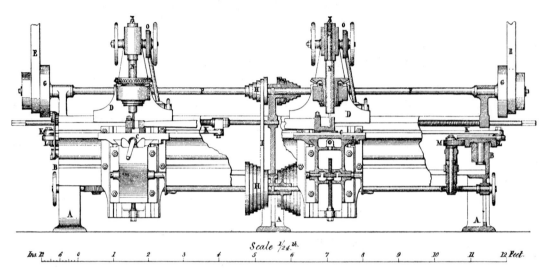

FIG. 24. Double-spindle vertical milling machine by Sharp, Stewart & Co., *Proc. Instn mech. Engrs*, 1856

Gear-cutting machines

Many of the gear-cutting machines produced during the early years of the period under consideration were not much more than enlarged versions of the old clockmakers' wheel-cutting engines, adapted to do heavier work. But others showed the result of the experience gained from the manufacture of other types of machine tool and formed the transition to the modern gear-cutter. Two forms of machine became common, the work axis being vertical in one and horizontal in the other, and both used formed cutters. A typical example of the first type is shown in Fig. 25. This was the design of F. Lewis of Manchester and was being made before 1840. In it the feed motion is given to the slide carrying the cutter spindle, and this could be tilted so that the motion could be either parallel, or at an angle, to the work axis. In some of Lewis's machines built about this time wheels up so about 12 ft in diameter could be cut and the cutter spindle could also be tilted so that oblique teeth could perhaps have been cut, but as no provision was made for giving any rotation of the blank as the cutter was fed across its face, it would appear that only plunge cuts could be employed, on wheels of small face width.

76

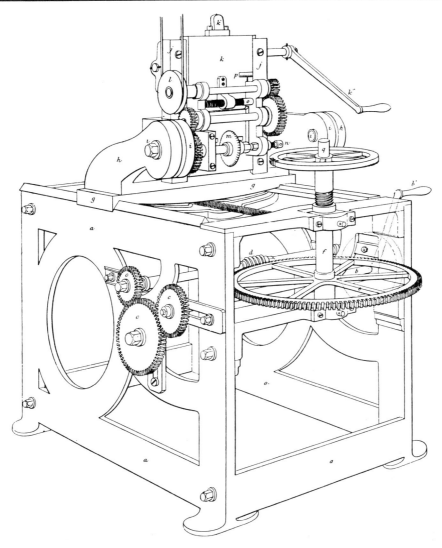

FIG. 25. F. Lewis's gear-cutting machine *c.* 1835. Buchanan,
Practical essays on mill work, 1841

Whitworth's gear-tooth cutting machine

This machine is of interest because it embodies the basic principle underlying the action of all gear-tooth hobbing machines. In his patent number 6850 of 1835 Whitworth describes his machine and says it is

applicable more particularly to the cutting of the teeth of screw wheels, or those which take into or gear with endless screws, or such other wheels as have their teeth formed at an angle to the direction of their axis; the principal novel feature being that a continuous rotary motion is given to the piece of metal or disc to be cut, at the same time a distinct continuous rotary motion is given to the cutting tool by which means the cutting of the

77

teeth proceeds round the periphery of the disc or wheel without intermission from the time it is commenced until it is finished.

The drawing accompanying the specification is reproduced in Figs. 26 and 27 and the construction of the machine will be fairly obvious. The blank is mounted on a shaft that is driven by a worm and wheel from the driving shaft. The cutter is of the nature of a hob but is made with a shank like a tap and this shank is fitted into the hollow end of a shaft that is carried in bearings in a saddle. This can be fed vertically on a dovetailed slide on the face of the base casting. The outer end of the hob is supported on a centre and the hob shaft is geared to a pinion on the end of the worm shaft through an intermediate gear. The latter is fixed on a slotted arm that can rotate about the axis of the worm shaft, and this motion enables the intermediate gear to maintain its mesh with the pinion and driven gear despite the vertical motion of the saddle. The downward motion of the saddle is imparted by a weight through a cord and screw and is limited by an adjustable stop. As there is no provision for the motion of the hob in the direction of the axis of the blank, the machine can cut only worm-wheels and wheels that are thin in relation to the diameter of the cutter, so that the curvature of the teeth cut on the blank is negligible.

Whitworth subsequently built machines that were a great advance on contemporary products in regard to rigidity, but none of them seems to have been a generating type. An early machine that is said to have been made some time between 1834 and 1844 is shown in Plate 60. The cutter is a milling cutter and the slide on which it is carried can be pivoted on the face of the angle bracket that carries it. Thus teeth can be cut at an angle to the axis of the wheel. The angle bracket can also be pivoted about a vertical axis so that bevel gears could at least have been roughed out. A dividing plate at one end of the bed is coupled to the work spindle through change-gears, a worm, and a large worm-wheel.

Bodmer's gear-cutting machine 1839

In his patent number 8070 J. G. Bodmer described several types of machine tool and one of these was a gear cutter that could cut the teeth of spur, bevel, and worm gears, and racks. In this machine he used his patent milling cutters. Parts of the very detailed drawings that accompanied his specification are reproduced in Plates 61 and 62 but as the construction is complex some description is necessary.

The machine consists of a bed (*a*) having dovetailed ways on its upper surface on which a saddle (*n*) can be traversed by means of a screw and nut. The saddle overhangs the bed at the rear and so an additional support (57) is provided. On its upper surface the saddle has dovetailed ways to carry a cross slide (*p*),

78

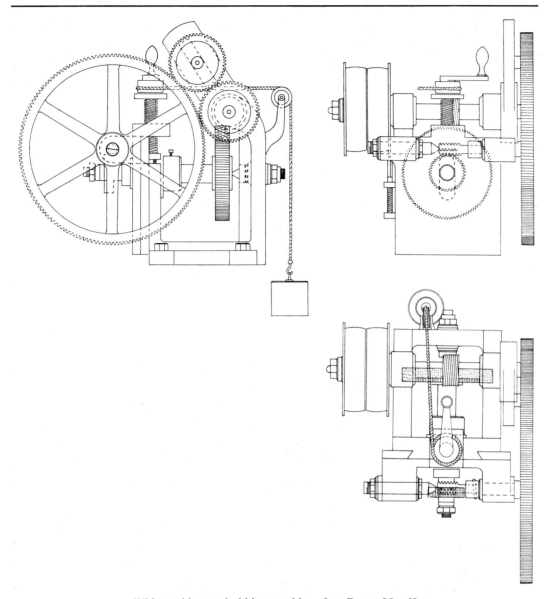

Whitworth's gear-hobbing machine 1835. Patent No. 6850.
FIG. 26. (above) Elevations. Fig. 27 (below) Plan

and on the top of this there is a table (u) that can be swivelled through 90° about a vertical axis. Bolted to this table is an angle bracket on which the lower member (v) of a tool-holder slide is carried on a pivot (w) so that the member can be swivelled about a horizontal axis. The cutter spindle revolves in a casting (7) carried by the upper member (4) of the tool-holder slide, and can be swivelled about a horizontal axis (s) at right angles to that on which the lower member can turn. The axis of the cutter can thus be rotated about three axes,

79

two of which are at right angles, while the third may be at any angle in the horizontal plane and at a limited range of angles in the vertical plane.

At the bottom end of the cutter spindle there are gears to couple it to a double V pulley; a rope provides the drive. The tension of the rope is maintained by a weight that acts on the carriage (*i*) seen at the right-hand end of the bed. The whole of the cutter spindle assembly (7) can be replaced by alternative forms for the cutting of worm gears, racks, and bevel gears.

The work is carried on the overhanging end of a spindle (24), which can rotate in bearings in a head (26) that can move up and down on ways on a casting (28) bolted to the end of the bed. The front end of the work spindle carries a large worm-wheel (25), which is engaged by a worm (39); this worm is split so that backlash can be eliminated. Bevel gears and key-wayed shafts couple the worm to a 'click crank' or dividing arm (38), which can be registered with one of a number of notches cut in a division plate. This latter assembly is bolted to the cross slide.

Spur gears are cut by formed milling cutters and indexing is by hand. For worm gears a hob is used; this can be geared to the division plate and thus to the work. Bevel gears are cut by a conical milling cutter, which revolves about an axis that can be moved in any direction about the apex of the gear. The axis of this cutter is approximately parallel to the generating line of the pitch cone of the gear being cut. A roller is situated beyond the end of the cutter and is free to rotate about the cutter axis; it bears on a former and lifts the cutter spindle upwards as the inward feed motion is given to the cutter. The tooth profile is thus a copy of the template or former. A separate cut is required for each side of a tooth.

In comparison with contemporary gear-cutting machines this one is much more versatile and it shows greater refinement of design. Perhaps the only criticism that can be made is that the complexity of the cutter-spindle assembly suggests that a lack of rigidity may have limited the cuts that could be taken. Whether this was so or not the machine is an outstanding achievement.

B. W. Bement's gear-cutting engine

This machine was designed and built about 1852 for the Lowell Machine Shop. It used a formed milling cutter and could cut spiral gears. The general arrangement of the machine is fairly clear from the drawing, Plate 63, but there are some points that require a little explanation. For straight-toothed gears the feed was provided by moving the saddle carrying the cutter spindle down the face of the head (*O*), which provided the adjustment for varying diameters of blank and gave the in-feed. Indexing was by the index plate (*D*), which was positioned by the spring-loaded pin (*K*). The spring carrying this pin was anchored to the end of an arm integral with the collar (*E*), but this collar was free to rotate on the frame of the machine. Its end, however, was held against an abutment (*F*) by means of a weight (*a*). When gears having inclined teeth were being cut, the abutment was tilted to the appropriate angle and the feed was then given by raising the work spindle (*C*). This was done by the wheel (*H*), on the inner end of which there was a toothed sector that meshed with a rack; the counterweight helped to reduce friction at the thrust bearing. In its upward motion the arm (*E*) and the dividing plate and work spindle received the required angular motion from the guide (*F*). The cutter spindle, of course, was tilted over to the appropriate angle. The machine was robust and well-proportioned and a notable feature is the grouping of all the controls for the convenience of the operator.

Schiele's gear-hobbing machine

In 1856 Christian Schiele of Oldham took out a patent, number 2896, for a gear-cutting machine, the principle of which is precisely that of modern gear-hobbers. The drawing (Plate 64) accompanying the specification shows two machines, one for small gears and the other for large ones. In both of them the cutter is clearly a hob, that of the large machine having inserted teeth. The spindle that carries the hob is coupled through change gearing to the spindle that carries the blank being cut. In the small machine the feed is imparted to the blank, which is moved upwards by a screw, while in the large one it is given to the saddle carrying the cutter. In the small machine the position of the hob in relation to the blank is adjusted by means of the worm, sector, and hand-wheel seen at the left; this rocks the frame carrying the hob spindle. In the large machine the adjustment is made by moving the saddle carrying the work along the bed. No provision is made for rotating the hob so that the tangent to its teeth can be brought parallel to that of the teeth being cut, but this is not essential since hobs can be designed to work at any angle, within limits. It is not known whether machines were ever built to these designs.

John Potts's bevel gear-cutting machine

In 1858 John Potts, who was a member of a well-known firm of clockmakers, took out a patent for a machine designed primarily for cutting bevel gears but adaptable for the cutting of spur gears. In his specification he describes two forms of his machine in one of which the axis of the blank is placed vertically and in the other horizontally. The tooth profile was copied from a former. Fig. 28 is produced from the specification and shows the horizontal machine.

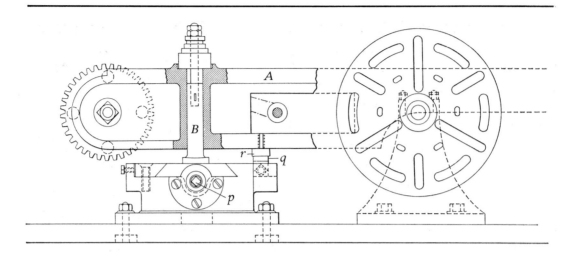

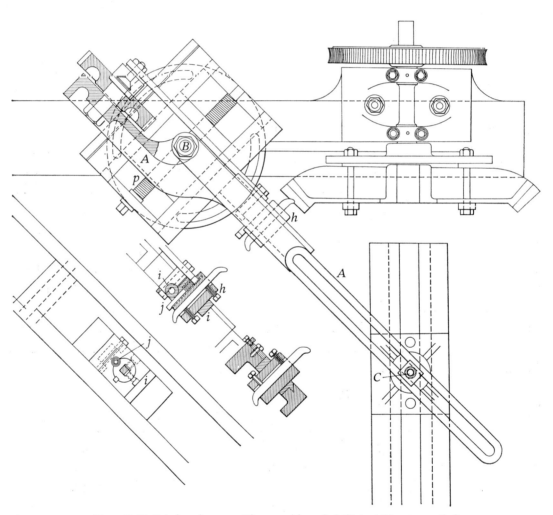

FIG. 28. Potts's bevel-gear cutting machine 1858. Patent No. 347—1858

The point B of the arm AA is moved along the slide by the screw p so that the arm swings about the pivot C. Because the point B moves along a straight line the arm A has to slide on the pivot block at C, and it may be observed that because the line of stroke of the tool does not pass through the axis at C, the line of cut passes through the apex of the pitch cone of the gear in only one position of the arm. The imperfection, however, would be very small. As the arm is moved along the slide a tracer piece r, carried by the arm and seen in the upper view, bears on the former q (carried by the base of the slide) and causes the end of the arm to be raised or lowered so that the tool reproduces the shape of the former. This motion of the arm is provided for by leaving the arm free to slide on the pivot at B, but it would appear that horizontal pivots would, theoretically, be required at both B and C, and at neither of these points is such a pivot shown in the specification. The tool holder h can be given a fine adjustment by means of the screw j and the outer member i is pivoted on a pin so as to provide relief for the tool on the return stroke. When the machine is being used for turning the blanks the cut is adjusted by means of the screw p. The slide assembly at B is adjustable along a radial slide and angularly on its circular base. The assembly at C is adjustable along the bed of the machine.

Humpage cites Potts's machine as the first attempt at planing or shaping gear teeth but, as has been mentioned, the Maudslay machines shown in Plates 36b and 36c may have been earlier and Glavet's patent of 1839 certainly preceded that of Potts. Whether machines were ever built according to Glavet's patent is doubtful but machines according to Potts's patent were built by Shepherd, Hill & Co. of Leeds and one is illustrated in Humpage's paper.

Peter Fairbairn's machine

In 1859 Peter Fairbairn took out a patent covering the use of a formed end-mill for the cutting of gear teeth and he manufactured machines employing such cutters. One of these is described in Wm. Fairbairn's *Mills and millwork*, Part 2, which was published in 1863. Fig. 29 shows this machine, which was designed to perform turning operations as well as to cut teeth; for the former purpose the worm shown engaging the larger worm-wheel was disengaged and the smaller worm-wheel was locked to the larger one. The mandrel carrying the gear was then driven by the cone pulley; a slide-rest assembly replaced the cutter head shown. When cutting teeth the larger worm-wheel was used to index the blank and its worm was coupled by change gearing to a dividing plate. The cutter slide could be placed at an angle to the gear axis and it was claimed that bevel teeth could be cut.

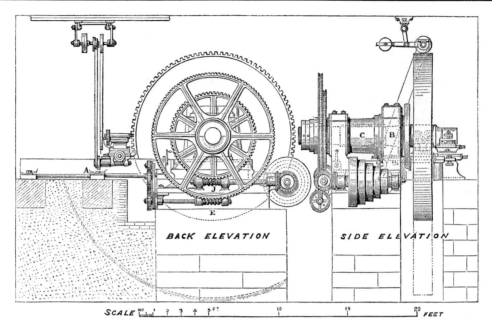

FIG. 29. P. Fairbairn's gear milling-machine *c.* 1859. Fairbairn, *Mills and millwork*, Pt. II

Grinding machines

In the early years of this period many efforts were made to produce grinding machines that were machine tools, but although some ingenious machines were devised, and probably built, it cannot truly be said that the precision grinding-machine was produced until the end of the period or even before the earlier years of the next one.

In 1834 an American, James Wheaton,[4] patented a machine that seems to have had many features later found in cylindrical grinders, but the drawing accompanying the specification is not very clear and for details the reader is referred to R. S. Woodbury's *History of the grinding machine*. A year later another American, J. W. Stone, took out a patent for a surface grinder in which the wheel axis was placed vertically and the face of the wheel was used, but it is doubtful whether a machine was ever built under this patent.

A few years later, however, the firm of Nasmyth Gaskell & Co. produced the machine shown in Plate 65 for the purpose of finishing the surfaces of large castings. The grinding wheels are composite structures consisting of heavy castings about 7 ft in diameter, each of which holds twelve abrasive blocks, and each block is provided with a separate axial-screw adjustment. The wheels are secured to the ends of a shaft mounted in bearings on a heavy base and are driven by a belt running on a cone pulley. Each of the two work-table assemblies can be traversed parallel to the face of its wheel along a bed that is raised slightly above the centre of the grinding wheels. The work tables are traversed by screws that carry two loose bevel-gears on their ends. The gears mesh with gears on a cross shaft at the front of the machine, and this cross shaft is in turn driven by bevel gears and a worm and wheel from the grinding-wheel shaft. Between the bevels on the end of the feed screws there are dog-tooth clutches and these provide the reversal of the feed motion. The clutches are actuated by rods that run parallel to the work-table ways and are moved by dogs carried by the work tables. The work is secured to the upper member of the work-table assembly and can be moved in a direction perpendicular to the wheel face. This motion can be made self-acting by means of a star-wheel that is situated on the end of the operating screw and comes into contact with adjustable abutments at the ends of the longitudinal motion.

In 1838 a machine for grinding the surfaces of pulleys was built by the American James Whitelaw,[4] who claimed that it was cheaper to build than a lathe and could produce work at a lower cost. In 1835 another American, Samuel Darling,[4] produced a surface grinder in which the wheel axis was horizontal and the periphery of the wheel was used. The work table of this machine was pivoted at one end about a horizontal axis, while the other end could be raised or lowered by means of a jack screw. This method of adjusting the cut was used subsequently in some milling machines.

Miscellaneous machines

A machine for turning, cutting, and shaping gear-tooth cutters in which a pantograph mechanism was used to copy the shape of an enlarged template was described by Bodmer in his 1839 patent. It consisted of a base with a large flat upper surface on which a lathe-type headstock was carried on a cross slide and of a tool holder that was mounted on one end of a pantograph linkage. The cutting tool for turning operations was circular in plan, and its diameter was proportionate to that of the roller that was situated at the other end of the pantograph and bore on the template. A reduction of seven to one was generally used. The workpiece was carried in a chuck on the nose of the headstock spindle and could be driven at speeds suitable for turning by means of a cone pulley and back gear. It could also be rotated at slow speeds by a worm that could be meshed with a large worm-wheel fixed to the spindle. This also provided means of indexing the spindle, an indexing arm and plate being provided. The links of the pantograph were heavy members and rested directly on the flat surface of the base. A milling cutter could be substituted for the turning tool for milling the sides of cutter teeth under the control of the template. The latter was carried in a bracket that could be fixed to the base in several positions, and adjustments were provided to enable it to be correctly orientated relative to the work. A copper cylinder or disc could also be used in conjunction with emery and oil for finishing hardened work.

P. Fairbairn & Co. in 1862 also produced a pantograph machine to enable gear cutters to be produced by milling. One of these machines was exhibited at the 1862 exhibition in London. Another of this firm's machines which could produce either plain or formed milling cutters and was built about 1850, is preserved in the Musée des Arts et Métiers.

A pitch-correcting machine

The screw-pitch correcting lathe devised by Maudslay in 1810 has been mentioned in the preceding chapter. A machine for the same purpose, but working on an entirely different principle, was amongst the numerous machine tools described by Bodmer in his 1841 patent. The principle will become clear if the procedure adopted in applying it is described; in this description the screw to be corrected will be referred to as the *long* screw. The first step is to cut a short screw having a very thin fin-like thread; this could be done on the same lathe as was used to cut the long screw or on some other lathe, its pitch being that of the long screw. This short screw was then mounted on one end of a long cylindrical rod, which had a key-way cut along its entire length and was supported in a gear-wheel mounted in a bearing in the frame of the machine. The gear wheel could be driven at a slow speed, and the end of the key-wayed shaft remote from the short screw was coupled by a muff coupling to the end of the long screw, which was supported by suitable bearings in a cast-iron trough. The short screw was then used to cut a thread in a long wooden nut, made in two halves clamped together. The hole in this nut was bored slightly smaller than the outside diameter of the short screw and so when the two halves of the wooden nut were clamped together with the short screw between them the thread of the short screw bit into the wood. Rotation of the short screw then caused it to cut a thread along the entire length of the wooden nut. This having been done the short screw was rotated back to the starting point and a cutting tool was mounted in a tool holder situated at the far end of the long screw. The short screw, together with the long one, was then rotated and the tool made the necessary correcting cuts. The principle is thus that the thread cut in the wooden nut would have a uniform pitch throughout its length and so would correct random variations of pitch in the long screw. If the pitch of the long screw was already uniform but slightly different from that required, the correction was obtained by giving the correcting tool a slight axial motion as the long screw moved past it. This was done by gearing a short lead-screw to the

86

gear driving the key-wayed shaft. In order to avoid errors due to temperature variations that would have had a greater effect on the long screw and key-wayed shaft than on the wooden nut, the former parts were immersed in cooling water in the trough in which they were supported.

Lapping

Bodmer, in the patent mentioned above, also illustrated several arrangements for lapping various surfaces. In one for lapping the bores of hardened bushes the lap was described as rotating at speeds of 3 000 to 4 000 rev/min. Another device showed two disc laps carried on a spindle placed just below and perpendicular to the axis of a rod mounted in a lathe. The device was carried on the saddle of the lathe and was traversed along the bed; the laps were rotated.

A lapping machine for flat surfaces was also covered by the patent. In this a disc lap was carried on a vertical spindle at the end of an arm like that of a radial drill; the arm could be raised or lowered. The work was carried on a circular table. This could rotate about its centre, which was coincident with the axis of the lap when the arm of the machine was in its mid-position. In order that long straight members such as small lathe beds could be lapped, the circular table was arranged to oscillate in unison with the oscillation of the arm of the machine, so that the lap could be kept in contact with the work without having to be much wider than the workpiece.

1860 to 1890

Lathes

THIS period did not see any fundamental changes in lathes for general turning purposes but improvements in detail and increases in size were made. An example of this development is the lathe shown in Plate 66, which was built in the Royal Gun Factory at Woolwich about 1865. It has a bed 36 ft long, with swing work up to 8 ft 6 inches in diameter, and weighs about 85 tons. Apart from its size there is little that is remarkable. The tailstock poppet is, however, locked in position by means of a conical split bush, which is forced in by a screwed plug so as to close on the poppet. Another example is the facing lathe shown in Plate 67 and a comparison of this machine with those from the Soho Foundry shown in Plates 40a and 41 shows that the chief improvement is a general tidying-up of the design and that fundamentally there is little change.

In the exhibition held in 1862 machine tools were a prominent feature; several firms showed lathes of fairly large size and many showed smaller lathes, up to 12 inches centre height. These did not have any special features except for an $8\frac{1}{2}$-in lathe by Smith, Beacock, and Tannett of Leeds, which had a template-controlled mechanism for the turning of non-circular pieces.[1] In general, the machines did not differ very much from those shown in the 1851 exhibition. In America in 1858 the George S. Lincoln company of Hartford built a wheel lathe[2] that could swing work 84 inches in diameter and had power feeds to both sliding and surfacing motions. The spindle of the tailstock was square in section and could be swivelled about a vertical axis to enable tapers to be bored; it could also be reciprocated by power so that key-ways could be cut.

In 1865 W. W. Hulse, whose Manchester works became famous during the second half of the nineteenth century, took out a patent (No. 1571) in which improvements to several types of machine tool were described. One lathe had a low bed-casting with dovetail slide ways machined on the front and rear vertical surfaces, and on each of these one or more saddles could be mounted. Two separate lead-screws were provided and the tailstock spindle was octagonal in section and was traversed by means of a pinion and rack. In a second lathe the saddle was mounted on the top of the bed in the conventional manner but two lead-screws were again used in order to eliminate any skewing of the saddles. In the last decade of this period Hulse's firm produced some very large lathes in which two lead-screws, which did not rotate, were used. Instead, a shaft could drive the nuts through clutches and change-gearing carried by the saddles. The clutches could be engaged in one position only, so that the cutting of screw threads was facilitated. It was possible in these lathes to have the tool slides, of which there were usually four, moving in different ways and at different speeds and this was in fact done for the purpose of turning tapers.[3] In one such lathe the bed was 75 ft long and jobs up to 60 ft long and 5 ft in diameter could be swung between centres. Steady rests fitted with rollers were provided. Up to four tools could be cutting simultaneously and each could remove up to 5 cwt of steel turnings per hour. The lead-screws were made in two parts.

Messrs. Tangye of Birmingham produced in 1865 a three-spindle centre lathe in which three jack screws could be machined simultaneously[4] and somewhat later they made a rather unusual lathe that is now in the Birmingham museum. In this the saddle is carried on the front of the bed as in Roberts's 1817 lathe, but the back gear is unconventional in that the pinion that drives the counter-shaft is placed on the right-hand side of the cone pulley and the gear that is fixed to the spindle is on the left. The face of the cone pulley is drilled to form a dividing plate, but finer dividing could be done by means of a worm that could be engaged with the teeth of the gear fixed to the spindle. The lead-screw has a thread with a rounded top and is supported at the right-hand end on a centre; it was also used as a rack to provide the hand traverse to the saddle.

A special-purpose lathe employing several tools simultaneously was designed and built by Thomas Ryder & Son of Bolton about 1885[5] for forming several necks in shafts for textile machines. The most interesting feature was that the cross slide carrying the tools was actuated by a Scotch-yoke mechanism arranged at the front of the saddle, with the axis of the crank shaft vertical. The crank pin carried a block, which fitted in a slot formed in the saddle and gave the latter a fixed in-and-out stroke. The tools were set to produce the required diameters when the crank reached the inner dead centre. The machines could also be used on the outer dead centre for internal work. Some of these machines are still at work and are highly regarded for their consistent accuracy. Similar machines were built in the years 1900–20 for producing motor-car components in quantity.

In a lathe built by Fairbairn, Naylor & Macpherson for the Great Northern Railway Works at Doncaster about 1890,[6] and employed on turning the webs of crank shafts and other jobs where the tool was cutting only over a short portion of each revolution, the work was speeded up automatically over the idle portions.

An account of the state of the art of machine-tool design in America during the period can be found in the report prepared by F. R. Hutton for the Census Office of the United States. This was published in 1885 and Hutton says that it represents practice up to the close of the year 1880. He regards the inverted V-type of way as characteristic of American practice except for large lathes but gives illustrations of lathes in which the saddle is carried on the front of the bed. However, in the range of lathes built by Wm. Sellers & Co., during the period rectangular section shears were used exclusively. In these machines the tail-stocks were positioned by forcing them into contact with the inner vertical surface of the rear shear; this was done by employing a rib with a sloping face on the underside of the shear. The typical American lathe of the period appears to be one having a four-step cone-pulley headstock with a conventional type of back-gear. The spindle runs in parallel bearings and the thrust is taken by collars at the left-hand bearing. The drive to the lead-screw is taken from a pinion situated either on the outer end of the spindle or on a short countershaft placed below, and a belt is used to take the drive to the lead-screw that is also used for the sliding feed. A rack is used for the hand traverse of the saddle and is placed beneath the front shear. In the more advanced designs the lead-screw had a key-way, and the feed motions were obtained by means of clutches and gears carried in the apron of the saddle. In general, a compound slide-rest was not fitted, but rising and falling tool-rests were common on the lighter lathes. Taper-turning attachments placed at the rear of the bed were coming into common use. Tailstocks mostly had set-over adjustments, but in the older designs the slide for this was placed high up, just below the poppet, while in the later designs it is low down as in modern lathes. The larger lathes were generally very similar to their English counterparts and had treble-geared head-stocks and an internal or external gear-drive to the outer edge of the permanently fitted face-plate for the lowest speeds. Compound slide-rests were commonly used but ratchet feeds were not unusual.

Hutton describes many special forms of lathe such as fly-wheel, pulley, wheel, and axle lathes, the last two being either single- or double-ended. An example of a facing lathe is shown in Plate 68a, while Plate 68b shows a pulley lathe made by the Niles Tool Works. In this the drive to the mandrel is by worm and wheel, and the ways on which the tool-slide traverses can be turned through a small angle about a vertical axis passing through the central plane of the worm that drives the feed shaft, so that pulleys could be crowned. After being turned the pulleys could be polished by mounting them on the end of the worm-shaft and it is said that this was commonly simultaneous with the turning of another pulley.

Vertical lathes or boring mills were in common use and two main types are illustrated by Hutton. In the first of these, two standards are used to carry an elevating cross-beam on which two tool saddles are mounted, one or both being capable of being tilted in order to turn tapers. In the second type, which was principally a boring machine, the body was a casting having a column with an extended upper portion in which a spindle that was co-axial with the work table could be moved vertically. Occasionally a radially disposed tool slide was provided so that the faces and rims of wheels could be machined as well as the bores.

In 1873 an exhibition of machine tools was held in Vienna, and J. Anderson, who at that time was superintendent of the Arsenal at Woolwich, wrote a report on the exhibits.[7] He was of the opinion that the tools shown by the French and German makers were, on the whole, not up to the standards of England and America. He comments on the absence of any machine in which coolant could be supplied to the edge of the cutting tool 'either through the tool or otherwise', and says that the first method was used in England fifty years previously, that is, about 1823. The writer has not come across any description of such an arrangement in any machine of that time. Anderson says that the best chucks in the exhibition were American but adds that 'there will be found in the Royal Arsenal at Woolwich at least forty constructions of chucks used in connection with the manufacture of shot, shell and fuses and a variety of other things and adapted for chucking from the inside of the article or from the outside all variously contrived but in such a manner as in each to ensure and maintain perfect concentricity; the greater part of them are in advance of anything that was shown at Vienna'. He goes on to comment on the extensive variety of American tools for the manufacture of sewing-machines, small arms, and the finest class of instruments of every kind, and in this field he singles out the firms of Pratt & Whitney and Brown & Sharpe.

Towards the end of this period the firm of Beyer & Peacock produced an interesting machine for turning long lengths of shafting. This is shown in Plate 69 and was designed and patented by Mr. Hunt, a member of the firm. The tools, of which four could be used, rotated about the shaft, which received an axial traverse. The shaft was gripped in the clamps B^1 and B^2, which could be arranged to grip either unmachined work for roughing cuts or turned work for finishing cuts. The clamps were operated alternatively so that when one reached the end of its travel the other could take over. Both were driven by a common lead-screw. Supports for the overhanging ends of the shafts were provided.

Another machine for turning in which rotating tools were used is the crank-pin lathe shown in Plate 70*a*. This was built by Booth & Co. of Halifax during the last decade of the period. The same principle was later to become common in machines for cutting off the heads of steel ingots and for similar work, but had also been used earlier by B. Gridley, the manager of the well-known Penn Works in London, who designed his machine in 1862, and it seems likely that a similar machine was working in the shops of Maudslay, Sons & Field ten years earlier when Gridley was employed there. A machine using the principle was exhibited in the Vienna exhibition of 1873 by the Chemnitz firm of R. Hartmann.

At the end of this period Thomas Shanks & Co. built a large triple-geared lathe[8] with a double bed and two lead-screws, and in this the tailstock casting had ways machined on its left-hand end to take a cross slide. This carried tools for facing the ends of jobs that would have been difficult to reach with tools held in the saddles. The machine is illustrated in Joshua Rose's *Modern machine shop practice*. A later example of this feature is shown in the lathe built by Sharp, Stewart & Co. in 1893 (Plate 106).

A machine that was built in France and was described as a lathe but could also be used for milling operations is shown in Plate 71. Its date of manufacture is uncertain but was probably towards the middle of the period. The illustration shows three of the operations, other than ordinary turning, that could be performed, namely, milling a rack, machining the teeth of a conical milling cutter, and machining the helical flute of a twist drill. Unless a separate saddle with a conventional cross slide and tool rest was fitted the machine would seem to be an awkward one for ordinary turning operations, but it is a good example of the intricacy of design that seems to have been a common feature of French design of the period.

Turret lathes

During this period the turret lathe developed from being a machine that was built by factories for their own use into one that was built for sale by numerous makers. The field of work also widened very considerably. In the early part of the period the turret lathe was still primarily an ordinary centre lathe in which the tailstock had been replaced by a turret, but at the end of the period it had become a distinct type of machine. This trend can be seen in Plates 70–3. In

Plate 70*b* the turret axis is vertical and its traverse is by means of a horizontal lever; the headstock is almost identical with that of any small centre lathe of the period, no saddle is fitted, and screw threads are produced by means of a chasing attachment. The lathe shown in Plate 70*c* shows a further step in development; the turret is more compact, a hollow headstock spindle is fitted, and a saddle carrying a tool post on a cross slide is used. Threads are still chased but the chasing attachment is operated by the lead-screw that controls the saddle.

Machines in which the turret indexed about a horizontal axis seem to have been as popular as the vertical axis machines. An early model is shown in Plate 70*d*, while Plate 73*a* shows a heavier machine of later date in which an important improvement is the use of friction clutches to give rapid changes of spindle speed. In the machine shown in Plate 73*b* a departure from both the types described above is made. The turret now indexes about a horizontal axis but this is perpendicular to the axis of the work.

In most of the machines of this period a three- or four-armed capstan or pilot wheel was used to traverse the turret, but sometimes a simple lever was used; the cross slide was usually operated by a screw and hand-wheel, but a lever moving in a vertical plane and acting through a pinion and rack was sometimes used.

Early in the 1860s the firms of Pratt & Whitney and Brown & Sharpe both started the manufacture of turret lathes and the latter firm became world famous in this field. An early Brown & Sharpe machine is shown in Plate 72. It is clearly no longer an adaptation of a centre lathe but has not yet reached the form that became almost universal a decade or so later.

In England at this time the turret was still frequently regarded merely as a useful addition to an ordinary lathe. In the machine shown in Plate 73*c* it is placed at the front of the cross slide and the tools that it holds are used just as any single tool might be used. The only saving effected, therefore, was the time that might have been needed to change tools. The fitting seen at the rear of the cross slide is an adjustable die carried on a separate saddle. It was used to cut large V and square threads. The machine shown in Plate 74*a* comes nearer to being a true turret-lathe since its turret is fitted with stops. It is representative of a class of machine commonly called 'brass finishers lathes', which were used in the manufacture of brass ware such as water taps, etc. An interesting feature is that the turret is provided with a cross-traverse motion. The longitudinal motion of the turret slide could be either by means of a screw operated by the hand-wheel seen at the right or, when this was disengaged, by the handle seen at the front, which operated a pinion meshing with a rack.

Automatic lathes or screw machines

The type of machine that is known in England as the automatic lathe or 'auto' and in America as the 'auto screw machine', is one that produces turned pieces without any attention from an operator except occasional supervision and replenishment of the stock bar from which the product is made. Such machines seem to have developed from machines for turning wood screws, and the earliest fully automatic machine for this purpose was that patented in 1842 by Cullen Whipple,[9] who was one of the founders of the New England Screw Co. In this machine all the operations were automatic, the motions being derived from cams. In 1846 another American, Thomas J. Sloan, patented a machine to make pointed screws, and in 1854 the firm of Nettlefold & Chamberlain of Smethwick acquired rights to the use of Sloan's patent and equipped their works with machines imported from America. The machines, shown in Plates 74*b* and 75*a*, are now in the Birmingham museum and are said to have been designed and built by Nettlefold & Chamberlain in 1860 or thereabouts. They undoubtedly derive from the machines brought over from America. The one on the left (Plate 74*b*) performs turning and slotting operations and that on the right (Plate 75) points and threads the screws. The first of these has two spindles, which can be indexed through 180° in order to bring the work from the turning to the slotting position; there it is held stationary by means of a brake while the slot is cut by a saw. The other machine has only a single spindle. The wood-screw producing machines were a somewhat specialized type and the automatic lathe that could be used on a variety of different jobs did not appear until some years later.

The first of such machines was designed and built by a German named Jacob Schweizer[10] and is shown in Plate 76. In this the feed motion for turning operations is given to the head carrying the spindle, which slides in ways formed on the bed. This type has consequently become known as the 'sliding head' type. It is also often called the Swiss type because of a misunderstanding arising from the name of the inventor. Schweizer's machine seems to have been an original conception and not just an improvement of an existing machine.

The fixed-head type of automatic was undoubtedly a development, admittedly brilliant, of the turret lathe and was due to Christopher Miner Spencer who took out a patent for his machine in 1893. His original machine, produced some few years earlier, was a conversion of a Pratt & Whitney turret lathe, but his patent covered a more sophisticated machine. Spencer subsequently became one of the founders of the Hartford Machine Screw Company and Plate 77 shows an early Hartford auto, now in the Birmingham museum. This does not, in all probability, differ appreciably from the first machines built under Spencer's patent.

In 1879 a patent was taken out by C. W. Parker for a machine for the automatic production of screws from bar or rod stock, and the Leeds firm of Greenwood & Batley subsequently built machines under this patent. The most novel feature of the machine was that the stock was fed through the chuck past stationary tools. This feed motion was produced by rollers carried at the rear of the hollow spindle which were driven so as to propel the rod through the spring-loaded chuck at the right-hand end. The machine employed a cam-shaft situated in the lower part of the box-like bed, and this actuated the front cross-slide so as to bring the turning tool into position, where it was held by a catch until the operation was finished. The catch was then released and the slide withdrawn. The rear slide carrying the parting-off tool and the spindle carrying the dies for cutting the thread were also operated by the cam-shaft. The die spindle was rotated at a slightly higher speed than the work spindle during the threading operation and was brought to rest when the thread was complete so that the dies unscrewed off the stock. An example of one of these machines is preserved in the Science Museum.

Boring machines

In this period the vertical boring-machine began to assume greater importance in relation to the horizontal type, although the latter still remained predominant. But it was not a machine like the Nasmyth & Gaskell design described in the last chapter that came to the fore but a machine whose design seems to have been influenced by the slotting machine. An example is shown in Plate 78. This was built by Smith, Beacock & Tannett in the early years of this period for the Arsenal at Woolwich. It had a spindle 12 inches in diameter and could bore holes up to 4 ft 6 inches diameter and 5 ft deep. This type of boring machine was also built during this period in America, but in smaller sizes, for boring the bosses of locomotive wheels. A typical example is shown in Plate 75*b*. Occasionally a radial slide was fitted so that the faces of the bosses and rims of the wheels could be machined, and often the machine was equipped with an integral crane for loading and unloading the wheels.

A new form of horizontal boring-machine was developed during the present period and it became very popular. It went out of favour about the second decade of the twentieth century although it is still occasionally built. It may conveniently be called the elevating-table type and its general arrangement is shown in Plate 79*a*. The spindle-head assembly resembles a lathe headstock, the

95

chief difference being that there is a boring bar or spindle that can be given an axial feed motion. Because the axis of the boring bar is fixed in space, the adjustments required to make it coincide with the axis of the hole to be bored have to be given to the work. This is done by carrying the work on a table that has a transverse motion on a saddle that can slide in an axial direction on an elevating bed. One end of the latter slides up and down vertical ways machined on the face of the spindle-head casting, and the other end is supported by an arched frame that also provides an outer bearing for the boring bar when necessary. Boring can be carried out in two ways on machines of this type, either by traversing the work along the bed or by feeding the boring bar through the stationary work. The headstock was sometimes arranged with an integral faceplate on which a head with a radial facing-slide could be mounted for the purpose of facing the end of the work. A point of some interest is that many machines of this type were made with the spindle head at the right-hand end of the bed and work table.

The type of horizontal boring-machine which at the present day is easily the commonest type, namely, that in which the spindle head slides up and down the face of a column, was developed during the present period. In the small and medium sizes the column was fixed, and the work was carried on a table that could be traversed across a saddle which itself could be fed axially along the fixed bed. An example of this type is shown in Plate 79b. For larger work it was found more convenient to keep the work stationary and to give the transverse adjustments to the column carrying the spindle head as in the machine shown in Plate 80a. This was built by Wm. Sellers & Co. and the principle of the belt drive to the spindle is slightly uncommon, the belt tension being maintained, as the spindle head moved up and down, by the weight of the floating countershaft carried by radius rods pivoted about the axis of the driving pulley in the base of the column.

A universal boring machine built by G. & A. Harvey of Glasgow about 1860 is shown in Plate 80b. The spindle head traverses along the face of a beam that can be rotated on its supporting columns about a horizontal axis, while the work table can be tilted about another horizontal axis but perpendicular to the first. The spindle axis can therefore be placed at any angle to the work within the limits of the adjustments.

Drilling machines

Probably the most important development in this period in relation to the drilling of holes was the appearance of the twist drill. This was invented in America at the beginning of the period and its production was greatly facilitated

96

by the development by Brown & Sharpe of their universal milling machine. The later development, by the same firm, of form-relieved milling cutters on a commercial basis must also have facilitated the manufacture of twist drills.

Pillar- and column-type drilling machines did not change much during the period, but radial drills were greatly improved and new types were brought out. One of these was the 'universal' radial drill and an early example is shown in Plate 81, from which it will be seen that two additional freedoms are now available to the spindle axis. Both freedoms are angular; the arm can be rotated about its longitudinal axis and the spindle head can be rotated about an axis that is perpendicular to both the longitudinal axis of the arm and the axis of the spindle itself. Towards the end of the period large radial drills were being provided with supports for the outer ends of their arms. These supports could be moved round by means of a pinion engaging teeth formed on an arc on the base-plate. It may also be of interest to mention that at this time there was at least one firm in the United States that specialized in radial drills and built nothing else.

Another type of drilling machine produced during this period is that shown in Plate 82. This particular one is a combined drilling and slotting machine, a combination that became popular in locomotive works for the drilling and slotting of holes in frame plates and also in bridge manufacture. The general arrangement is something like that of a travelling-standards planing machine and, in fact, the machine shown is equipped with a side tool-head to enable the edges of plates to be machined.

A multiple-spindle drilling machine with an original type of drive to the spindles was developed by the firm of Andrew Shanks about the beginning of this period. The principle underlying it is an extension of that of the triangular connecting rod for enabling one crank to drive two others. The 'connecting rod' became a rectangular plate, having holes into which the pins of cranks at the upper ends of the spindles entered from below, and the plate was given its driving motion by a similar crank above the plate. The principle was adopted several years later by an American firm. Perhaps the chief drawbacks are that the high inertia of the driving plate limits the speeds an which the drills can be driven and that it is not an easy matter to change the spacing of the holes. The Shanks firm also developed a machine in which four spindles were carried in a head that could be indexed round a central column. The spindles could be driven, at different speeds if required, by friction drives. Both of these machines of Shanks's were shown in the 1862 exhibition. The type of multiple-spindle drilling machine in which the spindles are carried in separate heads that can be moved along a beam supported by standards was built by several makers during the period. In such machines the drive to the spindles was usually either by bevel gears or worm gears.

A drilling machine built in 1887 by Thomas Shanks & Co. for the Ansaldo works in Genoa is shown in Plate 83. It was designed to accommodate loco-motive boilers of various sizes and the principles of its operation will be clear from the illustration. It is a good example of the machines that were being built at this time for the railway works then becoming common all over the world. Another arrangement that originated in railway works, where numerous holes had to be drilled in plates, was the mounting of several radial drills alongside a long table that carried the work; sometimes the columns of the machines were mounted on saddles that could be traversed along a bed placed beside the work table.

A machine for the 'drilling' of non-circular holes was being made about the end of this period by The Square Hole Drilling Machine Co. of London. The drill spindle was carried at its centre in a ball-and-socket joint and its upper end was controlled by templates.

Planing, slotting, and shaping machines

Developments in these machines during the period were mostly minor improve-ments in design, increases in capacity, and the building of special forms for particular purposes. The conventional planer was built in larger sizes and was sometimes fitted with two work tables, which ran on separate ways side by side and could be used either separately or together. The 'wall planer', utilizing the structure of the building housing it, was superseded by the 'side' planer built as a self-contained unit, and these were also built in some rather specialized forms. Special planers for machining the edges of long plates were built and attempts at employing double cutting continued. At the beginning of the period the American firm of Wm. Sellers patented and built planing machines employ-ing the spiral drive, which became very popular and was subsequently used by many other makers. The principle of this drive is shown in Fig. 30.

A patent was taken out in 1866 for a double-cutting planing machine in which two standards were provided, each with its own cross-beam and tool heads. The standards were placed back to back. Towards the end of the period Stewart, Beacock & Tannett made machines in which two cross-beams were used, one being placed on the front and the other on the back of the standards. But although this machine cut on both strokes, it was intended to be used to machine two separate pieces of work, and the tools did not operate on the same piece. In the late 1880s a new form of tool-holder, which enabled cutting to be done on both strokes on ordinary planers (assuming the standards and beam structure would permit it), was patented by J. H. Wicksteed of the firm of Joshua Buckton & Co. who built machines employing it. The principle underlying the device is shown in Plates 84*a* and 84*b*.

A combined horizontal and vertical planing machine was patented by W. W. Hulse in 1865. For horizontal planing the standards and cross-beam assembly travelled along ways formed on the vertical sides of the bed casting, and the

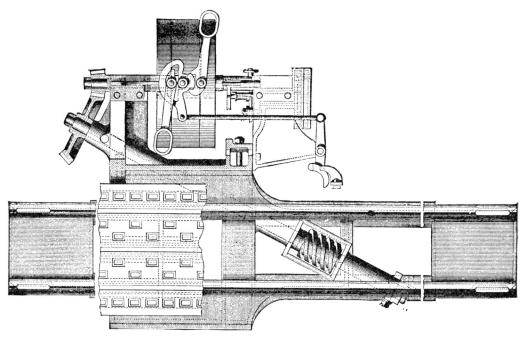

FIG. 30. Wm. Sellers's spiral drive for planing machines *c.* 1862. Sellers & Co., *Treatise on machine tools*, 1884

adjustment of the cut was given by the vertical and transverse movements of the tool in the ordinary way. For vertical planing the standards assembly was held stationary and the cutting motion was given to the long tool-head slide by means of a screw driven by separate pulleys and an open and a crossed belt. Cross motion of the tool head gave the feed motion and the depth of cut was regulated by moving the work table along ways on the top of the bed. A large planing machine with travelling standards and in which cutting could be performed, in addition to the normal planing motion, by giving the tool slide a motion across the beam or by giving it a vertical, slotting motion was exhibited by Wm. Sellers & Co. at the Paris Exhibition in 1867. Some ten years later the firm made an improved version of this machine in which a piece of work 24 ft long by 6 ft wide by 12 ft high could be machined on five faces without removing it from the work table.

In Hulse's 1865 patent a machine, which later came to be used extensively under the names 'side planer' and 'side shaping machine', was described. This is shown in Plate 84c. The tool-head assembly travels along the ways formed on the top of the fixed bed and is actuated by a screw driven by an open and a crossed belt. The work is secured to the top of one or more knee-type tables, which can be adjusted vertically and horizontally on the face of the bed. The tool head is moved along the arm to provide the feed motion and the depth of cut is adjusted by moving the tool up or down as in the ordinary planer or shaper. Machines of this type were introduced later, in 1882, by the firm of George Richards of Manchester and large numbers of them were produced. An illustration of one of the earliest of these appears in the *American Machinist*, vol. v, no. 24, 1882, and it is there stated that John Richards of San Francisco (father of George) and E. A. Walker of Philadelphia were associated with the design and production of the machine.

In a planing machine made by Francis Berry & Sons of Sowerby Bridge, Yorkshire, one of the standards that supported the cross-beam was adjustable outwards so that wide jobs could be tackled, and similar machines were made in America during the period. These call to mind Bodmer's design made nearly fifty years earlier.

A somewhat special form of machine for performing planing and slotting operations was built by Hulse & Co. towards the end of the period and is shown in Plate 85. It is noteworthy for the use of two screws for each of the planing motions. Planing was usually done by using the motion of the tool head across the beam, but could be done by reciprocating the work table if required. The tool head travel was 9 ft horizontally and 4 ft vertically, but objects up to 8 ft high could be slotted.

About 1865 Thomas Ryder & Sons produced a planing machine for grooving ten textile-machine shafts simultaneously. The shafts were held between simple chucks at one end and centres at the other and the chucks were geared together so that they could be indexed. The table carrying the shafts was operated by a crank and slotted link mechanism placed below it. The swinging link was pivoted to the table at the upper end and had a slot at the bottom end that engaged a block carried on a fixed pin. A second slot in the middle of the link engaged the block carried by the adjustable crank, which was driven by worm gearing. Indexing occurred at the end of the return stroke and was effected by means of a pawl and ratchet, which contacted a ramp carried by the frame. Some of these machines are still in use.

In 1866 Shanks & Co. produced a hydraulically operated slotting machine for a continental customer.[11] In this the ram was actuated directly by the piston of a hydraulic cylinder mounted on the top of the frame. A quick return was obtained very simply because the return cylinder had a smaller area than the working one. The hydraulic supply was from a pump running at a constant speed. The reversal was obtained by means of a valve controlling the flow to the cylinders.

Three special forms of shaping machine are shown in Fig. 31 and Plates 86*a* and 86*b*. The first was designed by F. W. Webb about 1865 for machining the

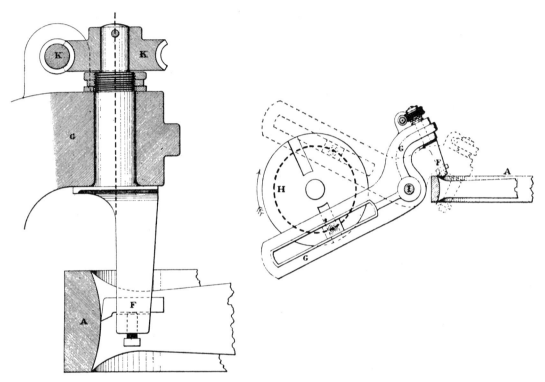

FIG. 31. F. W. Webb's curvilinear shaping machine. *Proc. Instn mech. Engrs*, vol. 17, 1856

insides of the rims of fly-wheels and locomotive driving wheels. The action will be obvious, but it may be pointed out that the tool can be rotated about an axis perpendicular to the axis about which the arm swings and this enabled the corners between the rims and the spokes of wheels to be machined. The second machine was designed by R. P. Doxford to copy three-dimensional surfaces such as the blades of screw propellors and the principle of this design will be clear from the illustration. The third machine was described as a planer and was built to machine the faces and ports of the cylinders of locomotives. It was installed in the Doncaster works of the Great Northern Railway.

An original design by the famous French firm of Ducommun et Dubied is shown in Plate 87. In this the work moves to and fro past the fixed tools so that the machine might be called a planer, but in its construction it is more like a shaper. It would seem to have been designed especially for machining the key-ways at the ends of axles and would not be very suitable for general work.

Milling machines

In this period the milling machine developed from a machine that was built by firms for their own use, usually for a particular type of job, until it became of equal or greater importance than the planing, slotting, and shaping machines and was being built for sale by numerous firms in most countries that had any machine-tool industry. One of the outstanding events was the production of the universal milling machine shown in Plate 88 by Brown & Sharpe. It was designed about 1862 by Joseph R. Brown, at the instigation of Frederick Howe, for the purpose of milling the flutes of twist drills. It soon began to be exploited in many fields and in 1867, when it was exhibited in Paris, it created quite a sensation. An example is preserved in the Science Museum.

A somewhat novel form of milling machine that was probably built about the beginning of this period is shown in Plate 89a, which is reproduced from Hutton's report. In this design the vertical adjustment of the spindle in relation to the work is obtained by rocking the spindle on circular arcs formed at the top of the column. The centre of the arc is displaced from the axis of the spindle but coincides with that of the driving-cone pulley, so that the rocking motion does not affect the belt tension. A slightly different arrangement was used later in this period in a fixed work-table machine built by Brown & Sharpe. In this the position of the spindle head was adjusted by pivoting the head on an axis parallel to, but displaced sideways from, that of the spindle. The adjustment was made by means of two nuts carried on a vertical screw at the opposite side from the pivot. The nuts embraced a lug projecting from the head. Machines of this design, with minor improvements, were still being produced in 1903. Another and similar machine, also by Brown & Sharpe, employed a pivoted spindle-head but used a different form of adjustment. These machines are shown in Plates 130a and 130b.

At the beginning of this period W. F. Batho of the firm of Batho & Bauer, which has been mentioned in the previous chapter, built a machine for milling simultaneously all six faces of hexagonal nuts.[12] These were carried on a vertical mandrel, held at the bottom in a chuck and at the top in a steady arm, and the mandrel was given a vertical feed motion. Six cutter spindles were arranged in a horizontal plane and carried fish-tail-shaped end-milling cutters, which were made wider than the faces of the nuts. To enable adjacent cutters to clear each other the spindles were geared together and alternate cutters were placed at right angles.

In 1874 a Frenchman, Pierre Phillippe Huré, who had started making machine tools in a works in Paris, developed a milling machine incorporating both horizontal and vertical spindles, either of which could easily be brought into the working position. A British patent was taken out in 1880 and Plate 90a shows one of the earliest machines built. The machine comprises a pillar on the front of which ways are machined to take a knee and work-table assembly. The top of the pillar has a cylindrical spigot on which the head casting can turn. The spindles are supported in bearings in the head and are driven by belts, the horizontal one directly and the vertical one over guide pulleys. The drive came from a swinging arm carrying a pulley on a countershaft, which was driven from a cone pulley arranged at the base of the machine. The swinging arm enabled the same belt to be used for driving both spindles. A friction clutch was provided for starting and stopping. The work table was made in two parts; the upper part could swivel about a vertical axis while the lower one travelled along ways formed in the saddle. This enabled the work table to be set at angles less than 90° to the knee ways.

In 1885 Joseph Saget of Puteaux took out a British patent for a milling machine and this is shown in Fig. 32, which is taken from the specification. The most interesting feature is, perhaps, the swivelling spindle-head that permits the spindle to be tilted about two mutually perpendicular axes. The spindle is shown in the vertical position, but by tilting the head on the circular face of the spindle carriage about the axis of the driving shaft D, it could be brought to the horizontal position. The other adjustment is about the axis of the crown wheel through which the drive is conveyed to the cutter spindle and is limited to about 30° either way. The machine was intended to mill cutters and other work of a complex shape by copying a template, which can be seen at G. In order to enable the template to be made with greater accuracy it was arranged to travel at twice the speed of the work table, thus doubling its dimensions relative to the work in one direction.

The ordinary horizontal-spindle machine was adapted for vertical milling by means of vertical spindle attachments and an example is shown in Plate 91a. This could also be used for the cutting of racks and similar jobs. At the end of the period such attachments had become standard pieces of equipment for horizontal millers.

A type of machine that is commonly called a sliding-head machine is shown in Plates 90b and 90c. This one was built at the end of the period by Lister & Co. of Keighley, but the type was being built by several makers. The principal claim

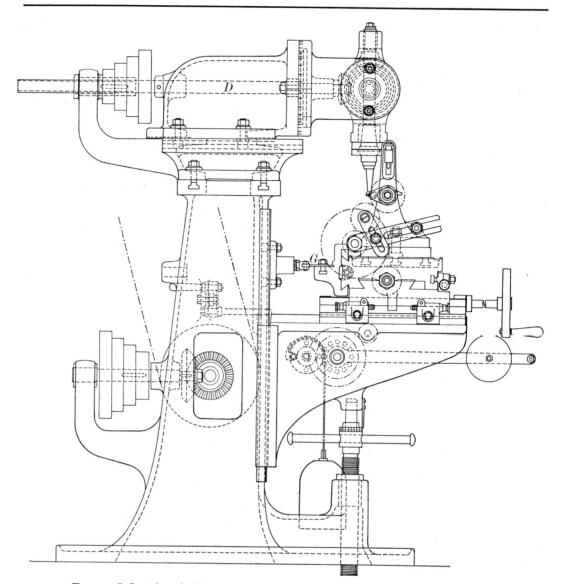

FIG. 32. J. Saget's swivelling-head milling machine *c.* 1885. Patent No. 6702—1885

made for this form of construction was that it enabled the knee assembly to be simplified and made more rigid, since the work table had only to move in the direction perpendicular to the spindle. In the Lister machine the drive to the spindle was by means of a long pinion that meshed with a gear carried by the spindle.

The Lincoln type of machine continued to be built in considerable quantities during the period but some improvements were made. To avoid having to shift the countershaft along on its brackets on the spindle-head casting whenever the spindle height was altered, the countershaft was carried on a rocking frame pivoted lower down, and the frame was coupled to the spindle by a radius rod, one eye of which was concentric with the spindle axis and the other with the axis of the countershaft. The Brainard Milling Machine Co. of Boston, Massachusetts, were using this arrangement in 1880 and may have been using it much earlier. The principle involved is the same as is used in the Fox lathe shown in Plate 26a and in the Sellers horizontal boring-machine shown in Plate 80a; it was also used during the period in the feed drive to the work table of a horizontal milling-machine. A variation on the Lincoln design that was produced probably during the early years of this period is shown in Plate 89b.

Three milling machines for producing plain and formed milling-cutters and similar work are shown in Plates 92, 93, and 94. All are of French design and they bring out the different lines of approach of their designers to the problem to be solved. The illustrations are taken from a portfolio of drawings published about 1882 by Armengaud aîné in Paris but it is probable that the machines were built several years earlier. The firm of Frey fils was a well-known maker of machine tools during the second half of the nineteenth century and Kreutzberger, the designer of the second machine, was a French engineer who had spent a considerable time in the Remington arms works in the United States of America. He was the patentee, in 1874, of a machine for sharpening milling cutters that was subsequently taken up by Brown & Sharpe and other firms. One of these machines is preserved in the Musée des Arts et Métiers.

An original form of vertical milling machine was introduced towards the end of this period by Brown & Sharpe and is shown in Plate 130c. The work table could traverse in two directions on the fixed base and the cutter spindle was housed in the overhanging portion of a heavy casting. The casting had a cylindrical portion of large diameter that could slide vertically in a bore at the rear of the base casting. This provided the vertical adjustment for the cutter. The type was subsequently used to a considerable extent and was still being manufactured in 1903, although of course with improvements. It has been called the *Pillar* type.

A single column, or open side, plano-type milling machine with a vertical spindle-head was built by Beaman & Smith of Providence, Rhode Island, towards the end of the period.

Also towards the end of the period the firm of Ludwig Loewe of Berlin produced the machine shown in Plate 91b. It was described as a circular milling-machine. The work was carried on a slowly rotating spindle mounted on a compound slide providing motions perpendicular and parallel to the cutter axis. The machine could take work up to 22 inches in diameter and was designed to finish it in a single cut. However, in 1866 Ramsbottom produced a machine on the same lines for machining the pins of forged crank shafts prior to turning, a large inserted tooth cutter being used. A similar machine was also made by Wilkinson & Lister of Keighley about 1888. In this machine the cutter was fed in until it reached the setting required by the diameter of the pin and the crank shaft was then rotated. In both machines the cut was over the full width of the pin being machined. Circular milling-machines on these lines have been built by various makers right up to the present day; they have not been widely used, however, but have found a place in the quantity production of certain articles.

A special machine built by Hetherington & Co. about 1887 is shown in Plate 95. It machined at one setting eight faces of a quadrant used in railway signal-gear, and was installed in the works of the London & North-Western Railway at Crewe.

A notable development during the period was the increased use of ganged cutters as a method of machining surfaces of complex form. One of the first firms in this field was the Ingersoll Milling Machine Co. of Rockford, Illinois, U.S.A., and one of their machines is shown in Plate 96a. Ruggedness was a major characteristic of these machines and the one shown could use cutters extending over work 36 in wide. This firm also produced a special type of cutter in which the cutting edges were formed on the ends of cylindrical inserts placed radially in a body member. Some of these cutters could be adjusted axially so as to maintain their effective width after grinding. An example of a gang of cutters is shown in Plate 96b and another form of adjustable-width cutter is shown in Plate 96c. In a plano-type milling machine built by Wm. Sellers about the middle of this period, and called a *slabbing machine* the work table was actuated by a spiral pinion (as used in his planers) which engaged a rack fixed to the front face of bed with its teeth in the vertical plane. The pinion shaft was carried by the work table at an angle of about 45° and was driven by a shaft through a bevel pinion and gear. The machine was designed particularly for cutting the recesses or flutes in locomotive connecting rods.

Gear-cutting machines

During this period gear-cutting machines developed in two important respects. First, they were made to work automatically so that after the workpiece had been put into the machine no further attention was required until all the teeth had been cut. Second, machines that generated the tooth profiles instead of merely copying formers were conceived, and later built. However, machines for cutting spur gears by the copying process still remained the most widely used type and their reign was undoubtedly extended by the introduction by Brown

& Sharpe of sets of eight form-relieved cutters that would cut gears ranging from twelve-toothed pinions up to racks. These sets were put on the market in 1874.

For the cutting of bevel gears the milling process was always unsatisfactory, and the shaping machine copying a template was the popular method until towards the close of the period under discussion, when generating machines were produced and came into use. That this was somewhat earlier than machines for spur gears was probably due to the fact that these were often required to be interchangeable, whereas bevel gears, from their nature, were not.

Some machines using the milling process and showing considerable refinement in design were produced in France during the period. The one depicted in Plate 97 was built by A. Piat, probably about the beginning of this period, and it is interesting to compare it with that of Whitworth's shown in Plate 60. Whereas Whitworth moves the work-spindle saddle in order to accommodate gears of different sizes, Piat moves the cutter head; Whitworth obtains the feed motion by moving the cutter along a slide on a bracket fixed to the bed, while Piat moves the spindle head on its saddle. In Piat's machine the work was indexed by hand through the worm *H*, which was coupled to an index wheel by the shaft *h*. The worm was carried in a bracket on the face of a second worm-wheel *G*, and this was geared through the shaft *p* to the feed motion and gave the required rotation of the blank when cutting helical teeth. A complete wheel *G* was not really necessary for this purpose since the extent of the motion required was small, but one was provided so that the effects of wear could be eliminated by turning the wheel round so as to bring fresh teeth into operation.

The credit for producing the first fully automatic gear-cutting machine is given to the firm of Gage, Warner & Whitney of Nashua, New Hampshire, who are said to have made one about 1860.[13] One of their machines was still working in 1896 and is illustrated in *Machinery* for November 1896. In 1867 Wm. Sellers & Co. exhibited an automatic gear-cutter at Paris and in 1868 Kendall & Gent of Manchester produced the machine shown in Plate 98*a*. This was made under a patent taken out by Thompson, Fitton & Fitton, who were concerned with textile machinery, and the machine is said to have been much used by makers of this kind of machinery. An interesting feature is that the feed rate was reduced during the entry and exit of the cutter into the work. In 1877 Gould & Eberhardt and Brown & Sharpe both produced automatic machines in America and Craven Bros. produced one in England. A Gould and Eberhardt machine made by John Lang & Sons of Johnstone, Scotland, under licence, is shown in Plate 98*b*. It incorporated a screw conveyor for the removal of the swarf.

Generating machines

We turn now to machines that generate the tooth profile. In about 1872, designs were put forward by one Hagen Torn[14] for machines to cut either spur or bevel gears. The designs do not seem to have been carried to the stage where workable machines could have been made from them and so far as is known they were never made. Similarly, in 1877 Gustav Hermann[14] published outline designs for machines for generating either epicycloidal or involute teeth. These seem more practicable than those of Hagen Torn but again the machines were not built.

The first generating machine to achieve success was that patented and made by H. Bilgram of Philadelphia in 1884–5 for machining the teeth of bevel gears. This employed a shaping process in which the tool represented one side of a tooth of a stationary crown wheel, and the gear being cut was given the motion it would have received if its teeth meshed with that crown wheel. For this purpose the blank rotated about its own axis while that axis rotated about the axis of the imaginary crown wheel. These motions were regulated by fixing a conical member, representing part of the pitch cone of the gear being cut, to the work spindle and making this cone roll on a flat circular member representing part of the pitch disc of the crown wheel. To prevent any slipping steel tapes were used as in Ramsden's screw-cutting machine. The design of Bilgram's machine seems to follow closely that shown in Hagen Torn's patent but whether there is any connection is not known. An example of a Bilgram machine as made by the Reinecker company during the last decade of this period is shown in Plate 139*a*.

In 1889 the American George Grant, who was an authority on toothed gearing, took out a patent for a bevel-gear shaping machine in which the generating motions were given partly to the blank, which rotated about its own axis, and partly to the tool that rotated about the axis of the imaginary crown wheel. The motions were co-ordinated by external gearing. However, it does not seem that machines were ever built under this patent.

In 1880 Ambrose Swasey designed, and the Pratt & Whitney company built, a machine for generating templates for use in the production of epicycloidal gear teeth on copying machines. The Pratt & Whitney company also produced a pantograph machine by means of which milling cutters could be produced from such templates. These machines will be found illustrated in Hutton's report to the U.S. Census Office. Towards the end of this period Ambrose Swasey also designed the novel generating gear-cutting machine shown in Plate 99. In this the rotary cutter is split on a plane containing its axis and each half can slide axially under the control of a helical cam seen on the right. During the period when one-half of the cutter is engaged with the blank it receives an axial motion at the same speed as that of the pitch circle of the teeth being cut, and during the period when it is out of contact it is moved back one pitch. The effect is, therefore, that of a continuously moving rack and thus with straight-sided cutters involute teeth are generated. The machine, though highly ingenious, was not a commercial success.

Grinding machines

At the beginning of this period grinding machines were still primitive and hardly deserved to be called precision tools, but by the end of it they were an accepted method of obtaining high accuracy and were becoming indispensable for all who were manufacturing precision mechanisms. The cylindrical and the surface types seem to have developed more or less concurrently but it will be convenient to consider the cylindrical machine first. As with many other machines there is some doubt as to who made the basic developments and for a detailed account of this aspect of the subject the reader is referred to Woodbury's *History of the grinding machine*.

It seems fairly certain that a simple and small, but accurate, cylindrical grinder was built about 1860 by Charles S. Moseley and that this machine is the one now in the possession of the Norton Company of Worcester, Massachusetts. There is also little doubt that another American, named Furbush, built a machine in 1873; he is said to have designed this some ten years earlier and it embodies many of the features that were present in a machine conceived by Joseph R. Brown, of Brown & Sharpe, about 1868. Brown's conception did not reach the stage at which it could be offered for sale until 1875. It was exhibited at Paris in 1876 and patented in 1877. Thereafter it had a great influence on the design of such machines. One of the earliest Brown & Sharpe productions is shown in Plate 100*a*; it embodies a swivelling work-head, a swivelling wheel-head, and a pivoted work-table, all of which features have remained basic elements of universal cylindrical grinders.

At first, however, these improved machines were not extensively available and more primitive machines were built and used. These were based on lathe construction and in many cases were actually lathes in which the saddle was replaced by a grinding-wheel carriage. The example shown in Plate No. 100*b* was made by Pratt & Whitney and known as a 'weighted grinding lathe' because the grinding-wheel-carriage was held down on the bed-ways by a weight, which can be seen below the bed. Weighted lathes were made at this time by many American makers and were not completely displaced by the gibbed-carriage construction until the end of the century.

Grinding machines for heavy work were later developments than machines for light work, but J. Morton Poole designed and built one in 1870 for grinding large rolls. Its most interesting feature is shown in Fig. 33. Two wheel-heads are used and are carried on slides on a frame that is supported by four pendulum links, one at each corner of the saddle of the machine. The whole wheel-

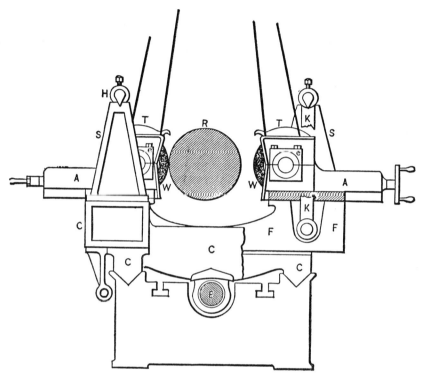

Fig. 33. J. M. Poole's roll-grinding machine *c.* 1870.
Rose, *Modern machine shop practice*

assembly could thus float perpendicularly to the axis of the roll, and the transverse forces acting at the contacts between the wheels and the work were, to a considerable extent, contained within the floating frame. The machine produced very accurate work and was used to a considerable extent during the following two decades.

A grinding machine that was considerably in advance of its contemporaries in respect of rigidity and also represented a radical difference in its general arrangement was made about 1883 by A. B. Landis, who with his brother founded the firm that subsequently became the Landis Tool Company. The original machine, restored by the company, is shown in Plates 101*a* and 101*b*. In it the longitudinal motion is given to the grinding wheel-head, and the work table is fixed but can be swivelled through a small angle. The use of a travelling wheel-head became fairly common later on, particularly in the larger and heavier machines.

Internal grinding machines

Machines for grinding holes can be divided into two groups, those in which the axis of the wheel spindle is fixed and those in which it rotates; the latter are commonly called planetary machines. The first type is used chiefly for small work although when the out of balance forces are small this type has been used for quite large jobs. The second type is most suitable for large and irregular shaped objects that would be difficult to rotate because of the out of balance forces.

The general design of internal grinding-machines when the work rotates follows similar lines to that of external grinders, and the chief difficulties are those due to the small wheels necessary when the hole is small and to the over-hang of the wheel when it has to operate at the bottom of a deep hole. Small wheels necessitate very high wheel-speeds and these give rise to troubles from vibration and overheating of bearings. The overhang of the wheel gives rise to vibration, and difficulties may also arise from the deflections that may occur. The wear of the wheel is also more serious than in external grinders where the wheels are large. However, these difficulties seem to have been easier to over-come in the first type of machine than those in the second type and so the latter were later in developing. Attempts were made to do internal grinding on the grinding-lathe type of machine but the results were poorer than when done externally. About 1880, however, Brown & Sharpe brought out an internal grinding attachment for use with their universal cylindrical grinders and this attachment was a success.

The second type of machine involves the use of a wheel spindle that rotates about its own axis while that axis rotates about the axis of the hole; it is there-fore necessary to be able to vary the position of the spindle axis in order to adjust the size of the hole being ground and this has to be done while the spindle is receiving its motions. This is fairly simple in principle but rather more diffi-cult to carry out successfully in practice. The first solution of the problem was made by Beyer & Peacock who patented their planetary-spindle grinding mach-ine in 1887. The underlying principle of this is shown in Fig. 34, where E is the spindle, D is an eccentric cylinder in which the spindle bearings are housed, B is an outer cylindrical member that rotates in its bearings in the frame A of the machine. The axis of B, of course, has to be made to coincide with the axis of the hole to be ground, and this is done by providing adjustment for the work in two directions at right angles. Rotation of the cylinder *D* about its axis provides the required variation of the radius of the hole. The author has not been able to find out precisely when Beyer & Peacock built their first machine under this patent, but a machine that bears the date 1892 was illustrated in *Engineering* of 16 January 1903. The planetary type of machine did not become widely used, however, until the increased production of motor-car engines employing cylinder blocks having several bores provided the field for them, and this was not until about the middle of the first decade of the twentieth century.

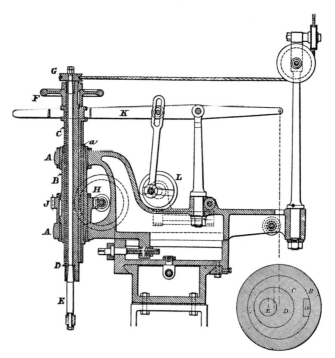

FIG. 34. R. Peacock's planetary-spindle grinding machine
c. 1887. Patent No. 696—1887

Surface grinders

The need to be able to grind plane surfaces was as pressing as that to grind cylindrical ones and so the surface grinder developed simultaneously with the cylindrical grinder. In both types the development was principally in America. Two main forms of surface grinder emerged, the edge-wheel and the face-wheel types. The progress of the surface grinder was, however, rather more dependent on the development of grinding wheels than was the progress with cylindrical grinders.

The early edge-wheel machines were, not unnaturally, based on the planing machine and were sometimes actually planers fitted with a wheel head. An early example of this type that was designed as a grinding machine is shown in Plate 102a. It was built by Brown & Sharpe about 1877. The wheel head traversed across the beam of the machine and this moved down the curved face of the standards to adjust the cut. As the axis of the driving-belt drum was made to coincide with the axis of the curved face the belt tension was not disturbed. This type of machine was built for many years but was eventually superseded by other types. One of the latter was the column or pillar type shown in Plate 103b. This also was developed by Brown & Sharpe some six years after the one described above. In this machine the wheel head is carried in a guide formed in a casting bolted to the base of the machine. In some other designs the wheel head was fixed and the work-table assembly was raised to adjust the cut; for this purpose the work table was sometimes carried on a knee casting on the face of the column or pillar as shown in Plate 103a. These types of machine were found to be more convenient than the planer type, at least for work of small or moderate size, and the first of them remains a popular type to the present day.

The face-wheel type of surface grinder has been built in two well-known forms, in one of these the wheel axis is horizontal as shown in Plate 103b and in the other it is vertical. The latter form was somewhat later in developing but is now probably more widely used than the other. In 1867 Sampson Fox of Leeds produced a machine of this type for grinding the guide bars of locomotives. The diameter of the wheel was made greater than the width of the job but nevertheless the wheel was oscillated from side to side during roughing operations although it remained in one position for finishing.

Magnetic chucks

These have greatly facilitated the holding of workpieces during grinding operations, particularly with surface grinders. One of the earliest to be produced was the invention of W. E. Newton about 1875. They were manufactured by the firm of Jacques, Oakley & Steemes.

Miscellaneous machines and matters

During the latter part of this period machines were developed for the express purpose of sharpening various forms of cutting tool. Some French ones have already been mentioned. A notable one was the twist-drill grinder produced by Wm. Sellers & Co. in the early 1880s. It is, however, convenient to leave the description of this machine until the next chapter.

The broach, which consisted of a metal rod having cutting teeth or edges formed on its circumference and was forced through a hole in order to produce a change of shape or size, is a very old tool. In its early days it was hammered through the hole but later on presses of various kinds were used. In 1839 J. G. Bodmer patented a machine for driving broaches in which a combination of blows produced by a cam together with a continuous feed from a screw was used. A press for pulling broaches through holes is illustrated by Rose in his book and he also shows some broaches but these are all short ones not exceeding about 8 inches in length. At the beginning of this period the pulling of broaches was being done in Birmingham and the practice is thought to have originated there. These broaches were quite short and could produce only small changes in the shape or size of the hole and consequently several had to be used on a single job. The introduction of the long broach which is pulled through the hole is attributed to W. P. Davis of N. Broomfield, Ontario Co., New York, who produced a key-way cutting machine with such a cutter about 1880. Davis's machine is described in the *American Machinist* of 11 November 1881. A machine of this type built by Smith & Coventry of Manchester is shown in Plate 104*a*. This appeared in *Engineering* on 22 March 1889.

At the beginning of this period R. Mushet made his important discovery of the effect of tungsten on the hardening of tool steel and 'self-hardening' steels subsequently came into extensive use. They had a profound effect on machine-tool design because the higher cutting speeds made feasible by these steels called for wider speed-ranges, greater rigidity, and better bearings.

Another development that had a profound effect on the design of machine tools was the application of electric power to the driving of them. Initially the application was to the driving of the line shafting of machine shops, and this was demonstrated at the Vienna exhibition in 1873, but the application to individual machines that came some twenty years later had a much more important effect. These, however, belong to the next period.

6

1890 to 1910

THIS period was marked by two opposite tendencies; in one direction the sizes of machine tools increased in order to enable them to deal with the increasing size of engines and other components such as stern frames, rudders, and propellor shafts for ships, while in the other direction smaller machines were built in greater quantities to deal with the numerous small components of the smaller higher-speed engines and electrical machinery that assumed such importance during the period. Development was also directed towards increasing the productive capacity of all types of machine tools. This took the direction of widening the speed and feed ranges, increasing the rigidity, and making the operation of the machines easier.

Lathes

From the beginning of this period lathes were mostly made with gibbed saddles, but as late as 1897 weighted carriages were still being fitted on some American lathes.[1] Considering the heavier lathes, Plate 105 shows a duplex lathe built in 1892 by G. & A. Harvey of Govan. This design has the merit of saving floor space. There are two spindles with their axes a short distance apart in the plan view and each is provided with its own driving gear. The tool slides at each end have independent self-acting motions and so the two ends can be used separately. Towards the end of the period this firm built a lathe for turning turbine rotors up to 10 ft in diameter, but in order to make the machine capable of dealing with the greater volume of smaller work required the normal centre height was made only 4 ft and this could be increased to 5 ft by using packing stools beneath the headstock, tailstock, and tool posts. The lathe had four separate shears and there were four independent carriages carrying the tool posts; two of these were carried on the front shears and the other two on the rear ones. The drive was by a 35 h.p. electric motor mounted on the headstock.

The lathe shown in Plate 106, which was built about 1893 by Sharp, Stewart & Co., affords a good example of the large lathes being built by several makers at that time. This particular machine could handle work up to 6 ft in diameter and 40 ft in length, and it will be noticed that there is a tool slide machined on the front face of the tailstock, a feature that had been employed earlier, as mentioned in the last chapter. The saddles were fitted with change gearing for varying the rate of the cross feed so that tapers could be machined by using a combination of the longitudinal and cross feeds. Some seven years later this firm produced a double-ended lathe having a headstock at each end of its bed which was 86 ft in length. Two tailstocks were provided at the centre but these could, of course, be removed in order to accommodate very long jobs. Between each headstock and tailstock there were two carriages, each having two tool posts, one at the front and the other at the rear. The centre height was 3 ft.

A typical large gun-turning and boring lathe is shown in Plate 107. It was built about 1893 by the Niles Tool Works of Hamilton, Ohio, but lathes of similar size and general design were being built by makers in several countries at that time. Jobs up to 91 inches in diameter could be swung over the bed-ways and those up to 70 inches over the saddles, and work up to 45 ft long could be accepted. Lathes with much shorter beds but equally massive headstocks were also built at this time for the machining of large forgings and castings of short length.

A machine that was described as an Ingot Boring machine but which is conveniently included with lathes is shown in Plate 108. It could employ either trepanning bars or boring bars and could take ingots up to 12 ft long and 5 ft 6 in across the corners and its foundation casting was 44 ft long. Facing heads for machining the ends of the ingots could be substituted for the trepanning bars. The machine was built in 1899 by Craven Bros. About 1904 the Niles-Bement-Pond Company built a lathe for boring ingots but in this the ingot was rotated.[2] The lathe incorporated several original features. The boring-bar carrier that occupied the place of the conventional tailstock was arranged to act as a hollow piston so that the feed could be imparted by hydraulic pressure. In order to control the feed and to prevent any jump when the resistance to motion was suddenly reduced, the outside of the piston had a screw thread machined on it and the helix angle was made such that the torque, which was exerted on the nut by the axial thrust and tended to rotate the nut, could do so but could be easily controlled by a mechanical drive applied to the nut. The company used the same principle in a double-ended lathe built about the same time as the above for the purpose of boring gun forgings. In this machine the work was driven from the centre.

The machine shown in Plate 109 was built by Hulse & Co. in 1899 for turning the ends and drilling the flanges of the flues used in Lancashire boilers. The

116

main spindles are carried in headstocks bolted to massive base castings, the left-hand one being bolted to the base casting while the right-hand one can be moved along ways to accommodate flues of different lengths. The tools for turning the edges of the flanges are held in compound rests mounted on projecting portions of the spindle bases, and the tool travel is limited to that provided by the top slide of the rest. Also mounted on the castings that carry the headstocks are four drilling spindle heads, and these can be adjusted so that the drill axes are at the appropriate distance from the axis of the work. The flue is driven from the right-hand headstock and the left-hand one is arranged to provide the indexing of the work for the drilling operations. The drilling spindles are interlocked with the main spindles so that they cannot be operated when the latter are rotating.

A lathe was built about 1908 by Macdonald Swinburne & Co. of Barrhead for turning and grinding lengths of shafting up to 22 ft long and 4 inches in diameter and to an accuracy of 0·00025 in.[3] The machine had a fairly normal headstock but at the front end there was a four-spindle rotatable head, the spindles of which were driven through gearing from the main spindle of the headstock and could be indexed in steps of 90°. A similar head was provided at the other end of the machine. On the front of the bed a saddle carrying a tool rest was mounted, and at the rear there was a grinding-wheel head that could traverse along separate ways. The bars to be machined were loaded into the machine by a mechanical conveyor at the bottom station, were turned at the front station, and ground at the rear one. The top station was an idle one and in this position the bar did not rotate. The patentees of this machine were the Phoenix Ground Shafting & Power Transmission Company. In 1890 a lathe that machined eight shafts simultaneously was seen by an engineer visiting the United States.[4]

Although lathes specially designed for the machining of crank shafts had been built from about 1840 onwards, lathes for small crank shafts began to become common only during the last half of the present period. An example, made by Thomas Ryder of Bolton, is shown in Plate 104*b*. This is clearly an adaptation of a general purpose lathe. The machine shown in Plate 110*a* and made by L. Gardner & Sons of Patricroft is a specialized one and the design is still current. The headstock 'spindle' is a large drum that is supported in bearings at each end and is fitted with clamps to hold the crank shaft in the correct position and so that the pin being turned is close to the outer end of the drum. A tailstock supports the outer end of the crank shaft. A long cross-slide carries the roughing tool at the front and the finishing tool at the rear; both tools take plunge cuts along the whole length of the pin. An accuracy of 0·0005 in is held on the diameter. A separate tool at the rear can machine the faces of the crank webs.

In 1903 the firm of Pollock & Macnab of Bredbury made special lathes for the sole purpose of turning cast-zinc cylinders into shavings. Two tools were used, one at the front and the other at the rear. They were mounted in special holders, providing both top and side rakes with very simply shaped tools, and took cuts about 1¼ in wide. The feed motion was imparted by a central screw actuated by a pawl and ratchet. This had the advantage of causing the chips to be broken into short lengths instead of coming off in long coils; interruption of the feed in this manner was used for the same purpose many years later in capstan and turret lathes.

About 1904 John Lang & Sons of Johnstone produced lathes that were fitted with headstocks incorporating a double expanding-pulley type of variable-speed drive, which gave an automatic increase of spindle speed during facing operations as was done in Clement's lathe in 1826. In a lathe made by W. F. & J. Barnes of Rockford, Illinois, about 1894, the spindle carried two discs against the peripheries of which a third disc was pressed so as to provide friction drives.[4] One of the discs was fixed to the spindle and gave a reverse drive, while the other could be moved along so as to provide a variable-speed forward drive.

An example of a lathe specially designed to bore and turn wheels, pistons, pulleys, etc., at high speed and with heavy cuts but also with accuracy is shown in Plate 110b. It was produced about 1893 by the Ohio Machine Tool Works and could take jobs up to 26 inches in diameter. It will be noticed that the taper- and contour-turning fitments are of an unusual type.

Pittler's universal lathe

This was primarily a lathe but could also be used to perform milling operations. It was designed by W. von Pittler of Leipzig about 1893 and made by the Deutsche Werkzeug 2 Maschinen Fabrik of Chemnitz in several sizes, both as a floor-mounted and as a bench lathe. The general arrangement can be seen from Plate 111a. The trapezoidal section-bed carries a saddle with a cylindrical outer surface on which is mounted a bracket that can be clamped in any position or be left free to rotate. This bracket has a cylindrical bore at the front and in this one leg of the L-shaped tool slide is carried. This tool slide can also be clamped in any position or be left free to rotate. The tool can thus be given four motions—longitudinal traverse, traverse at an angle to the axis of the work, rotation about the cylindrical leg of the tool slide, and rotation about the cylindrical surface of the saddle. The first three can be self-acting and the fourth can be under the control of a template as, for example, when backing-off taps or milling cutters. The self-acting feeds are derived from the worm that is seen at the left of the headstock and is geared to the spindle. The wheel that meshes with this worm is carried on a shaft in a bracket that can be swivelled about the axis of the lead-screw, and at the bottom of this inclined shaft there are two bevel pinions, either of which can be meshed with a third bevel gear mounted on the lead-screw. This arrangement gives a forward or reverse drive or a neutral position. The inclined shaft can also drive the wheel seen at the front of the headstock so that motion can be transmitted through the universally jointed telescopic shaft to the saddle. In some versions of the machine there is a second worm, behind the first, and driven from the spindle through a 2 to 1 spur-gear pair. The worm-wheel can be swung round so as to engage this second worm, thereby giving a feed rate of double the normal rate. The worm can also be mounted on the inclined shaft and the worm-wheel on the shaft geared to the spindle so that the latter can be given a slow rotation in synchronism with that of the lead-screw, thus enabling helices to be milled by cutters carried in the saddle in an attachment that replaces the tool slide.

A lathe designed specially for cutting long screws such as lead-screws is shown in Plate 111*b*. It was made about 1902 by J. Parkinson of Shipley who took out patents in 1899 covering its novel features. The thread is cut by a succession of cuts by a single-point tool that is fed in, traversed, and disengaged, and then returned to the starting point ready for the next cut, all these actions being automatic. The sequence goes on until the tool has been fed into the correct depth, when the machine stops itself. When multiple threads are being cut a traverse is made for each thread at one depth of cut and then the tool is fed in for the next cut, all automatically. A number of machines of this design are still in use and can compete with much more recent designs embodying different principles. A similar machine was also built about this time by the Automatic Machine Co. of Bridgeport.

A somewhat unusual form of lathe, described as a hollow mandrel lathe, was built by Wm. Muir about 1910. It was double-ended, one end being adapted for turning and boring operations and the other end more particularly for facing.

In the lighter lathes a notable development during the present period was the increased facility with which changes of spindle speed and of feed rates could be obtained. Headstocks embodying change gears, which could be brought into operation by sliding gears or clutches along their shafts or by engaging friction clutches, became much more common. Enclosed change-gear boxes in which the same principles were used or in which a sliding key was employed also became common. But perhaps the most important design was the Norton tumbler gear-box, which was patented about the beginning of this period. This was first fitted, about 1893, by the Hendey Machine Co. of Torrington, which subsequently became the Hendey-Norton Co. An early example is shown in Plate 112*a* and Fig. 35 but the mechanism is so well known that description is not required. The provision of an easy reverse drive to the lead-screw, which was also the feed shaft and was operated from the saddle, was one of several features that made this lathe a particularly popular one. Many other change-speed mechanisms, some similar and others very different in principle, were invented in the following decades.

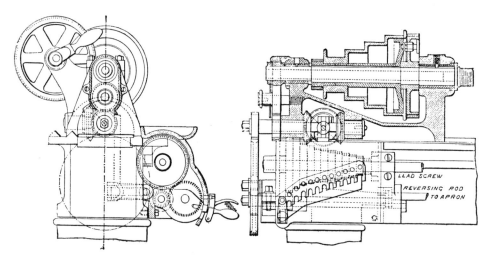

FIG. 35. The Norton gear-box, *Engineer, Lond.* 19 January 1894

Another direction in which progress was made was towards the elimination of the cone-pulley belt drive. It was gradually replaced by the all-geared head-stock and single-pulley drive and this development greatly facilitated the introduction of the individual electric-motor drive and the elimination of line-shafting and overhead countershaft gear. Towards the end of this period the belt drive between the electric driving-motor and the machine tool was eliminated and built-in motors directly coupled to the gear-boxes of the machines came into use.

Vertical lathes

The use of the vertical lathe and boring mill was greatly extended during this period, due to some extent to the increase in size of the pieces to be machined and the fact that these were easier to handle on the horizontal table of the vertical lathe. Increases in size were even greater than in conventional lathes. The culmination of this was the 60-ft machine designed by John Riddell, the superintendent of the General Electric Company of America in whose shops the machine was built and used. The general design was conventional, comprising a cross-beam that could be elevated on standards and carried two tool heads, and a rotating table. The latter was surrounded by a fixed annular work-table on which work could be mounted for boring operations, the tools then being mounted on the rotating table and the standards and cross-beam structure being removed. The fixed work-table had two tracks machined on it, one 30 ft and the other 40 ft in diameter, and on these the outer ends of tool slides carried by the rotating table could be supported. For a full description of this machine the reader is referred to the *Transactions of the American Society of Mechanical Engineers*, vol. xxiv, p. 1288, 1903.

Another large vertical-axis lathe, in which the column and cross-beam structure was dispensed with, was built in 1903 by the German Niles Tool Works of Berlin.[5] This machine consisted essentially of a rotating table surrounded by a fixed annular base-plate. For normal external turning operations the work was carried by the rotating table while the tools were carried on column assemblies that provided vertical and horizontal feeds and were bolted to the annular base. For boring operations the work was secured to the annular base and the tool assemblies to the rotating table. To facilitate the centring of the work the annular base could be moved in two directions by means of hydraulic jacks. This machine could take a dynamo stator having an internal diameter of 30 ft.

The use of small vertical lathes continued to increase during the period. In 1893 the Bullard Company of Bridgeport, Connecticut, who specialized in this form of lathe, were making one with a table 57 inches in diameter, and in 1907 a 24-in machine was put on the market. Both of these had turret tool-holders carried on a cross-beam, and the later one had one on the face of the single column which, with the beam, formed an L-shaped structure. In 1895 the Richards Machine Tool Co. were producing the small vertical lathe shown in Plate 112*b* for the turning of piston rings for small steam-engines. They also made a small machine in which the column carrying the vertical tool-slide itself traversed along ways in the bed-casting at about the work-table level. In 1901 Webster & Bennett of Coventry started producing double-table machines such as that shown in Plate 113*a* and they continue to make them. In 1902 G. Wilkinson, of Keighley, brought out the machine shown in Plate 113*b*. This is notable for the use of separate standards carrying tool heads for external turning operations. The work-table diameter was 2 ft 6 in.

Turret lathes

During this period the turret lathe came to be the most important type of lathe for any machine shop where articles were produced in numbers exceeding about a dozen. The improvements were chiefly that manipulation was easier, power return-motion of the turret saddle became common, an increased range of tools available for any job was provided, and capacities increased. Thus in 1899 turret lathes that would take bars 6 inches in diameter were being built by the German firm of Droop & Rhein and other firms also made machines of similar capacity. The length of the job that could be turned was increased by the introduction of the 'flat turret' lathe in 1891 by Jones & Lamson of Vermont. This was the invention of James Hartness of that company and it permitted work to pass through the turning tool and over the top of the turret; it also gave a better support for the turret as the bearing surface was out at the edge and it reduced the overhang of the tools carried. An example of this type of machine is shown in Plate 114a. Other firms subsequently built this type.

In 1897 J. Brockie took out a patent (No. 4201) for a system of electro-magnetic and hydraulic control of capstan lathes and automatics. The elements of the machines were to be actuated by hydraulic cylinders, the valves of which were controlled by the stops on the machine elements through switches, relays, and a commutator that was also actuated by the machine motions. Brockie envisaged the use of pre-set commutators for particular jobs; these would be kept in the tool stores when not in use.

A turret lathe that acquired a very good reputation in the larger size-range was made by the Gisholt Co. One of their machines, made in 1893, is shown in Plate 115. The inclined axis for the rotation of the turret enabled longer boring bars and lengthy multiple tool-heads to clear the cross-slide turret without having recourse to a very lengthy turret-slide travel. The headstock of this lathe incorporated friction clutches for the spindle drive and a power-operated chuck was also fitted on some models.

The use and production of turret lathes lagged somewhat in England at this time but there were several firms who built them, for example, Alfred Herbert, H. W. Ward, James Archdale, Bradbury & Co., John Lang & Sons, and Pollock & Macnab. Many other makers used turrets on their lathes, but merely as a convenient method of holding a variety of tools that were then used as in a centre lathe. This, of course, missed the most important advantage of the turret lathe proper, in which all the tools were set to cut the required diameters and stops regulated the lengths turned, so that the subsequent operation of the machine required very little skill. An unusual form of turret lathe was brought out in 1899 by the Wolseley Machine Co. of Birmingham and is shown in Plate 114b. The horizontal axis adopted for the turret was a departure from contemporary practice but, as has been pointed out, it was used in the early part of the preceding period. Advantages claimed for it were that the swarf fell away

122

from the tools and clear of the bed-ways and that the operator had easier access to the tools.

In a lathe made by the American Turret Lathe Co. of Wilmington, Delaware, under patents taken out by Conradson, a very large turret slide was provided which, in addition to the main turret itself, carried a small turret on a cross slide that could be actuated by hand or power. This eliminated the normal cross-slide saddle.

An unusual design was produced about 1892 by Herr Wilhelm von Pittler and a later example of it which shows its general arrangement is shown in Plate 116a. The Pittler Company later built an automatic with the same general arrangement. The horizontal position for the axis of the turret is a reversion to that adopted in the first turret of the early days. An interesting machine was made on the Continent about 1900. It was a four-spindle *turret* lathe and its design was undoubtedly based on that of the four-spindle automatic invented some five years earlier. The spindle head indexed from station to station and the turret and cross slide were traversed by hand, but a vertical tool-slide at the top was power-actuated and could be fed into depth and then traversed axially. A radical departure from conventional design is shown in the 'ring' turret lathe illustrated in Plate 116b and produced about 1905 by the Massey Machine Tool Co. of Waterton, New York. Some six years later Drummond Bros. of Guildford built a lathe on the same principle but using the cylindrical bed that they had popularized on their 4-in bench lathes.

Automatic lathes

Perhaps the most important development during this period was the introduction of the multi-spindle automatic lathe, but many innovations and improvements were made in single-spindle automatics including the introduction of automatic loading for chucking machines.

An interesting machine designed by C. M. Spencer, who invented the automatic lathe, is shown in Fig. 36. It is virtually two machines combined into one and has two spindles, that at the left being the main one that takes the rods from which the articles are to be machined and that at the right being an auxiliary spindle into which the work is transferred for further machining when the operations at the first spindle have been completed. The auxiliary spindle thus does the work that a second-operation automatic lathe would normally perform. The turret consists of two disc-like members one of which (K) is fixed to the shaft (L) while the other (K') is carried by a hollow shaft surrounding the first. The two discs are fixed together rotationally by pins (h) and the right-hand one (K') is also fixed axially. The left-hand member is traversed by cams carried on

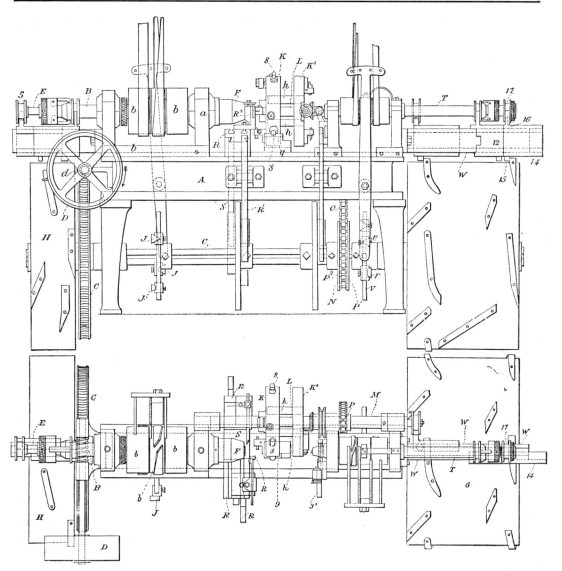

FIG. 36. Spencer's double-ended auto screw machine. *Engineering, Lond.* 30 October 1898

the drum (*G*). The rotational motion for indexing is derived from the chain drive (*N, O, P*) of which the sprocket (*N*) is loose on its hub and is driven by friction discs on either side. This drive tends to rotate the turrets all the time but they are held, when tools have to operate by the stops (8) that come against the fixed abutment (9). When the stop passes off the end of the abutment the indexing occurs, at other times the sprocket of the chain drive is slipping. The forming and parting-off tool slides are operated by levers and cams (*S, R*) in the ordinary manner. The two turret discs are provided with a large hole through which the auxiliary spindle can be moved up to receive the piece of work when it is parted off from the bar in the main spindle. The disc (K') carries a milling cutter for nicking the screw heads.

A 'Hartford' automatic made by the Pratt & Whitney Company about 1899 is shown in Plate 117. The general design calls for no comment; it is given as an example of magazine loading.

The Cleveland automatic that was introduced about 1897 differs from most contemporary designs in that it employs a cylindrical turret, which indexes about its axis and has a fixed forward and backward stroke, whereas the stroke of the turret slide of the conventional auto could be adjusted by changing the strip cams on their drums. The design is shown in Fig. 37. The drum (R)

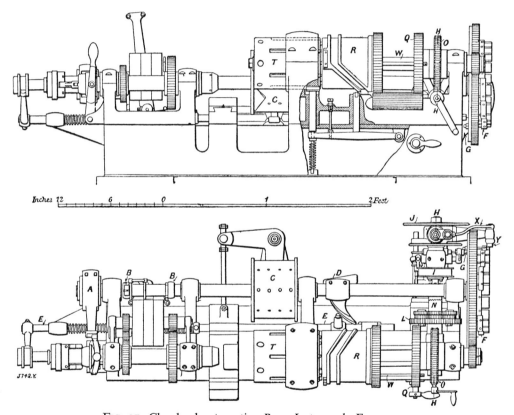

Fig. 37. Cleveland automatic. *Proc. Instn mech. Engrs*, 1901

rotates independently of the turret and can be driven at a slow speed, which can be varied, for cutting operations, and at a high speed for idling motions. The rotation is converted into an axial motion by the cam groove in the circumference of the drum, which engages a fixed roller. A cam-shaft at the rear is driven by the large spur-gear seen at its right-hand end and its cams operate the chuck, the bar feed, the spindle drive belts, and, by means of cams bolted to the drum (*C*), the cross slides. This cam-shaft can be driven at a high speed for the idle motions, while the slow speeds for the cutting operations can be varied by means of a double-disc friction drive, the driven disc of which is moved between the driving ones by the cams (*F*). The dogs (*G*) control the change of speed of the cam-shaft from slow to fast.

Another automatic lathe which used a cylindrical turret that indexed about its axis was the Wolseley, first produced in 1899 and shown in Plate 118*a*. It also incorporated a double-disc variable-ratio drive. Two years later the Wolseley Company brought out a vertical automatic lathe. Its most important advantage was the saving made in floor space.

A third machine that employed a horizontal turret axis was that shown in Plate 118*b*, which was designed by J. Brockie about 1900 but was envisaged in his patent of 1897. In this machine, however, the turret is a disc-like member and is carried on the end of a heavy spindle that is moved axially for the turning and drilling feeds and is rotated for indexing. Another somewhat unusual feature was that the forming and parting-off tools were carried in arms at the end of spindles that were rocked about their axes to give the feed and return motions.

About 1902 A. C. Dormer, an engineer of Rolle, Vaud, designed and produced the unusual form of automatic lathe shown in Plate 119*a*. In this four tools that can be used for turning operations are carried on four compound slides so that they can be given motions parallel and perpendicular to the spindle axis. In addition there is a telescopic spindle co-axial with the work spindle and this carries a die or tap. These were driven at a speed slightly slower than the work when screwing and at a higher speed when they had to be retracted. One advantage claimed for the tool-slide arrangement was that several tools could be in operation simultaneously; thus a finishing tool could start on its cut as soon as the roughing tool had machined a short length and did not have to wait for the completion of the roughing.

During the first decade of the twentieth century the Gridley single-spindle automatic was produced by the Windsor Machine Co. of Windsor, Vermont. The Gridley machine was later made by Craven Bros. of Manchester and one built about 1910 is shown in Plate 119*b*. One of its most important features was that the tool holders were bolted to long slides formed on a rotating drum; the feed motions were provided by the slides and the indexing by the drum. This was claimed to give greater rigidity to the tools.

Multi-spindle automatic lathes

The invention of the automatic lathe having several spindles, so that the time when the tools were idle was very much less than in the single-spindle machine, was made by the Americans Reinholdt Hakewessel and E. C. Henn in 1895, when they built a four-spindle machine for the manufacture of bicycle parts in a factory at Hartford. Subsequently a company was formed to manufacture the machines, and in 1902 this concern moved to Cleveland and became the National Acme Company. One of the earliest Acme four-spindle automatics is shown in Plate 120 and this basic form has been retained up to the present day. The four-spindle head indexes from station to station and the four-station 'turret' traverses along to provide the feeds. The cutting-off and forming slides of this early machine follow the practice used in the single-spindle automatics of that time.

Another company that was early in the field with a four-spindle automatic was the Windsor Machine Company, which has been mentioned as the manufacturer of a single-spindle machine. In the next twenty years multi-spindle autos were built in most of the industrial countries of the world. The majority of these were variants of the original Acme but some entirely different designs were brought out. One of these is shown in Plate 121. It was built by the Prentice Company about 1906 and was designed for the machining of small castings. These were loaded by hand into one of five chucks or fixtures carried in a turret that could be indexed from station to station. Opposite the other four stations there were four spindles rotating about fixed axes and carrying tools for boring, turning, and facing the workpieces. The axial feed was obtained by moving the turret along.

Boring machines

At the beginning of this period several makers were building vertical machines that were basically the same as that of Billingsley, built in 1802. These consisted of a large arch or portal frame, usually constructed of two columns united at the top by a bridge member that carried the driving mechanism for the spindle. The arch was fixed to a base casting that carried the work and also provided a bottom bearing for the boring bar along which the cutter head travelled. A machine of this type was built as late as 1906. In that year a horizontal machine almost identical with that built by Murdock and employing a travelling cutter-head was also built.

An impressive boring, turning, and drilling machine was made in 1892 by Rushworth & Co. of Sowerby Bridge.[6] Two drilling and boring heads were carried on a cross-beam supported on standards similar to those of a planing machine, and the work was carried on a rotating table on a saddle that could be traversed along the bed between the standards. The cross-beam also carried a turning tool and an auxiliary standard carried a tool head for turning the peripheries of jobs. The capacity of this machine was 4 ft in diameter and 8 ft in height. The machine shown in Plate 122*a* was built by G. & A. Harvey in the same year for machining circular and elongated circular holes in boiler plates. For the latter purpose the spindle head was given a motion along the beams by means of the crank seen at the right.

In a small vertical-spindle boring-machine for pulleys produced by the Richards Machine Tool Co. of London in 1893 all the driving and feed mechanism of the spindle was carried below the fixed work table as in key-seating machines. In 1896 Cunliffe & Croom made the two-spindle machine shown in Plate 122*b* and four spindle versions as well. The work table indexed from station to station and the operator loaded and unloaded the jobs at the front stations while the spindles operated at the rear.

The elevating-table type of horizontal boring machine continued to be produced, and some innovations were made. A duplex machine with two independent headstocks and work tables placed side by side was built in 1902 by G. Wilkinson, and a machine with spindle heads at both ends of the elevating table by the Newark Machine Tool Co. of New Jersey in 1903. Sharp, Stewart & Co. had produced in 1892 a machine that had a headstock and bed very much as in a lathe but was fitted with a boring spindle; in this machine a saddle traversed along the fixed bed and carried an arch-shaped member that could be raised and lowered by jack-screws. Ways machined on the front and back of the saddle guided this arch-shaped member, the top of which was machined to provide ways for a cross-traversing table. Pivoted at the centre of the latter there was a square table with T-slots to which the work was secured. This work table could thus be swung to any position to enable holes to be bored at any angles.

The elevating-head type of machine, however, gradually came into favour, and by the end of the period it was ousting the elevating work-table type. Two forms of drive to the spindle of the elevating-head type of machine became common, one employed a belt and the other shafts and gearing. The principle of the belt drive was that used by Sellers in the travelling-standards planing machine and shown in Fig. 19. The belt ran over fixed pulleys at the top and bottom of the column and over and under pulleys carried by the spindle head. One of the latter pulleys drove the spindle. A pipe-facing and boring machine employing a shaft drive is shown in Plate 123*a*. It was built by George Richards & Co. in 1898 and differs from a general purpose machine of the same form only in that it is not fitted with a traversing boring-bar spindle. In the larger elevating spindle-head boring machines the work was usually carried on a fixed work-table base and the horizontal motion was given to the column, which could slide along ways on a bed.

For machining holes whose depth is not great and where the cuts have to be heavy, or where the hole in the work is blind, the 'snout' type of boring machine has great advantages. One built by Joshua Buckton & Co. in 1899 is shown in Plate 123*b*. The snout form of construction later became common in vertical-spindle machines for boring the cylinder blocks of motor-car engines.

Horizontal spindle machines, in which no provision was made for vertical adjustment of the spindle or work, were built during the last half of the period for jobs required in large numbers. The jobs were then carried in fixtures that were designed for them and positioned them correctly in relation to the spindles of the machine. An example of a four-spindle machine of this kind is shown in Plate 124*a*. It was built by the Newton Tool Works for boring the motor- and gear-cases of electric trains and trams. The axial feeds are given to the spindles and the centre distances between these can be adjusted to suit different jobs. In the two-spindle machine of somewhat similar design shown in Plate 124*b* and built in 1904 by Ward, Haggas & Smith of Keighley for boring and facing the stator castings of electric motors, the work table could be adjusted in a direction perpendicular to the spindle axes. The two heads carrying the facing cutters were adjustable along the bed of the machine and one of them was fitted with the boring bar, which traversed axially.

Multi-spindle horizontal boring machines were built during the first half of this period specially for the machining of the cylinder castings of Corliss-type steam engines. They had a main spindle for the bore of the cylinder and four auxiliary spindles at right angles to the main one for boring the valve bores. The auxiliary spindles could be adjusted both vertically and horizontally to suit different sizes of cylinder.

In 1908 the firm of De Fries of Dusseldorf built some large horizontal boring and milling machines in which the spindle heads could be rotated about horizontal axes on their saddles so that their axes could be tilted out of the horizontal. The column carrying the saddle could be rotated on its base about a vertical axis and the base itself could travel on the bed casting. The machine was made in two sizes, the large one having a spindle $7\frac{1}{2}$ inches in diameter.[7]

In 1908 Henry Broadbent Ltd. of Sowerby Bridge built a special duplex horizontal boring, milling, drilling, and tapping machine for working on the body castings of horizontal gas and oil engines. The main spindle for machining the cylinder bore was carried by a head that could move vertically on a column, and the column could be traversed along ways at the end of the large fixed work table. On either side of this there were ways to carry two columns that together supported a cross-beam. The latter could be elevated on the columns and could also be tilted about a horizontal axis; it carried two spindle heads that could thus be tilted out of the vertical. One of the columns carried all the driving gear for the cross-beam heads and in addition was fitted with a spindle head for the boring of the bearing housings for the crank shaft of the engine. Thus all the principal bores and holes in the casting could be drilled and tapped, or bored, and milling operations be performed, all at one setting.[8]

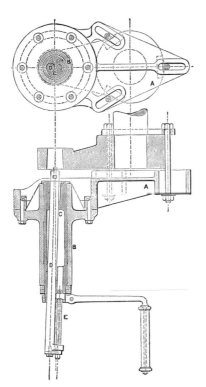

FIG. 38. Taper-hole boring bar.
Engineer, Lond. 2 February 1894

A portable boring bar, patented in Germany about 1893, is shown in Fig. 38 chiefly because the principle involved was used a decade later in the size adjustment of a planetary-type internal grinding machine. As the tool bar is fed along its axis the radius of the circle in which the cutting edge of the tool moves is changed and so a tapered hole is produced. If the feed motion is given to the outer member (C) a parallel hole will result and the motion along the axis of the tool bar itself will then provide a size adjustment.

Drilling machines

The principal improvements made to drilling machines during the period concerned spindle drives and feed gears, but the controls were grouped together and made more convenient for the operator to reach without having to move away from the spindle and work. There was also a great increase in machines employing a number, up to twenty, of separate drill heads mounted on a common beam-member along which they could be adjusted to vary the centre distances between them. In these machines the feed was sometimes given individually to each spindle but sometimes to the work table. In some machines the centre distance between the spindles was fixed. The multi-spindle machine, in which the centres of the drills could be adjusted in two directions so as to accommodate a wide variety of jobs, came into use at the beginning of the period and was well-established at the end of it. The use of several radial drilling machines, all mounted on a common bed along which they could be moved so that the whole area of a lengthy piece of work could be covered, was common, particularly in railway works and shipyards.

An elaborate machine for drilling boiler shells and similar work was built in

1893 by Scriven & Co. of Leeds. In this the work was carried on a rotatable circular table, which was placed between two columns that could be moved radially and transversely and could also be rotated about their vertical axes. Each column carried two saddles that could slide up and down; each saddle had a circular face on which was mounted an angle bracket and each bracket carried two independent drill heads.[9]

A machine for drilling twelve holes in the rims of railway-carriage wheels was built by George Richards & Co. in 1895 and is shown in Plate 125a. It is interesting to see that the work is mounted in a fixture and brought to the machine along rails and is then raised in the machine by power-operated brackets at each side. This is very similar to what is done in some transfer machines at the present day.

In 1891 a double-arm radial drilling machine was built by J. H. Hamilton, in which one arm was mounted on a vertical pillar in the ordinary way but a second arm and spindle head were carried on a horizontal pillar fixed to the end of the box-like bed.[10] The second arm was counterbalanced and its spindle could drill holes in the end of a piece of work at the same setting as for the drilling of holes in the top. An 'end-drilling' machine was made about 1900 by W. F. & J. Barnes for drilling holes in the ends of long work that could not be got under an ordinary drilling machine.[11] The spindle was carried in a head that could move along an arm pivoted on a horizontal axis at the bottom of one end of the box bed, to the upper surface of which the work was secured. The arm was counterbalanced and the arrangement was on the same lines as that of the second arm of Hamilton's machine.

About 1905 Wm. Asquith & Co. produced various forms of radial drilling machine in which the spindle was centrally placed between the two walls of a hollow-beam casting so that the thrust of the drill was taken centrally.[12] A somewhat similar arrangement was used by the Bickford Drill Co. at about this time. This form of construction, however, although it had a fairly wide vogue for some years, has not persisted.

In 1893 the Dusseldorf firm of Habersang & Zeizen made an adjustable centre distance multi-spindle drilling machine in which the spindles were driven by telescopic shafts provided at each end with a claw coupling centred on a ball.[13] These couplings functioned as variable-angle bevel gears. But a few years later Pratt & Whitney were producing machines with up to sixteen spindles in which universally jointed telescopic shafts were used, and in 1911 this firm was making a portal-frame type of multi-spindle machine in which the head moved vertically between the uprights of the frame. Drills up to $1\frac{5}{16}$ inches diameter and up to ten in number could be used.[14] They were also making multi-spindle machines in which the spindle axes were disposed horizontally.

In the five-spindle machine shown in Plate 125*b* the spindle heads can be indexed about the pillar so as to bring any of them into the operating position. This was produced about 1907 by Schuchardt & Schutte of Berlin, but the principle had been used by Thomas Shanks in 1860, and Pratt & Whitney had made a four-spindle machine in which the work-holding fixtures could be indexed round the pillar in 1880.

A massive machine that could be used for drilling, slotting, and milling operations was made in 1899 by the Société Russe de Constructions de Locomotives of Kharkoff and this seems to have been an impressive piece of engineering.[16] The drilling and slotting head was carried in a saddle and the slotting ram was screw operated. The saddle could be tilted about a normally horizontal axis and could travel along the face of a cross-beam. The cross-beam was carried at its ends on circular faces formed on two uprights, so that the beam could be tilted about a horizontal axis as in G. & Λ. Harvey's boring machine shown in Plate 80*b*. The uprights carrying the beam could be traversed along ways placed at each side of a base-plate on which the work was mounted. Ernst Schiess of Dusseldorf built a similar machine in 1909 but in this the drilling and slotting heads were separate, one being mounted on the front and the other on the rear of the beam.[16]

Planing, slotting, and shaping machines

No great changes occurred in the basic features of these machines during this period but some unusual machines that come under this heading were produced and changes comparable to those that occurred with other types of machine tool were made. The side, or wall, type of planer was built throughout the period but was waning in popularity by the end of it. The open-side or single-standard type of planing machine increased in popularity and some large ones were built, particularly in America.

A machine that was called a 'circular' planer, but which was more of a slotter than a planer, was built by Campbells & Hunter of Leeds in 1897. The tool travelled up and down the face of a column as in a side planer but the work was carried on a circular table and the feed was rotational. Six castings carried the work and could be moved radially on the surface of the work table rather like the jaws of a huge chuck.[17]

In 1897 Alexander Gordon of the Niles Tool Works took out a patent covering the use of compressed air to operate the clutches of planing-machine drives. One of the chief claims made for this was that it gave more rapid reversals.

In 1902 Hulse & Co. built a planer in which the cross-beam could be tilted so that the feed motion was at an angle to the surface of the work table and the inclined faces of castings could be machined without recourse to awkward packings.[18] One end of the beam was carried on a pivot on a saddle that moved up and down on one of the standards, and the other end was carried by a saddle that was similar but had provision for absorbing the variation in the effective length of the beam as it was tilted. The beam was locked to the saddles during cutting but the two saddles could be elevated together as required. The same firm also made a planer in which the tool slide was coupled by a radius rod to a pivot on a vertical bracket carried at the middle of the bridge member connecting the tops of the standards. The beam was left free to move on the standards and so the traverse of the tool slide across the beam caused the tool to move in a circular arc. The position of the pivot was adjustable.

Plate-edge planers continued to be built, and in one made by the Niles Tool Co. in 1893 an auxiliary bed and tool head was provided to enable the ends of plates to be machined at the same setting as the edges. The auxiliary bed could be swivelled so that the end of the plate was at any angle between 75 and 105° to the long edge.[19] A plate-edge planer, in which the tool head travelled on ways on the back of the beam that carried the holding-down jacks for the plate instead of travelling on a separate bed at approximately floor level, was built by G. Addy of Sheffield in 1899.[20] A machine that was called a 'breast side' planer was made in 1897 for machining the edges of armour plates. The tool head was carried in a slide that could move up and down in a saddle that could slide along the beam. The latter was supported at its ends on circular faces formed on heavy standards bolted to the foundations, and it could therefore be tilted so that the tool slide, which normally gave the feed motion but could be used for slotting, was out of the vertical. The main cutting motion was obtained by moving the saddle along the beam.[21]

Pit-type planers were built during the period to handle the very large components of the engines then being built. The 'pit', however, was formed by side castings bolted to a base-plate and machined on their upper faces to carry the travelling standards and cross-beam assembly. In one machine built in 1903 there was a separate work table that could be adjusted vertically, by small steps, between the side walls.

A wall planer, in which the slide for the travelling tool-head assembly was carried by the building housing the machine, was built as late as 1891, but this construction was soon displaced by the self-contained machine in which the 'wall' was a massive casting bolted to the base. These were built in large sizes. One built by Ernst Schiess in 1910 could machine a surface $32\frac{1}{2}$ ft long by 21 ft high.

Throughout this period the Manchester firm of George Richards was prominent in the production of the side-planing machine in which the tool travelled and the work was stationary. In its usual form the tool head was carried on the face of an overhanging arm along which it moved to give the feed motion, while the arm was carried by a saddle that travelled along ways formed on the top of the bed casting to give the cutting motion. In some machines these motions could be interchanged so that they could also be used as a travelling-head shaper. The face of the bed was machined to carry one or more work tables as in the travelling-head type of shaping machine. The saddle was usually actuated by means of a screw and reversal was by open and crossed belts, but towards the end of the period electric drives were being used. In the machine illustrated in Plate 126a two saddle and arm assemblies were used; one of these had a stroke of 12 ft and the other of 13 ft and the strokes overlapped. It was therefore possible to machine a surface up to 24 ft long by $3\frac{1}{2}$ ft wide. In 1910 the firm built a side planer in which the saddle was moved by an endless chain that ran over sprockets at the ends of the bed, and it was claimed that this form of drive required less power than a screw. The firm also made a variation of the type in which the normal arm and tool head could be removed and be replaced by an 'arm' that hung down in front of the face of the bed. This member carried the tool head, which could thus be given a vertical feed motion. As the arms could be changed over quite rapidly it was feasible to plane the top and the faces of castings at the same setting, the work being bolted to the base-plate of the machine. By mounting two side-planing machines face to face on a large bed-plate the equivalent of a pit planer was produced.

A special machine resembling a side planer of the type just described was made in 1896 by Hulse & Co. and is shown in Plate 127a. The construction will be clear from the illustration but it may be pointed out that the cutting motion could be either by the tool head moving along the arm or by the arm and saddle moving on the bed-ways. In an open-side planer built by the German firm of Billeter & Klunz about 1908 a cylindrical pillar was used to carry the cantilever arm and this could be elevated as in a radial drilling machine.

In 1905 Sir W. G. Armstrong Whitworth & Co. built a planing machine with travelling standards for machining large armour plates and this type of machine was also built by Joshua Buckton & Co. in the same year.[22] This type of machine was said to be particularly steady when cutting and to require less power than travelling-table machines.

The common open and crossed belt reversing mechanisms for planers was improved by the introduction of clutches to eliminate the shifting of belts, and some of the clutches were electro-magnetic. Fly-wheels were also incorporated in the mechanisms to increase the speed of reversal and to lessen the peak demand for power when electric motors were used for the drive. Electric-motor drives, however, by the middle of the period were by means of motors directly coupled to the driving pinion, the reversal being obtained by electrical means. A difficulty experienced with these direct-coupled electric drives was due to the inertia of the motor armatures, and so clutches were sometimes used to obviate this. During the last years of the period the German firm of Felten & Guillaume Lahnmeyerwerke and the Lancashire Dynamo Company in England developed rather more complex electric drives employing motor-generator sets to feed the main driving motor. This drive was known in England as the Ward Leonard drive and became the standard drive for the larger machines.

A special machine was made in 1903 by the Stettiner Maschinenbau A.G. for planing the blades of screw propellors. The general arrangement is obvious from Plate 127b. The cutting motion was given by the rotation of the arm about the central pillar and this motion was geared to the vertical motion of the ram carrying the cutting tool so that in conjunction with the feed motion along the arm a helical surface was produced.

Slotting machines

By the middle of this period slotting machines in the small and medium sizes had assumed the form common today but in the early and middle parts of the period some very large and unconventional machines were produced. That shown in Plate 128 was built by Thomas Shanks in 1892 and bears a close resemblance to a side-planing machine. The ram had a maximum stroke of $3\frac{1}{2}$ ft but the slide assembly in which the stroke occurred could be adjusted vertically by $2\frac{1}{2}$ ft.

The multiple-head slotting machine, introduced during the preceding period for the machining of the long frame of locomotives and in which the rams were carried on cross beams and standards as in planing machines, continued to be built but incorporated the detail improvements found in the conventional machines of the period.

The pillar type of shaping machine shown in Plate 126b became the most popular for the smaller and medium sizes and usually employed the crank-and-slotted lever-driving mechanism, but some variations of this were used. Thus, instead of pivoting the lever at the bottom and using a short connecting rod to couple it to the ram at the top, the arrangement was reversed; and instead of the connecting rod a second slot-and-pivoted block was sometimes used and this also could be at either the top or the bottom. In 1902 the Hendey Machine Company introduced a range of machines in which the ram was actuated by a pinion and rack, open and crossed belts being used for the reversals, and a little earlier the Morton Manufacturing Co. of Muskegon Heights, Michigan, produced a pillar-type shaping machine in which the cutting was done on the inward stroke of the ram. The method of altering the stroke of the driving crank of the conventional type of machine was improved and made easier to operate and self-acting feeds to the tool-head slide were improved. Tilting work tables became fairly common.

The travelling-head type of shaper remained popular for the larger machines. In one of these machines, built by Ernst Schiess in 1909, the ram slides were carried on the saddles on ways formed to the arc of a circle in the vertical plane. The rams could thus be tilted out of the horizontal through angles up to 15°. The machines were used for machining armour plate and enabled slight tapers to be formed at the edges.[23]

Milling machines

These were well-established at the beginning of the period and their popularity increased considerably, so that at the end of the period they were probably next only to the lathe in importance. The basic forms did not change much but some new forms came into use, chiefly for somewhat specialized work. In the smaller sizes of machine the knee type of construction was mostly used but the Lincoln type and other types employing fixed beds and elevating spindle heads were also used considerably. For the larger machines the plano type of construction was most common. The designs of all types showed improvements in such things as spindle bearings, gear-boxes, and feed gears. The lathe type headstock fitted with a cone-pulley and back-gear disappeared and all-gear drives became common. Belt-driven feed gears gave way to gear-driven ones, and telescopic universally jointed shafts for carrying the feed to the work table began to give way to drives using only key-wayed shafts and bevel or worm gears. Screws were generally used for the work-table feed but racks and pinions were not entirely displaced. The Brown & Sharpe Company, who were pioneers in the milling-machine field, were manufacturing machines with rack and pinion drives until well beyond the end of the present period. In the smaller sizes of machine there was a tendency to build such things as spindle and feed gear-boxes as units that were subsequently assembled into the body of the machine. Towards the end of the period these units were being made so that they could be used in more than one type of machine, for example, in both horizontal and vertical models.

Plates 129 and 130 show some types of milling machine being made by Brown & Sharpe in 1895 and 1913, the illustrations being taken from catalogues issued at those dates. Some of the machines were being built several years earlier than the dates of the catalogues. The plates bring out the changes in design that occurred over the period and also show the longevity of some of the basic forms. The universal machine at (*a*) in Plate 129a shows how the design has been stiffened up since the first machine was built in 1862, other changes being in the provision of back-gear and the use of a hollow spindle and an overarm support; while comparison of this machine with that at (*b*) shows greater changes, of which the most important are the use of gear-boxes for the spindle and feed drives. These changes are even more apparent between the two plain machines shown at (*c*) and (*d*). The No. 13 plain machine seen at (*a*) in Plate 130a has a fixed work table, the vertical adjustments being obtained by pivoting the cutter spindle head. The later version of this type of machine, seen at (*b*), shows a general increase in robustness and the introduction of a brace between the bed and the overarm support, while the locking of the spindle head has been improved. Other improvements between all the earlier and the later machines were increases in the number of spindle speeds and feed rates available. The vertical machine seen at (*c*) in Plate 130 had been built for some years before 1895; the chief differences between it and the later version seen at (*d*) are the use of a chain instead of a belt for the drive from the vertical shaft to the spindle, the use of a telescopic shaft and a gear-box in the feed gear, and a much heavier work-table assembly.

From the beginning of this period horizontal milling machines were frequently supplied with vertical milling attachments and by 1903 slotting and rack-cutting attachments were also common. Plate 131*a* shows two designs by Brown & Sharpe. In both the attachment is carried primarily on the face of the column but with support from the overarm. In both, the spindles can be swivelled to any angle in a plane perpendicular to the spindle axis of the machine. A model in which the spindle of the attachment could be placed at any angle was being made in 1903.

In 1894 the French firm of P. Huré brought out the ingenious spindle head whose construction is shown in Fig. 39, where the spindle axis is shown in the horizontal position. By rotating the lower portion of the head on the inclined circular face the spindle axis can be brought to the vertical position. The head can also be swivelled on the circular face by which it is attached to the column of the machine, and by a combination of this motion with the former one the spindle axis can be placed at any angle to the direction of the table axis whilst remaining in a horizontal plane, so that helices can be milled although the work table does not swivel. An overarm is provided to support the outer end of the spindle when in the horizontal position. This design is still in production by the firm, now known as Leon Huré S.A.

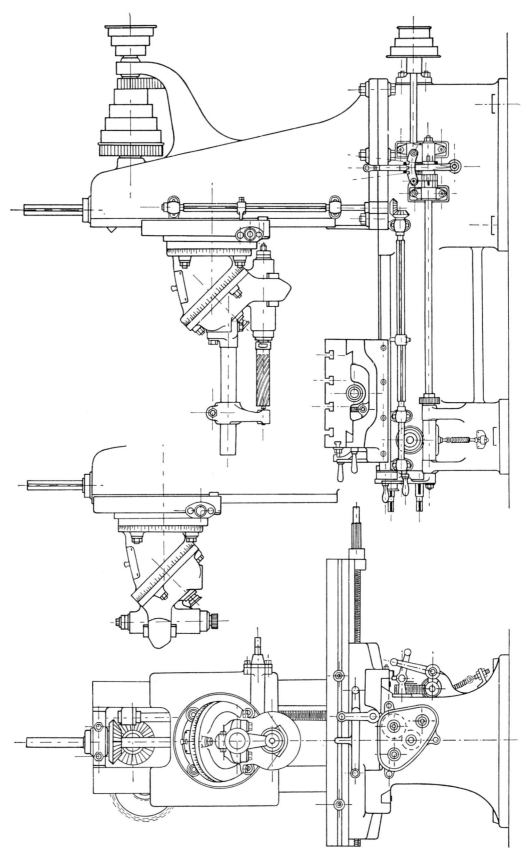

FIG. 39. Huré swivelling-head milling machine. Patent No. 2381–1896

Also in 1894 the Van Norman Company in America manufactured a milling machine in which the spindle was carried in a head that was permanently attached to the column but which could be swivelled so as to lie at any angle from the horizontal to the vertical.

In 1892 C. H. Phillips, an American, took out a patent for a brace that coupled the overarm to the knee of horizontal milling machines. These subsequently became universal fitments and before the end of the period the brace had been extended so as to couple the knee to the base of the column as well as to the overarm.

About 1900 the Grant Machine Tool Co. of Cleveland, Ohio, brought out machines of the type shown in Fig. 40, in which the spindle is carried in a drum

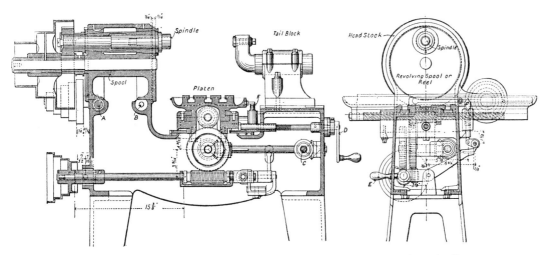

FIG. 40. Grant's drum-spindle-head milling machine. *Engineer, Lond.* 20 April 1900

that can be rotated in the head of the machine in order to vary the height of the spindle above the work table. The outer end of the spindle was supported in a cranked member that could be pivoted about the axis of the drum. This construction carries to the limit the principle used in the oscillating-head machine shown in Plate 89*a* and in the pivoted-head machines shown in Plates 130*a* and 130*b*.

Vertical spindle machines made greater progress in the larger sizes than in the smaller ones during the earlier years of the period but the smaller sizes made great progress in the latter half of the period. The machine shown in Plate 131*b* is fairly typical of the kind of machine that was being made by several English makers during the first decade of the period. It was made by Kendall and Gent and is belt driven. There is also a support for the lower end of the cutter and this was a feature that was common throughout the period for this size of machine, which was frequently employed on heavy profiling work. Some makers of this type and size of machine preferred to use a gear drive to the spindle.

Plates 132a and 132b show two milling machines by Alfred Herbert of Coventry. That at (a) was made in 1900 and has a work-table assembly that slides directly on the bed, the vertical adjustments being given to the spindle head—an arrangement that was unusual in relatively small machines at that time. The second example was made in 1906. This type became very popular and was subsequently built by many makers.

In 1891 E. Rivett of Boston, Massachusetts, produced a vertical milling machine. This was fitted with a turret containing six spindles that could be indexed about a horizontal axis so as to bring any spindle into the working position. The spindles were driven by conical friction gear and those not in use did not revolve.[24]

The type of milling machine shown in Plate 133a was variously known as a 'power', 'manufacturing', 'slabbing', or 'double-head' type. It was being built in small sizes in the previous period and is really only a development of the Lincoln type but it became virtually a distinct type when used in the larger sizes. The example shown was made by H. W. Ward & Co. of Birmingham about 1901. The work table was 7 ft by 2 ft and had a traverse of 6 ft. A quick return was provided for the table. The columns carrying the spindle head and the outer support bearing were adjustable transversely through a distance of 6 in. In the double-head machines a second spindle head occupied the place of the outer support column; these machines were used mostly with face cutters operating on the side faces of the work.

A 'double column' milling machine, in which the work table elevated on slide-ways formed on the inside faces of a U-shaped box-base casting, was being manufactured by Pratt & Whitney in 1898 in two forms. In one form there was a single spindle head on the top of the left-hand leg and an outer mandrel support on the right-hand leg. The second form had two spindle heads, one on each leg. Machines of this general form are still being built today. A plano-type milling machine built by Wm. Muir in 1892 is shown in Plate 133b. Towards the end of this period some very heavy plano-type millers were built in England, America, and Germany for milling armour plate; these, however, were designed to use slab milling cutters and they could take cuts of the order of $\frac{3}{8}$ in deep by 2 ft wide at feed rates of 4 in/min. In 1899 Cunliffe & Croom made a plano-type miller in which two separate work tables, each 8 ft long and $2\frac{1}{2}$ ft wide, were carried on a common bed, and two spindle heads were fitted on the cross-beam. The plano-type miller was also used for heavy profiling work. In 1899 Wm. Muir made one with a work table 10 × 5 ft with a circular table 5 ft in diameter; it had two spindle heads, which could be coupled together and be guided by a single tracer or could be used separately. In 1896 Kendall & Gent built a combined milling and drilling machine which had two standards and a cross rail. On the latter were mounted a vertical-axis milling head and a saddle carrying the arm of a radial drill. The work table was circular and could be traversed along ways perpendicular to the cross rail. The machine could handle work up to 7 ft 6 in diameter and 8 ft 6 in high.[25]

Machines, which were called 'rotary planers' but which used face milling cutters, were used to a considerable extent for machining large girders and similar work. The cutters were sometimes as much as 10 ft in diameter and had inserted teeth resembling lathe tools. The cutter spindle head could slide along ways on a bed that could be swivelled about a vertical axis and incorporated an apron that projected in front of the cutter and provided a support for the ends of the girders.

During the second half of the period some machines of unusual form were made by Curd Nube of Offenbach am Main. The one shown in Fig. 41 has three spindles—a vertical one above the work table, a vertical one below it, and a horizontal one in the usual position. The work table has a hollow space at its centre to provide room for the bottom spindle and it could traverse in two directions and rotate about a vertical axis. It is carried on a knee that can be raised and lowered on the face of the column. Machines having two vertical spindles, one above and one below the work table, which could be tilted, were made by the Thurston Manufacturing Co. of Providence, Rhode Island, about this time.

In 1898 a multiple-spindle automatic milling machine was built by James Gregory of Bridgeport, Connecticut, for milling the hexagonal faces of valve caps. There were eight spindles to carry the work and these were indexed from station to station and rotated about their vertical axes as this was done. At six of the stations spindles carrying milling cutters were carried on short slides along which they were given a short traverse during each cycle. At the remaining stations the work was automatically ejected and manually loaded respectively. The machine could handle 350 caps per hour.[26]

Thread milling became fairly common during the latter half of the period and one of the first machines made for this purpose is shown in Plate 134a. It was designed by H. Liebert, who took out patents for it in 1897, and was made by John Holroyd of Milnrow, the firm of which he was manager. The spindle head B can be rotated about a vertical axis and be moved vertically and horizontally. The vertical motion had a rapid withdrawal. The gearing that determines the pitch of the thread is placed at the end of the bed and an indexing plate enables multiple threads to be indexed. A steady, Q, is provided below the work and is adjustable in two directions, while a second steady, Y, is available for the ends of long jobs. In a smaller machine made by the same firm the general constructional form was that of a knee-type horizontal milling machine. The table that carried the work was mounted at a point near to its end on a circular facing on

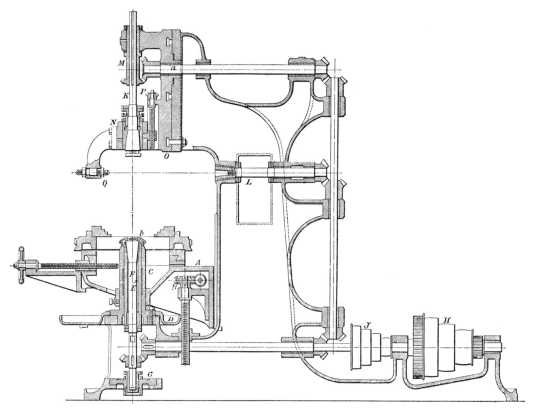

FIG. 41. Three-spindle milling machine by Curd Nube. *Engineering, Lond.* 22 January 1904

the top of the knee. Thread milling machines were also made about this time by the German firm Reinecker of Chemnitz and one produced about 1900 is shown in Plate 134*b*. During the second half of the period Pratt & Whitney manufactured a range of thread milling machines.

Gear-cutting machines

Remarkable progress was made during the period both in the improvement of existing methods of cutting gear teeth and in the development of new methods, particularly those in which the tooth shape was generated instead of being copied. The milling process that employed a form-relieved cutter and produced a single tooth at each traverse remained the principal machine for manufacturing work throughout the period but it was being displaced by other types towards the end of the period. The great activity in respect of generating-gear cutters was evident not only in regard to spur gears but also in regard to bevel gears. Spur-gear cutters will, however, be dealt with first.

The earliest rival to the milling process for spur gears was the hobbing process. It has been mentioned that Bodmer's machine could be arranged for hobbing and that Christian Schiele in his patent showed two constructions of hobbing machines. The earliest hobbing machine was actually built and about which there is definite knowledge was one that was working in 1893 in the works of George Juengst & Sons of Croton Falls, New York. This was illustrated in Humpage's paper to the Institution of Mechanical Engineers in 1908, in which he gave the name as Juenpt. The hob was carried on a slide that could traverse along ways on the top of a pedestal. It was driven through a spur pinion and wheel from a belt pulley that was carried on the slide, and the hob axis could be swivelled about a vertical axis through a small angle. The work-piece was overhung on a spindle, which was carried in a head that could be raised and lowered in a guide formed in a column integral with the pedestal. The hob and work-spindle were geared together by a worm and worm-wheel, a pair of bevels, and change gearing, the latter being mounted on a bracket on the work-spindle head. Key-ways along the shafts allowed for the motions of the hob slide and the work head. Because of the limited swivel motion of the hob this machine was restricted to the cutting of straight-toothed gears.

In 1894 the German firm of J. E. Reinecker started to produce gear-hobbing machines and one design built throughout the next decade is shown in Plate 135*a*. This quickly achieved a great reputation. It could cut worm-wheels as well as both straight and helical-toothed spur gears. For cutting worm-wheels tapered hobs fed axially were used, a method devised by the firm. Fly-cutters could also be used and could be given an axial motion so that they swept out a surface equivalent to that of a hob. This, of course, was a slow method but was useful when a suitable hob was not available. The two component motions required by the work because of the rotation of the hob and its feed motion were combined in this machine by means of a differential. This enabled the feed rate to be changed readily. A smaller machine is shown in Plate 135*b*.

The hobbing machine in which the work axis is horizontal soon achieved a conventional form similar to the common form of the formed-milling cutter machine. In this the hob was carried on a saddle on ways on the top of the bed and the work on a mandrel carried by the spindle head. The head could be raised and lowered on a column at one end of the machine, while another column, usually mounted on the bed-ways, carried a bearing to support the outer end of the work mandrel.

In an alternative form introduced by the Pfauter Company and which became common during the latter part of this period the work axis was placed vertically and the head carrying the hob was given its feed motion on the face of a column at the end of the bed. An example of this type is shown in Plate 136a. It was made by John Holroyd & Co. in 1904.

The next development was that made by E. R. Fellows in 1897 when he patented the pinion-cutter process. In this the cutter takes the form of a spur pinion, which is rolled in unison with the blank to provide the generation of the tooth shape and is reciprocated axially to give the cutting motion. A relief motion is provided to take the work out of contact with the cutter on the return stroke. The main difficulty with this process, which was known in theory many years previously, was the production of the cutters, and perhaps Fellows's work on this aspect of the problem was of greater importance than his invention of the machine for carrying the process into effect. The basic form of the Fellows machine did not change subsequently during the period under discussion and a typical example is shown in Plate 136b.

The principle of generating spur-gear teeth by rolling a blank with a toothed rack had been known since Edward Sang gave his paper to the Royal Scottish Society of Arts in 1837. It underlies the action of the hob but it was not embodied into a practical machine until some eighty years later, although the principle was used by Fellows in the production of his pinion-type cutters. Towards the end of this period machines embodying the rack-cutter principle were produced by Reinecker in Germany and Parkinson in England. The former used a tool that represented a single tooth of a rack and this was given a reciprocating motion to provide the cutting action. The generating motion was given entirely to the blank, which was rotated about its own axis as that axis received a translation tangential to the pitch circle. The general form of the machine is seen in Plate 137a. Its chief disadvantage was its low rate of production compared with the other methods available at that time.

This disadvantage was overcome in the Sunderland gear-planer patented by Sam Sunderland in 1908 and made by J. Parkinson & Son of Shipley. This uses a cutter having several teeth but, as it was impracticable to have enough to enable the cutter to be rolled right round the blank, Sunderland devised a 'step-back' motion. When sufficient motion had been given to the rack cutter and the blank to enable one tooth to be generated the cutter was disengaged from the blank and stepped back one tooth space so that eventually all the teeth of the gear were cut. In some cases the step-back motion embraced several teeth. An early Sunderland machine is shown in Plate 137b. The head carrying the cutter moves up and down the face of the saddle member, which itself moves along the bed-ways. The blank is carried on a mandrel that rotates about a fixed axis. The head carrying the slide in which the cutter reciprocates can be swivelled about an axis perpendicular to the axis of the blank so that helical teeth can be cut as easily as straight ones. Machines were made under licence from the Parkinson company in some European countries, in particular by the Maag Company of Switzerland.

A spur-gear tooth-generating machine that employed two rack type cutters, one at each side of the blank, was patented in 1907 by F. J. Spencer and J. Speirs of Huddersfield, and is shown in Plate 138a. The cutting motion is given to the blank, which is carried on the top of a ram that is reciprocated vertically by means of an adjustable crank and a connecting rod whose upper end is spherical. This enables the ram to be rotated in order to give the blank its generating motion, which is derived from a worm that engages a large worm-wheel secured to a sleeve splined to the ram. The cutters are carried in compound slides and can be traversed tangentially to the blank in opposite directions to give them their generating motion. This also is derived from a worm that engages a worm-wheel concentric with the ram and to which a large spur gear is attached. This gear meshes with racks carried by the cutter slides. The two worms are geared together by change gearing so as to give the correct ratio between the generating motions. A form of clapper box provides relief for the cutters on their return strokes. The upper members of the compound slides provide for the adjustment of the cutters radially. In this machine the length of the rack cutters is made sufficient to enable each to cut rather more than half the teeth required on the blank so that no step-back motion is necessary. In a larger machine described in the patent the blank is rotated forwards when the cutters reach the ends of their generating motions and they are thereby enabled to function on their return strokes; the blank, of course, then rotates backwards in unison. The cutters are built up of pieces of tool steel machined at one end to the shape of one tooth of the generating rack, and the pieces, which are ground all over, are clamped in holders. The machine does not seem to have been manufactured to any great extent.[27]

A copying-type machine, which embodied some novel features, was designed by Pedersen about 1908 and is shown in Plate 138b. Two cutters were used, one taking a roughing cut and the other the finishing one. They were carried on a reciprocating slide, one cutting towards the right and the other to the left. They were mounted on a member that could be rocked about a pivot so that the cutting edges were moved out of contact with the work on their return strokes.

At the end of this period, or perhaps just afterwards, Sir Charles Parsons and his colleagues developed the 'creep' method of hobbing large gears. In this the work was mounted on a sub-table that could rotate on the top of the main table to which it was geared so that it received a slow motion relative to the main table, the extent of this supplementary motion being about 1 per cent of the total motion. Any errors in the worm-wheel of the main table were thereby distributed in a spiral formation round the periphery of the wheel instead of being concentrated in lines parallel to the axis. Fig. 42 shows the arrangement of the machine for carrying out this principle.

Machines for cutting bevel gears

Up to the beginning of this period most bevel gears had been cut on machines employing the template copying process such as has been described earlier in this book, and this type continued to be widely used and built right up to the end of the present period. However, towards the end of the previous period Hugo Bilgram had produced his generating machine and this was used to a considerable extent during the whole of the present period and an automatic version was produced about 1901. An example is shown in Plate 139*a*. Its limited production capacity caused it to go out of favour subsequently. At the end of this period the copying type of machine was clearly becoming obsolescent except for certain specialized purposes.

About 1898 H. C. Warren, who was employed in a cycle factory of the Pope Company at Hartford, Connecticut, produced a machine for cutting the bevel gears used in the firm's cycles, for which purpose the machine is said to have been used extensively. It seems to have been envisaged in two distinct forms. In one version the imaginary generating crown wheel was simulated by a pair of milling cutters with straight sides and carried by slides, so that they could be traversed along lines converging on the apex of the gear. In the other version multi-toothed straight cutters resembling external broaches are said to have been used. In both cases the generating motion was given partly to the blank, which rotated about its own axis, and partly to the cutter slides which rotated about the axis of the imaginary crown-wheel. It does not seem that the second version of the machine was ever actually built but a machine of the first kind was put on the market by a German firm and their product is shown in Plate 139*b*.

In 1898 the Gleason Company of Rochester, New York, who had become one of the leading firms in the production of copying-type machines, patented a generating type. In the next few years the machine was built and its general appearance can be seen from Plates 140*a* and 140*b* which, however, show a rather later production. Two reciprocating cutters were used and represented the sides of a tooth of the imaginary crown wheel. The generating motion was given partly to the blank and partly to the cutters, as in the Warren machine. The cycle on which the machine worked was roughly as follows. With the cutters at the bottom of their generating motion they were fed into depth by

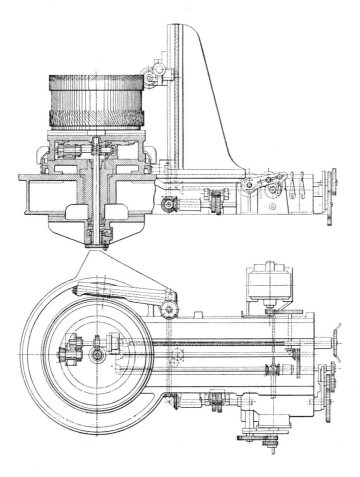

FIG. 42. Parsons's 'creep method' gear-hobbing machine.
Engineering, Lond. 14 March 1913

rotating the member carrying them about a vertical axis passing through the apex of the blank. A cam then commenced to raise the curved arm seen in the illustrations and as this was keyed to the spindle carrying the blank the latter was rotated about its axis. The curved arm carried a short toothed sector that meshed with another toothed sector secured to the member carrying the cutter slides, so that this member was also rotated, but about the axis of the crown wheel. The toothed sectors were, in effect, enlarged portions of the crown wheel and of the gear being cut and so gave those members the correct relative motion. The generating 'roll' could only encompass the generation of one tooth space and so at the end of it the cutters were withdrawn from the blank and both were brought back to their starting positions. During this time the blank was indexed round one tooth and the cycle then recommenced. The machine was fully automatic and, in its various models, became one of the most widely used bevel-gear cutters throughout the world.

Generating machines were subsequently built in several other countries. About 1900 the Reinecker company started to make the Bilgram machine in Germany. At about the same time the Ateliers de Construction Mecanique, of Mulhouse, who were the successors of the firm of Ducommun (a name that has appeared several times previously in this book), produced the Nardin machine shown in Fig. 43. It uses reciprocating cutters to represent the crown wheel and these are situated below the blank in the lower part of the machine. The whole of the generating motion is given to the blank, which rotates about its own axis, while the saddle carrying it rotates about the vertical axis of the crown wheel. The connection between these two motions, however, was entirely by gearing. Again a step-back motion was necessary.

In 1906 F. J. Bostock, of Birmingham, took out a patent (No. 5290) for a machine for generating bevel-gear teeth by means of a hob that he had patented in 1905 (No. 22142). The hob increased in diameter, and its teeth in size and pitch, from one end to the other. The machine and hob are described in an article by E. Gregory in the *American Machinist* of 21 March 1908. In a later article (6 June 1908) Gregory said that a machine had been built and was in the experimental stage. However, machines using taper hobs for cutting bevel gears were not built commercially until some thirty years later when they were developed in Germany.

A bevel-gear cutting machine of a type that has sometimes been described as a 'describing generating machine' was produced in 1895 by Smith & Coventry[28] and one made about 1900 is shown in Plate 141a. It was used to some extent during the next two decades. It employs straight-sided cutters, but these cut on their ends and do not represent the teeth of a crown wheel. They reciprocate in unison, being operated by a crank and connecting rod coupled to a slider, which in turn is connected to the tool slides by other connecting rods. The tool slides themselves are set to converge on the apex of the blank. The latter is secured to a spindle, mounted in a carriage that can rotate about a vertical axis passing through the apex of the blank, and this motion enables the blank to be fed into the correct depth. The carriage is geared to the slotted link seen low down on the left and this link is coupled by the connecting rod, which

148

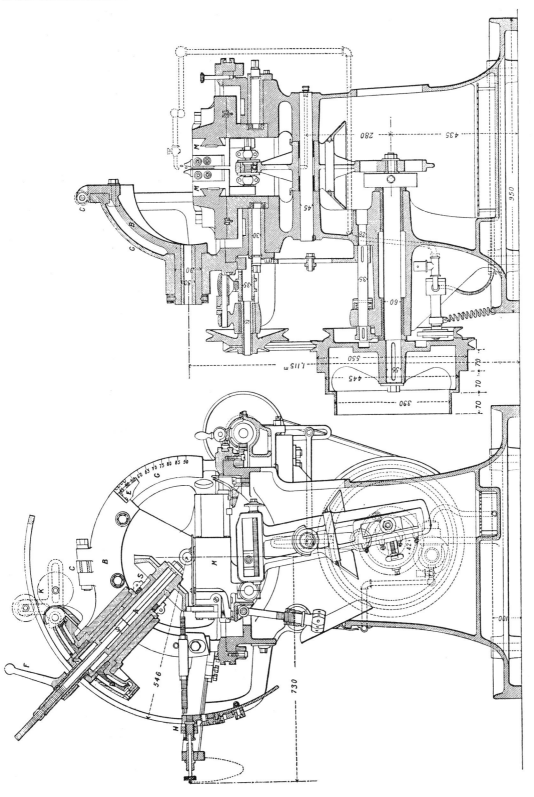

Fig. 43. The Nardin bevel-gear generating machine. *Engineer, Lond.* 25 November 1906

can be clearly seen, to one of the bars of a double parallel motion. These bars are pivoted at one end to the frame of the machine and at the other end to two slotted guides, one above and the other below the centre line of the cutter assembly. Thus as the slotted link moves upwards the slotted guides move apart and, as they are engaged by pins fixed in the ends of the cutter slides, the latter are also moved apart. Hence as the blank is fed into depth the cutters are moved apart so as to produce the profile of the tooth being cut. This profile is only a close approximation to that corresponding to generation by a straight-sided crown-wheel tooth. Both sides of a tooth are finished at each indexing cycle and the rate of production is fairly high.

Another machine of this type was brought out in 1906 by the Societa Anonima Dubos of Turin and is shown in Plate 141*b*. A round-nosed tool was used and it reciprocated along a slide that could pivot about a horizontal axis at its centre. This pivot was in a C-shaped frame that could itself pivot about a vertical axis in the frame of the machine, and the two axes intersected at the apex of the pitch cone of the gear being cut. The two pivoting motions were geared together through change gears and a double crank and connecting-rod mechanism so that, as the C-frame moved round, the cutter slide was rotated about its pivot and the line of stroke of the tool was raised. This gave the profile to the tooth being cut but again that profile was only an approximation. Only one side of a single tooth was machined at one time.

The 'Rice' bevel-gear machine that was made in Hartford, Connecticut, about 1910 employed a somewhat hybrid principle. The blank was carried on an arbor, which could rotate about a horizontal axis and had a 'master' gear fixed to it at its outer end. The frame carrying the arbor could be rotated about a vertical axis passing through the apex of the gear being cut. The master gear-teeth engaged an abutment that was fixed to the frame of the machine and represented the cutter. The latter was a large disc with cutters inserted in its periphery and it rotated about a fixed axis. This machine is described in *Engineering* of 19 October 1900 and also in the *American Machinist* of 26 May 1900.

A copying-type machine, which was particularly suited for the cutting of small gears and fine pitches but could also cut large gears, was brought out by Greenwood & Batley towards the end of the present period. One is shown in Plate 142*a*. The template from which the tooth shape was copied was attached to an arm fixed to the lower end of the spindle carrying the blank and represented an enlarged version of at ooth of the wheel being cut. The template was held against a fixed abutment representing an enlarged version of the cutting tool, by means of a dead weight. The cutting tool was given a simple reciprocating motion along a horizontal slide. As the quadrant carrying the spindle and blank was given a feed motion about its horizontal pivot, so the template produced a rotation of the blank and the tool produced a copy of the template. Only one side of a single tooth was cut at a time.

A very similar machine was patented about 1904 by J. H. Gibson who was associated with the firm of Lairds of Birkenhead, and somewhat similar machines, adapted to cut spiral as well as straight bevels, were made at this time by Usines Bouhey of Paris. The spiral tooth was obtained by imparting a rotation to the blank during the cutting stroke of the tool.

Machines for spiral bevel gears

A machine designed to produce spiral bevel gears was made about 1900 by Maison Colman of Paris, to the design of M. Monneret, and is shown in Plate 142*b*. The blank is carried on a spindle mounted in a saddle that can be rotated about a vertical axis, and this enables the correct depth of tooth to be obtained. The straight-sided cutter represented a tooth of an imaginary crown wheel, about the axis of which the cutter slide can rotate in the headstock of the machine at the right. This rotation had to produce a corresponding rotation of the blank in order to generate the tooth profile and gearing was provided to do this. The cutter was reciprocated by a crank and connecting rod and, in order to obtain a spiral tooth, this motion had to produce a corresponding rotation of the blank. The latter therefore received two component motions, one from the rotation of the cutter slide and the other from the reciprocation of the cutter along the slide. These two motions were transmitted through separate trains of gearing and were combined by making one of them rotate a worm that meshed with a wheel on the spindle carrying the blank and making the other give the worm a translation along its shaft. The assembly in which this was done can be seen at the left of the saddle carrying the blank.

Towards the end of the nineteenth century the Bilgram machine was modified so as to enable spiral gears to be cut, and again the spiral was produced by giving the blank a slight rotation as the tool travelled across the face of it.

Machines for spiral and worm gears

Spiral gears and worms can, of course, be cut on universal milling machines, and worms can be cut in lathes. Both these methods were common after the universal milling machine had been developed. But from the beginning of this period special machines for these purposes began to appear. These almost invariably employed milling cutters and were, in fact, specialized forms of milling machine. The cutter was carried in a head that could be rotated so that its central plane could be brought tangential to the helix being cut and two arrangements were used to produce the helix. In one of these the blank rotated and the saddle carrying it was fed along axially, while in the other the blank rotated but the axial motion was given to the cutter head. The second arrangement was mostly used in the larger machines. An example of the first type is shown in Plate 143*a*. It was made by Greenwood & Batley about 1906. The cutter head is placed above the work and is rotatable about a vertical axis; it can also be moved up and down vertically on a slide on the frame of the machine. The gear blank is carried on a mandrel in a saddle that can slide along the ways on the top of the bed, and the mandrel is geared to the lead-screw producing this motion through change gearing seen at the end of the bed. In the larger machine, shown in Plate 143*b* and also built by Greenwood & Batley, the work only rotates and does not translate. The cutter head can now swivel about a horizontal axis in its head and the latter can slide along ways on the base of the machine.

For some hundreds of years worm-wheels have been cut by means of a hob that was a replica of the mating worm, gashed and hardened to make it cut. These cutters were commonly not backed-off and were generally used to produce the rotation of the worm-wheel being cut. Roughing-out was done by means of a fly-cutter producing a single tooth space at a time. This process, however, was suitable only for gearing in which the pitch of the worm thread was small. A backed-off hob that was geared to the blank in the correct ratio was used, as mentioned by Whitworth in 1835 and by Bodmer a little later. Such hobs were fed radially into the blank and this is unsatisfactory when the lead of the worm is large. At the beginning of the period now being considered machines intended solely, or chiefly, for hobbing worm-wheels began to appear. An example made by Greenwood & Batley, who produced them in a range of sizes, is shown in Plate 144*a* and another, larger machine by the Niles Tool Works is shown in Plate 144*b*. The axially-fed hob was introduced by the Chemnitz firm of Reinecker in 1894 and in 1895 J. H. Gibson took out a patent covering a machine in which a fly-cutter was made to simulate a hob. The cutter was carried on a mandrel that was threaded at one end. The thread had the same pitch as the hob being simulated and engaged a nut that was geared to the worm driving the work table that carried the blank. The nut had a spur gear fixed to it and another spur gear, with fewer teeth, was splined to the mandrel. Both gears meshed with a planet pinion carried by a cage that was free to rotate; the assembly thus constituted a double-sun epicyclic gear. During each revolution of the blank the epicyclic gear rotated 'solid' and so the mandrel speed was the same as that of the nut. But once during each revolution of the blank a cam on the work table caused a striker to move forward so that it engaged a star-wheel fixed to the pinion of the epicyclic gear, thus causing that pinion to rotate about its own axis. The mandrel was thus made to rotate relative to the nut and the fly-cutter made to sweep out the surface of the worm it was simulating.

Machines especially designed for hobbing worm-wheels with a tangentially fed hob were produced during the latter half of this period and an example made by Henry Wallwork & Co. is shown in Plate 145a.

The cutting of the Hindley or globoidal type of worm and its mating wheel has always been an operation for which special methods and machines have had to be used. Those for cutting the worm take the form of a cutter, which repre-sents the tooth of the worm-wheel and is mounted so that it can rotate about the axis of the wheel in relation to the blank, the two spindles then being geared together in the proper ratio by external gearing. The worm-wheel has been hobbed by reversing the process and using a cutter or hob that is a replica of the worm, suitably gashed, and is mounted in the correct relationship with the blank to which it is geared externally. The feed motion has to be radial in both cases. An example of a special machine of this kind is shown in Plate 145b. It was designed and used by the Lanchester Motor Car Company for the production of the Lanchester-type worms and wheels used in their cars around the turn of the century.

Grinding machines

This period was one of great activity in respect of all types of grinding machine and during it grinding developed from a process used mainly for finishing hardened articles and where great accuracy was required, into a process that could produce work faster and better than other, equally available, methods. Although the basic forms were not changed much, some new types of machine appeared. The improvements were mostly in greatly increased rigidity and in details and components. Better bearings made it possible to use larger wheels running at higher speeds and also made overhung wheels feasible. Wheel drives, wheel-head slides, feed gears, and steady rests were all improved, and the prac-tice of grinding on dead centres was introduced. More attention was paid to keeping dust out of slides and bearings and the use of a coolant became much more common. But perhaps the most important developments were in the grinding wheels themselves. These, however, are outside the scope of this book.

A machine that had a great influence on the design of subsequent grinding machines was designed by C. H. Norton and built by the Norton Grinding

Company of Worcester, Massachusetts, in 1900. The wheel was 24 inches in diameter by 2 inches face-width and the machine could take work up to $5\frac{1}{2}$ feet long. The most notable feature of the machine, however, was its great ruggedness and consequent rigidity. The design is shown in Plate 146*a*, but here the work table has a gap which makes the machine particularly suitable for grinding such things as pistons integral with, or mounted on, their piston rods. This variant was introduced about a year later.

About 1902 the Landis Tool Company of Wayneboro, Pennsylvania, built the machine shown in Plate 146*b*. This required no countershafting and, although not a universal machine, the work-head could be swivelled through 90° and the work table through a small angle. The wheels used were 30 inches in diameter and 2 inches in face-width, and in a trial a 6-in diameter cast-iron test piece 44 in long was reduced in diameter by $\frac{3}{32}$ inch in 11 min. This was the first large machine to be built in which the wheel-head travelled past the work instead of vice versa. All the ways of this machine were protected against the ingress of dust by means of permanently fitted covers.

In a machine made by Wm. Muir about 1902 the in-feed was obtained by traversing a saddle that carried the work table instead of by traversing the wheel-head.[29]

The German Reinecker company also built some large grinding machines at this time. In one of these, made in 1903, the saddle carrying the wheel-head was mounted on ways placed on the rear face of the bed, as in the Landis machine mentioned above, and in another machine wheel-heads were similarly mounted on both the front and the back of the bed. This machine, which was built about 1907, could take work up to 33 ft long and nearly 3 ft in diameter.

In the same year the automatic loading of jobs such as ball-bearing races was introduced by the Norton Company. Automatic sizing was introduced by the Pratt & Whitney company in the following year. About 1910 the Churchill Machine Company of Manchester introduced a machine in which three separate spindles were mounted in a turret that could be rotated about a vertical axis so that any one of the spindles could be quickly brought into position.[30] One spindle was for cylindrical work, one for internal work, and the third for facing work. In the same year the Garvin Machine Co. developed an air-operated chuck which greatly facilitated the loading and unloading of the workpieces.

Internal grinders

Internal grinding continued to be done extensively by means of attachments used on external grinders, but machines particularly adapted for this work were also developed. When the work was small it was generally rotated and two forms of machine emerged. In one of these the wheel-head was carried on a cross slide mounted in a saddle that could traverse along the bed-ways, while in the other type the cross slide carrying the wheel-head was fixed, and the traverse was given to the work-head, which was mounted on ways. Examples are shown in Plates 147*a* and 147*b*.

For larger and irregular work planetary spindle machines were used. The inventors of this construction used it in the present period in a number of machines built specially for grinding the curved slots of the expansion links used in the valve gears of locomotives. An example of one of these, made in 1892, is shown in Plate 148*a*. The lever carrying the counterweight was oscillated by an adjustable crank and imparted an axial reciprocating motion to the wheel spindle. It could be disengaged to enable the spindle to be withdrawn so that the hole being machined could be measured. In an alternative form of curved-slot grinding machine, built about the same time by other makers, the grinding wheel rotated about a fixed axis and the link was carried on a table at the end of a radius rod whose pivot could be adjusted in relation to the axis of the wheel, so that the cut could be regulated by moving the work. Machines of this latter type were made in a vertical form, particularly by continental makers. The Beyer Peacock company also used their planetary spindle heads in machines built to grind the crank pins of locomotive axle and wheel assemblies when the pins were on the outside. The principle patented by this company for the spindle adjustment was adopted by other makers in both Europe and America during the first decade of the twentieth century. Amongst these companies were Mayer & Schmidt and F. Schmaltz in Germany and the Heald Company in America. The first of these firms also produced an alternative method of adjusting the spindle. This will be clear from Fig. 44 and will be seen to be the same in principle as the portable boring-bar described in an earlier section of this chapter.

An entirely different principle for machines for grinding holes in large and irregular pieces was patented by Reid & Neilson of the Park Engineering Works, Glasgow, about 1895, and machines using the principle were built in 1896.[31] The wheel spindle rotated about a fixed axis and was given a vertical reciprocating motion, while the work was carried on the upper member of a compound slide whose slides were at right angles and were free in the sense that no screw or rack was used to control them. Instead, the upper slide was engaged by the pin of an adjustable crank placed underneath and rotating about a vertical axis. This gave the work a motion of translation in a circular path having the same radius as the crank. As this radius was quite small, as a rule, the out-of-balance forces were kept low even though the axis of the hole being ground was at a considerable distance from the centre of mass of the work. The same principle was used by the Pratt & Whitney company in the machine shown in Plate 148*b*, which they produced in 1899 for grinding the ball tracks of cup-and-cone ball-bearings. In this machine, however, the compound slides carried the wheel-head and two cams were used to oscillate the slides. This enabled non-circular shapes to be ground. The machine was made in two slightly different forms, one for external and the other for internal work. In 1906 the Pratt & Whitney company also built a grinder, having the general form of a facing lathe, for the purpose of

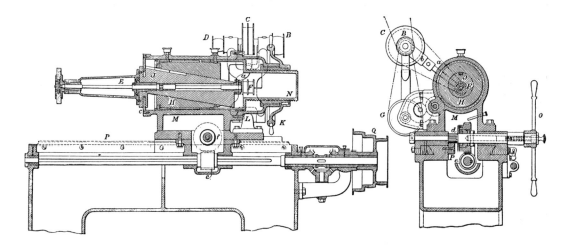

FIG. 44. Mayer & Schmidt planetary-spindle grinding machine. *Engineering, Lond.* 26 December 1902

grinding the circular tracks, up to 40 inches in diameter, of gun mountings. The work was carried on a large faceplate in front of which there was a T-shaped bed integral with the base of the machine. The cross of the T was parallel to the faceplate and carried two wheel-heads, one at each end, while the stem of the T carried a saddle and column on the face of which a horizontal spindle could be raised and lowered. This spindle was used chiefly for internal grinding and the other two for facing and external work.

In 1908 the Bryant Chucking Grinder Co. of Springfield, Vermont, produced the original design shown in Figs. 45 and 46. This was intended for the production of articles in considerable quantities, and it could grind both holes and faces or shoulders. There are two spindles *B* and *C*, one for the internal wheel and the other for the facing wheel, and these are carried in a housing that is part of the cylindrical member seen at the top. The facing wheel is traversed across the face of the work by means of an oscillation of the housing about the axis of the cylindrical member, and for grinding holes the housing is held against an adjustable abutment.

156

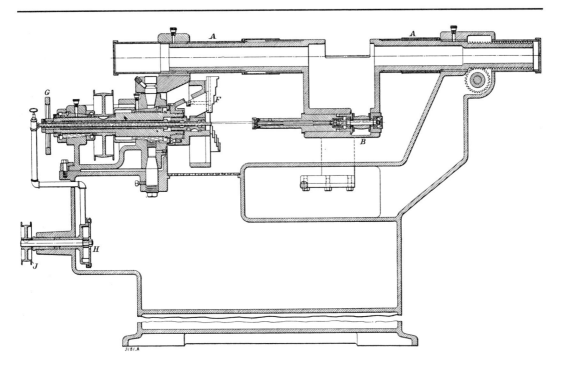

FIG. 45. The Bryant hole-and-face grinding machine. *Engineering, Lond.* 17 January 1913

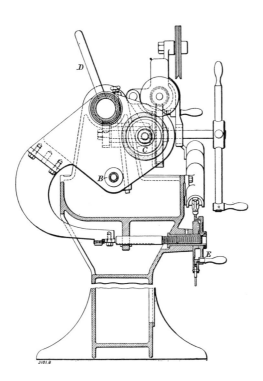

FIG. 46. The Bryant hole-and-face grinding machine.
End view, *Engineering, Lond.* 17 January 1913

157

Cylindrical grinding machines, specially arranged for grinding the cams of automobile cam-shafts, were developed during the period. Two types were evolved. In one the cam-shaft was carried between centres in a cradle that could rock about an axis at a lower level, and a master cam on the driving spindle bore against a fixed roller so as to rock the cradle. In some early machines of this type only a single master cam was used and this had to be indexed in relation to the cam-shaft in order to get the required angular spacings. In later examples a complete master cam-shaft with the cams properly spaced angularly, but closer together axially, was used. At the end of the period fully automatic cam-shaft grinders were being designed and they appeared shortly afterwards. The second type of machine moved the grinding wheel to and fro instead of the cam-shaft. This type was introduced by J. Holroyd towards the end of the period. The principle of the construction was somewhat similar to that of the Bryant machine just described. The master cam-shaft was carried low down under the bed of the machine and rocked the grinding wheel, which was carried on an arm pivoted above the work, to and fro.[32]

Surface grinders

At the beginning of this period most of the present-day forms of surface grinding machine had been produced, included the planer type, the elevating wheel-head pedestal type, the fixed wheel-head elevating-knee type, and the horizontal wheel-axis face-wheel type. Most of these were further developed and some new ones were introduced, amongst these being the open-side and the circular- or ring-table types. Considering the open-side machine first, there were two arrangements for traversing the wheel across the work. In one of these the wheel was moved and in the other the work was moved, the former being mostly used. The wheel-head was generally carried in a saddle that could move up and down the face of a column; in some machines the whole column assembly was moved to give the traverse as in the machine by Mayer & Schmidt shown in Fig. 47, while in others the wheel-head was carried on the end of a ram or slide that could be traversed in the saddle. When the work table was moved to give the traverse it was carried in a saddle that could move on ways perpendicular to the longitudinal travel of the table. When the wheel axis was fixed the vertical adjustment was provided by making the work-table assembly elevate; this was commonly done by employing a knee as in milling machines.

In the smaller machines the pedestal type with an elevating wheel-head was the most popular and an example with a duplex head is shown in Plate 148c. This was made by O. S. Walker of Worcester, Massachusetts, about 1902. The wheel at the front is a face wheel and the edge wheel is at the rear, the positions being changed over when required by rotating the assembly about the axis of the cylindrical post that carried it. This could be done without any interference with the belt drive to the spindles. The post and wheel-head assembly could also be raised and lowered without affecting the belt tension. The cross traverse was given to the work-table assembly.

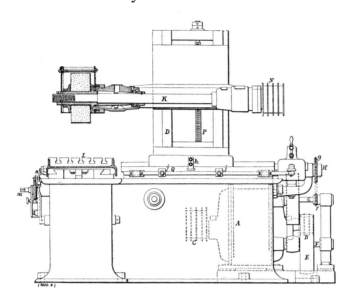

FIG. 47. 'Openside' surface grinding machine.
Engineering, Lond. 19 September 1902

The circular-table type of machine was introduced by the Reinecker company in 1902 and is particularly suitable for grinding the faces of discs and rings. An example made by the Churchill Machine Tool Co. towards the end of this period is shown in Plate 149*a*. In some machines of this type the table assembly could be tilted slightly so that conical surfaces could be ground. The success of this and of other surface grinders was due to a great extent to the use of magnetic tables for holding the work.

The vertical axis face-wheel surface grinder did not increase much in popularity until the end of the present period. An example made by the Churchill Company is shown in Plate 149*b*.

Tool and cutter grinders

Grinding machines for sharpening cutting tools may be divided conveniently into three groups: those for lathe- and planer-type tools; those for twist drills; and those for milling cutters, reamers, and similar cutters having multiple edges. At the beginning of this period most lathe-type tools were ground by off-hand methods by the operator of the machine using them, because very few machines were available for doing them otherwise. Such machines were, however, produced during the period and an early example made by the Gisholt Company about 1898 is shown in Plate 150*a*. In this the tool holder can be rotated about two perpendicular axes and the whole assembly can be rocked to and fro about an axis parallel to the axis of the grinding wheel. The various faces of the tool can therefore be brought to the proper positions relative to the face of the wheel and then be moved to and fro across the face of the wheel. Another firm that produced this type of machine in several forms was Wm. Sellers & Co. and one of their machines is shown in Plate 150*b*. In this the grinding wheel was given an automatic axial reciprocating motion when the periphery of the wheel was being used but this motion could be stopped when desired.

There was a good deal of controversy regarding the best method of sharpening twist drills during the last decade of the preceding period and this continued into the early days of the present one. Two methods were generally advocated. In one the end face or lip of the drill was ground by moving the drill axially and rotating it about its own axis at the same time, so that a helical surface was produced, but sometimes an additional rocking motion was also given to it. In the second method the drill was rotated about an axis lying at a small angle to the axis of the drill itself. This gave a lip that was conical and a clearance behind the cutting edge that varied from the centre outwards, being greater at the centre. Fig. 48 shows a machine made by L. Sterne & Co. of Glasgow about 1904 in which the first method is employed. As the chuck carrying the drill was oscillated about its axis by means of the handle

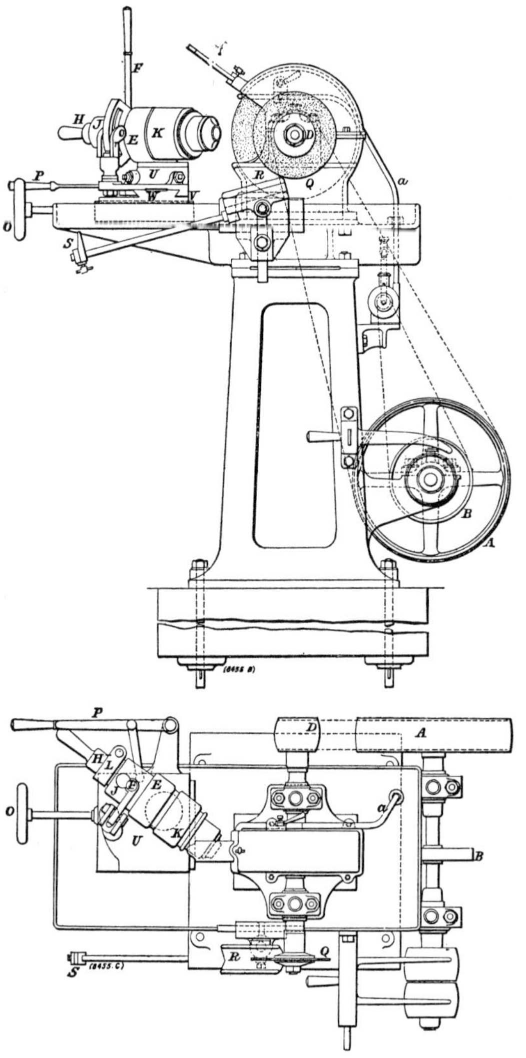

Fig. 48. L. Sterne & Co.'s drill grinding machine. *Engineering, Lond.* 28 October 1904

160

F, an internal cam surface, held against a roller by a spring, imparted an axial motion; at the same time the whole chuck assembly was rotated slightly about a vertical axis. This latter motion was effected by a spiral slot in the flange seen at *J* which engaged a roller. The chuck assembly was fed along the slide *W* in order to bring the drill into contact with the grinding wheel. A separate wheel was provided to thin the centre of the drill when required. A machine first made by Wm. Sellers & Co. in the early 1880s is shown in Fig. 49. In this the drill is held in a chuck (not shown), which can be rotated about an axis *aa* placed at an angle to the axis *bb* of the drill. The clamping device that gripped the drill automatically positioned it and raised the centres of small drills higher than those of large ones so as to produce a smaller radius of curvature on the lip. The member *A* that carried the grinding wheel could pivot about and slide along the axis *O* and its axial position was regulated by the wheel *Q*. This enabled the wheel to be brought into contact with the end of the drill and then be oscillated slightly by means of the lever *R*.

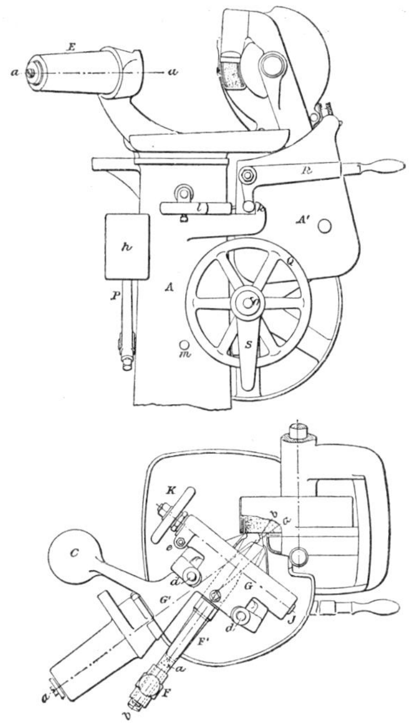

FIG. 49. Sellers's twist-drill grinding machine. *Engineering, Lond.* 11 November 1904

Cutter grinders were produced throughout the period in a great variety of forms but can be roughly divided into two groups, those manually operated and those having some self-acting motions. These machines used disc, coned, or cup wheels and frequently two kinds of wheel were permanently fitted. The wheels could usually be placed either parallel or perpendicular to the length of the cutter edge. Three typical examples are shown in Plates 151*a*, 151*b*, and Fig. 50. The first of these was made by the London Emery Works Company about 1895. The work-table assembly is carried on a compound slide at the top of a pillar and this provides the vertical adjustment and also permits the assembly to be rotated about a vertical axis. The slide motions are operated through screws and the cutters are positioned by a guide finger, carried by the post seen at the front. The upper part of the work table can be tilted, by means of the screw seen at the left, to enable taper reamers and cutters to be ground. The second machine was made by the American Watch-Tool Company of Waltham, Massachusetts, at the middle of this period. The table is again carried on a pillar on a compound slide and can be both elevated and swivelled about a vertical axis; its upper portion could also be swivelled about a vertical axis relative to the lower portion so that tapered articles could be ground. The work table was traversed by means of a pinion and rack. The spindle carrying the two grinding wheels could also be raised or lowered. The third machine is rather more elaborate and was made by F. Schmaltz about 1904. The wheel-head is reciprocated along an arm by

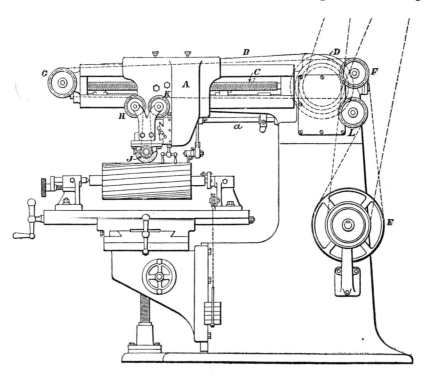

FIG. 50. Cutter grinding machine by F. Schmaltz. *Engineering, Lond.* 15 July 1904

means of the screw *C*, which is driven through a bevel-gear cluster and dog-clutch reversing mechanism. It could be adjusted vertically and laterally on slides. The wheel is driven by a belt that runs over several pulleys (*F* to *L*). Automatic indexing could be used when required. In other machines made by this firm the wheel-head was carried on the end of a ram as in a shaping machine and the work table was carried on a knee.

In some machines no vertical adjustment was provided for the work-table assembly. Instead the grinding wheel was carried on the end of a long arm that was pivoted at or near to its other end so that the wheel could be raised or lowered. The arm was sometimes positioned by means of a screw and nut at some point between the pivot and the wheel. This arrangement was adopted by H. Ernault of Paris in a machine made to the design of F. G. Kreutzberger in 1904. By leaving the arm free about its pivot and letting its end rest on a former or template carried by the work table, cutters having curved shapes could be ground. This was done in a machine made by J. Holroyd, also in 1904.[33]

Gear-tooth grinding machines

Machines for grinding the profiles of gear teeth are, basically, similar to machines for that purpose using other forms of cutter. They can consequently be divided into copying and generating types. But for both of these the substitution of a grinding wheel for some other form of cutter was found to involve a major difficulty—the wear of the wheel during the grinding of a single gear was sufficient to reduce the accuracy attainable to unacceptable limits. This difficulty was ultimately overcome in one of two ways. In one the wheel was trued repeatedly at short intervals so that its shape was retained and adjustments were made to allow for the variation in size of the wheel, while in the second method the wheel was made so large that the wear of the wheel was reduced to an amount that was acceptable. Machines using the latter method were not developed, however, until after the end of this period and machines using the first method not until nearly the end of the period. In effect, the chief advance made during the period was the great advance made in wheel manufacture. This reduced the wear problem to more manageable proportions.

As early as 1899 the American firm of Leland & Faulconer produced a machine for grinding the teeth of small bevel gears used in the pedal bicycles they were making at that time. The machine is described in the *American Machinist* of 6 June 1899. The work spindle was carried in a T-shaped frame that was pivoted about a horizontal axis passing through the apex of the pitch cone of the gear being ground, and the frame was moved about this axis so that the corner of the grinding wheel traversed up and down the face of the tooth. The grinding wheel was carried in a slide and was reciprocated so that the corner of the wheel could grind the length of the tooth. To produce the correct profile the grinding-wheel slide was pivoted about an axis perpendicular to that of the work-spindle frame, and motion about this axis was produced by a former, which was attached to the frame and engaged a follower on the wheel slide that represented the corner of the wheel. The follower could be changed over easily so that both sides of a tooth space could be ground at each indexing of the work.

About 1907 Humpage used a corundum hob to grind spur-gear teeth and he mentions this in his paper to the Institution of Mechanical Engineers but the idea was not successfully exploited commercially until some thirty-five years later.

Towards the end of this period Reinecker produced the generating spur-gear tooth grinding machine shown in Plate 152a. The grinding wheel is V-shaped and represents one tooth of a rack and it rotates about a fixed horizontal axis. The whole of the generating motion is given to the work, which rotates about its axis as the slide carrying it traverses to and fro perpendicular to the work axis.

The formed-wheel gear-tooth grinding machine has some advantages over the generating types, one important one being the ease with which modifications to the pure involute profile can be made, but until the difficulty of wheel wear was overcome it did not become practicable. The credit for overcoming the difficulty goes to Ward and Taylor of the Gear Grinding Company of Detroit[34] who conceived and realized, about 1908, an automatic method of truing the wheel at frequent intervals. Two pantograph linkages were used to cause truing diamonds, one for each side of a tooth, to copy enlarged templates. In addition a diamond was arranged to true the periphery of the wheel. Machines of this kind were subsequently used extensively. The automatic truing of the wheels of generating-type gear grinding machines would seem to be an intrinsically simpler operation than the truing of formed wheels, but nevertheless machines in which it was done were not produced until after the end of the period covered by this book.

Miscellaneous machines

Machine tools that are portable can, of course, be placed under the headings of their type but it is more convenient to take them together. They are used chiefly when the job to be operated on is heavy or bulky or in an inaccessible position, so that it becomes easier to take the machine to the job. Except that they are designed to be as compact as possible and completely self-contained, they do not differ from machines that are fixed to foundations. Drilling machines were the first to be used in portable forms, but from the latter part of the last period and throughout the present one many other types of machine have been built in portable form. Thus a portable slotting machine was built in 1899 by Buckton & Co. and a portable planing machine in 1902 by Hulse & Co. The machines described in the previous chapter for machining the valve faces and ports of locomotive cylinders were built also in portable form, as were machines for re-boring the cylinders and re-turning the crank pins of locomotive crank-shafts. A machine that could be described as a portable vertical lathe was built about 1906 by Napier Bros. of Glasgow for turning and boring naval barbette mountings. It consisted of a base member that carried a rotatable double arm, on one end of which there was a turning-tool slide and on the other end a grinding wheel-head. The rotating member was driven by two electric motors mounted on it and coupled to two spur pinions that meshed with a circular rack fixed to the base. The latter incorporated arrangements to enable the machine to be centred on the barbette. Surfaces up to 30 ft in diameter could be machined.[34]

A machine for cutting blind holes was made by the Smith Slotting Machine Co. of London about 1907. It resembled a knee-type milling machine but employed a cutter of the form shown in Fig. 51. This was mounted on an overhanging arm on the end of the horizontal spindle of the machine and was oscillated about an axis coincident with that of the circular toothed portion of the cutter at a rate of 800 strokes/min. A vertical-feed motion was given to the knee and work table. An important field for a machine of this type is in die-sinking, particularly dies for drop-forging and machines of a similar nature were subsequently built in other countries.

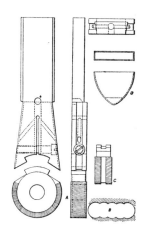

FIG. 51. Blind-hole cutting machine. *Engineering, Lond.* 1 October 1907

The use of broaches for cutting key-ways and for more complicated internal shapes increased during the last decade of the period, but the machines that used the broaches did not change much, although they were improved in detail and made in a variety of sizes. An early broaching machine made by the Lapointe Machine Tool Co., is shown in Plate 152*b*. This firm subsequently played a leading part in the development of the broaching process.

The term 'universal' is used somewhat loosely in respect of machine tools but always carries the implication that several different types of operation can be performed. In milling machines the term commonly means only that the work table can swivel, that a vertical spindle attachment is provided, and that a dividing head is available so that helices can be cut. Usually the operations that can be performed in a universal machine all lie within one general field, for example, turning, grinding, or milling, but from time to time efforts have been made to produce machines that will perform operations in several fields. An example of this is the drilling, slotting, and planing machine by Sharp, Stewart & Co., shown in Plate 82. Usually such machines have been made for use either on jobs that are difficult to move from one machine to another or in a particular situation, such as on board ship or in a mobile workshop, where space is limited. They have also been produced to meet the demands of small users who cannot afford the capital outlay involved in purchasing a number of separate machines. Two examples that were produced during the present period are shown in Plates 153*a* and 153*b*. The first shows some machines, made by the London Lathe & Tool Co. about 1888, which can perform drilling, turning, and milling operations and, in some forms, grinding also. The second shows a more ambitious design, made about 1902 by a Mr. Linley, which was used on board naval vessels. It can turn objects up to 14 in long, can swing pieces up to 5 ft in diameter, and can perform drilling, slotting, and both horizontal and vertical milling operations. Basically it consists of a compound slide work-table mounted on a knee and of a complex spindle-head mounted on the face of a column. This head could be swung so that the spindle axis could lie at any angle between the horizontal and the vertical. For turning operations with the spindle axis horizontal, a tailstock could be mounted on the end of the knee and a slide-rest on the work table, and this slide-rest could also be mounted on the end of the spindle. Other firms produced machines that provided facilities for turning, drilling, and milling or shaping in which only the basic casting and the driving mechanism were common.

REFERENCES

CHAPTER I

1. KLEMM, F. *A history of western technology* (trans. D. W. Singer), Plate 5 facing p. 64. Allen & Unwin, London (1959).
2. USHER, A. P. *History of mechanical inventions.* Harvard University Press, Cambridge, Massachusetts (also Oxford University Press) (1954).
3. WOLF, A. *A history of science, technology and philosophy 16th and 17th centuries*, p. 168. Allen & Unwin, London (1935).

CHAPTER 2

1. HOGG, O. F. G. *The Royal Arsenal*, p. 258. Clarendon Press, Oxford (1963).
2. ROLT, L. T. C. *Tools for the job*, p. 42. Batsford, London (1965).
3. —— *Tools for the job*, p. 45. Batsford, London (1965).
4. RAISTRICK, A. *Dynasty of ironfounders*, p. 132. Longmans, Green, London (1953).
5. KLEMM, F. *A history of western technology*, Fig. 30, p. 97. Allen & Unwin, London (1959).
6. SMEATON, J. *Trans. R. Soc.* (1785).
7. RAMSDEN, J. *Description of an engine for dividing mathematical instruments.* Commissioners of Longitude, London (1777).
8. WOODBURY, R. S. *History of the lathe.* The Society for the History of Technology, Cleveland, Ohio (1961).
9. ROLT, L. T. C. *Tools for the job*, p. 163. Batsford, London (1965).

CHAPTER 3

1. HOLTZAPFFEL, C. *Turning and mechanical manipulation*, vol. ii, p. 651. Holtzapffel, London (1856).
2. BATTISON, E. A. Eli Whitney and the milling machine, *Smithsonian Journal of History*, vol. 1, no. 2. Smithsonian Institution, Washington, D.C. (1966).

CHAPTER 4

1. *James Nasmyth* (Ed. S. Smiles), p. 403. Popular Edition, 1897.
2. FITCH, C. H. *United States Census Report 1880. 10th Census. Manufacture of interchangeable mechanism.* Government of the United States of America, Washington, D.C. (1880 and subsequent years).

References

3. HUTTON, F. R. *United States Census Report 1880. 10th Census. Report on machine tools and wood-working machinery.* Government Printing Office, Washington, D.C. (*c.* 1885).
4. WOODBURY, R. S. *History of the grinding machine.* The Technology Press, Cambridge, Massachusetts (1960).

CHAPTER 5

1. CLARK, D. K. *The exhibited machinery of 1862: a cyclopedia of the machinery represented at the international exhibition.* Day & Son, London (1864) (preface only dated).
2. ANON. *A century of machine tools.* Taylor & Fenn, Hartford, Connecticut (*c.* 1935).
3. HULSE, W. W. Modern machine tools and workshop appliances for the treatment of heavy forgings and castings, *Trans. Instn civ. Engrs,* vol. 86, Pt. IV, Paper 2158 (1885–6).
4. *Engineering, Lond.* 12 January 1866, p. 22.
5. Communication from Thos. Ryder & Son, Bolton.
6. *Engineer, Lond.* 16 December 1892, p. 525.
7. ANDERSON, J. *Vienna Universal Exhibition 1873, Reports* Part II, *Report on machine tools.* H.M.S.O., London (1874).
8. ROSE, J. *Modern machine shop practice,* 2 vols. Virtue & Co., London (undated but probably about 1887).
9. DICKINSON, H. W. Origin and manufacture of wood screws. *Trans. Newcomen Soc.,* vol. xxii, 1941–2, p. 79 (1946).
10. ANON. Bechler sliding head automatics. *Mach. Tool Rev.* Jan.–Feb. 1954, p. 15.
11. *Engineering, Lond.* 29 June 1866.
12. BATHO, W. H. Shaping machine for nuts. *Proc. Instn mech. Engrs,* vol. 20, p. 317 (*c.* 1870).
13. HUMPAGE, T. Evolution and methods of manufacture of spur-gearing. *Proc. Instn mech. Engrs,* vol. 3, p. 651 (*c.* 1909).
14. WOODBURY, R. S. *History of the gear-cutting machine.* The Technology Press, Cambridge, Massachusetts (1959).

CHAPTER 6

1. Pratt & Whitney Co.'s catalogue 1897.
2. *Engineering, Lond.* 27 May 1904.
3. *Engineering, Lond.* 25 December 1908.
4. *Engineer, Lond.* 12 December 1890.
5. *Engineering, Lond.* 14 September 1903.
6. *Engineer, Lond.* 19 January 1893.
7. *Engineering, Lond.* 25 September 1908.
8. *Engineering, Lond.* 20 November 1908.
9. *Engineering, Lond.* 17 March 1893.
10. *Engineering, Lond.* 27 November 1891.
11. *Engineer, Lond.* 6 September 1901.
12. *Engineer, Lond.* 6 January 1905.
13. *Engineer, Lond.* 24 August 1894.
14. Pratt & Whitney Co.'s catalogue 1897.
15. *Engineering, Lond.* 1 January 1899.
16. *Engineering, Lond.* 24 September 1909.

17. *Engineer, Lond.* 20 August 1897.
18. *Engineer, Lond.* 11 December 1903.
19. *Engineering, Lond.* 15 December 1893.
20. *Engineering, Lond.* 28 July 1899.
21. *Engineering, Lond.* 19 November 1897.
22. *Engineering, Lond.* 21 July 1905.
23. *Engineering, Lond.* 13 August 1909.
24. *Engineer, Lond.* 30 March 1900.
25. *Engineer, Lond.* 17 August 1896.
26. *Engineering, Lond.* 15 July 1898.
27. *Am. Mach. Lond.*, vol. 31, 198–200 (1908).
28. GILBERT, W. K. *Machine Tools—Science Museum catalogue*, Item 180. H.M.S.O., London (1966).
29. *Engineering, Lond.* 18 September 1903.
30. *Engineering, Lond.* 13 October 1911.
31. *Engineer, Lond.* 21 August 1896.
32. *Engineering, Lond.* 25 October 1912.
33. WOODBURY, R. S. *History of the grinding machine.* The Technology Press, Cambridge, Massachusetts (1960).
34. *Engineering, Lond.* 26 October 1906.

INDEX

Pages containing text figures are in bold type

Index

Index

NOTE ON THE PLATES

WHERE only the name of the author is given as the source of a plate the full references are as follows:

Armengaud
Albums Armengaud Aîné, *Atlas de machines-outils*, extrait de *La Publication Industrielle*. Paris.

Buchanan
Robertson Buchanan, *Practical essays on mill work and other machinery*. London, 1841.

Byrne
Oliver Byrne, *Handbook for the artisan, mechanic and engineer*. New York, 1853.

Clark
D. K. Clark, *The exhibited machinery of 1862*. London, 1864.

Diderot
Denis Diderot and Jean le Rond d'Alembert, *Encyclopédie*. Paris, 1762–72.

Hutton
F. R. Hutton, *Report on machine tools and wood-working machinery* in 10th U.S. Census, 1880, and published separately, Washington, 1885.

Monge
Gaspard Monge, *Description de l'art de fabriquer les canons faite en execution de l'arret du Comité de Salut Public de 18 pluviose de l'an 2 de la Republique Française*.

Plumier
P. C. Le Plumier, *L'art de tourner en perfection*. Lyon, 1701.

Rose
Joshua Rose, *Modern machine shop practice*. London, 1887.

Taylor & Fenn Co.
A century of machine tools. Hartford, U.S.A., 1935.

Thiot
Antoine Thiot, *Traité de l'horologie*. Paris, 1747.

PLATE 1

a. Clock-wheel cutting machine. Seventeenth century. Photograph from the Science Museum, London (Crown copyright reserved)

b. Tour à réduire les médailles de Mercklein 1767. Conservatoire National des Arts et Métiers, Paris

PLATE 2

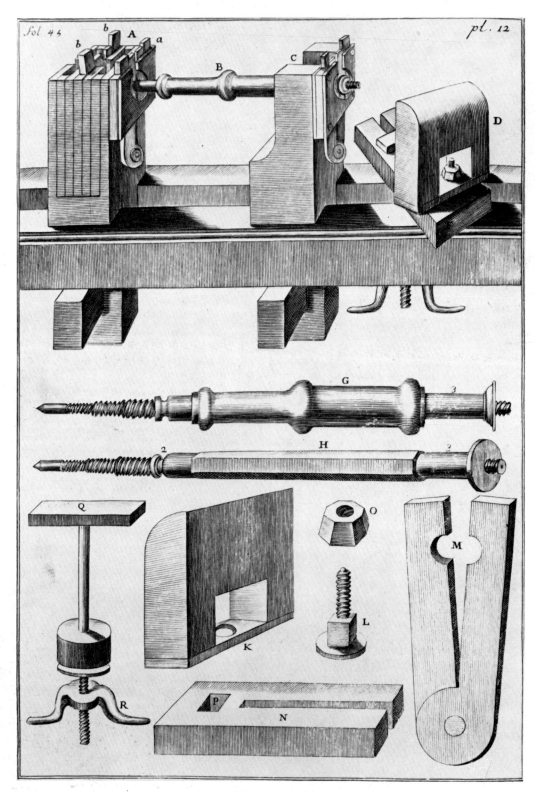

Mandrel lathe *c.* 1700. Plumier

PLATE 3

Pole lathe *c.* 1800. Photograph from the Science Museum, London (Crown copyright reserved)
Thos. Noakes & Sons Ltd.

PLATE 4

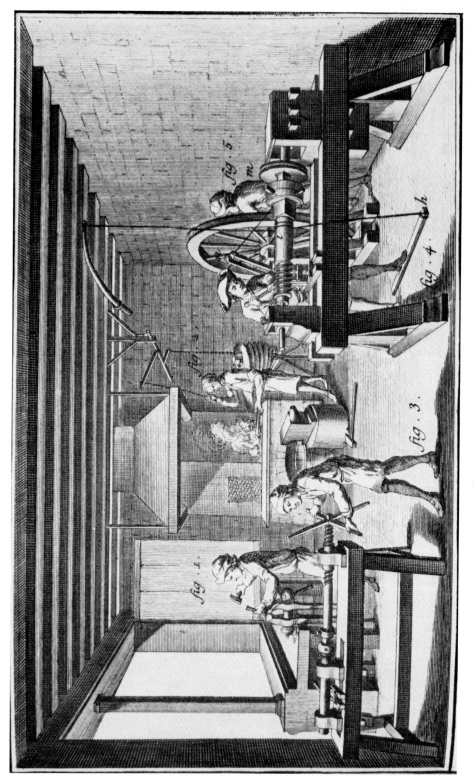

Mandrel lathe and screwing machine. Diderot

PLATE 5

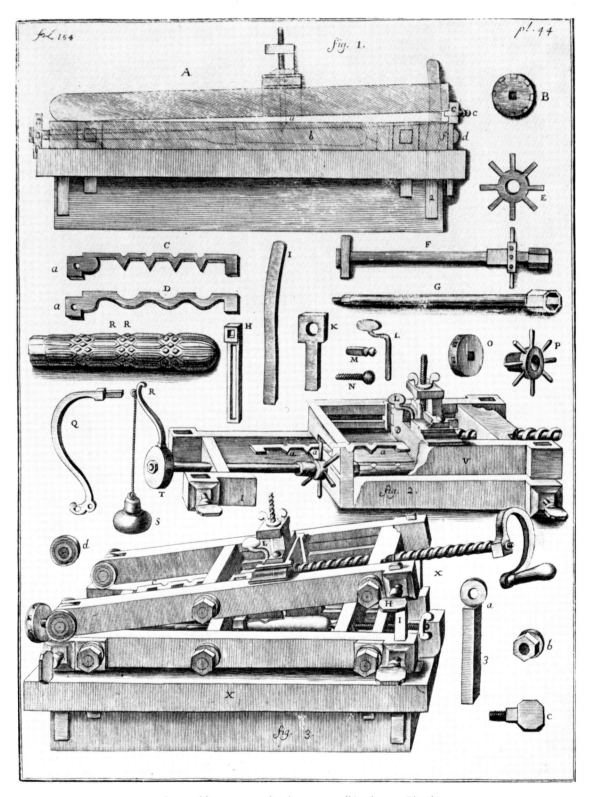

La machine aux manches à couteaux d'Angleterre. Plumier

PLATE 6

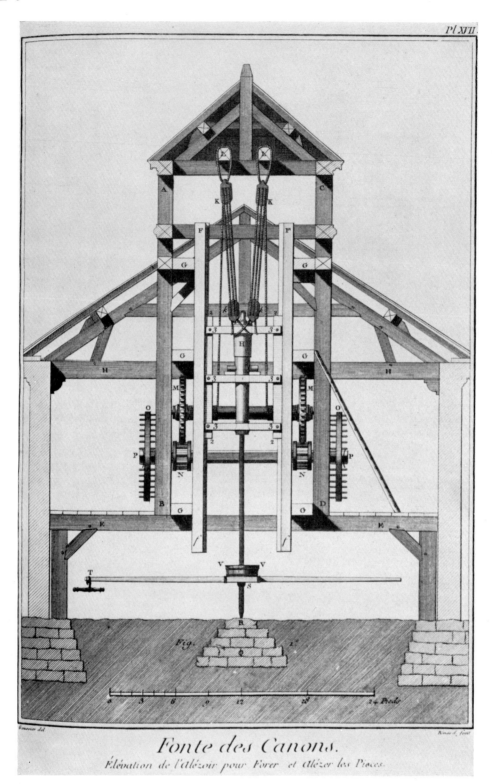

Fonte des Canons.
Élévation de l'Alézoir pour Forer et Alézer les Pieces.

Vertical gun-boring machine. Diderot

PLATE 7

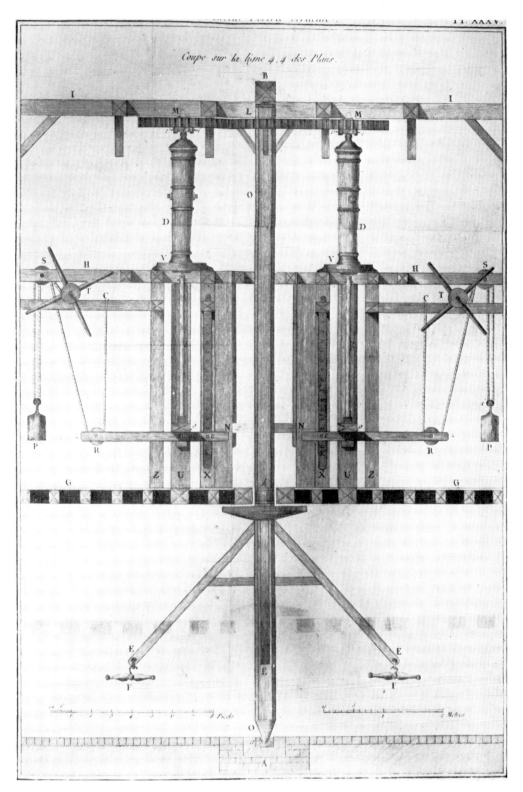

Four-station gun-boring machine. Monge

PLATE 8

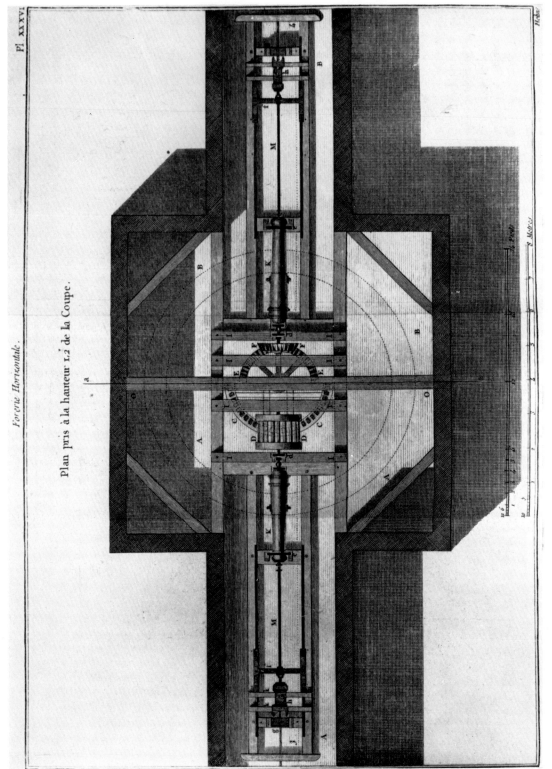

Two-station horizontal gun-boring machine. Monge

PLATE 9

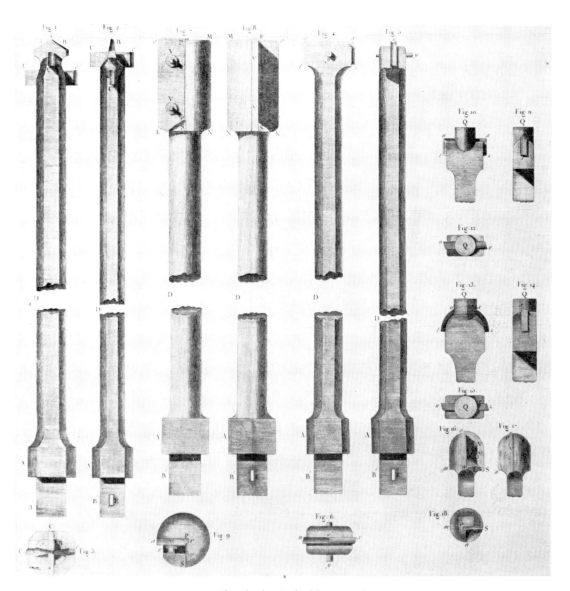

Gun-boring tools. Monge

PLATE 10

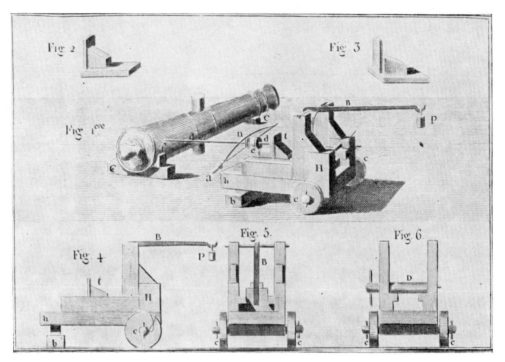

a. Bow drill for touch-holes of guns. Monge

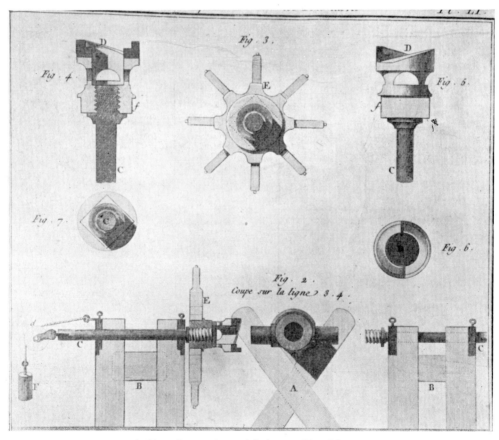

b. Trunnion turning and facing machine. Monge

PLATE 11

a. Ornamental lathe *c.* 1740. Photograph from the Science Museum, London
(Crown copyright reserved)

b. J. A. Schega's ornamental lathe *c.* 1767. Deutsches Museum, Munich

PLATE 12

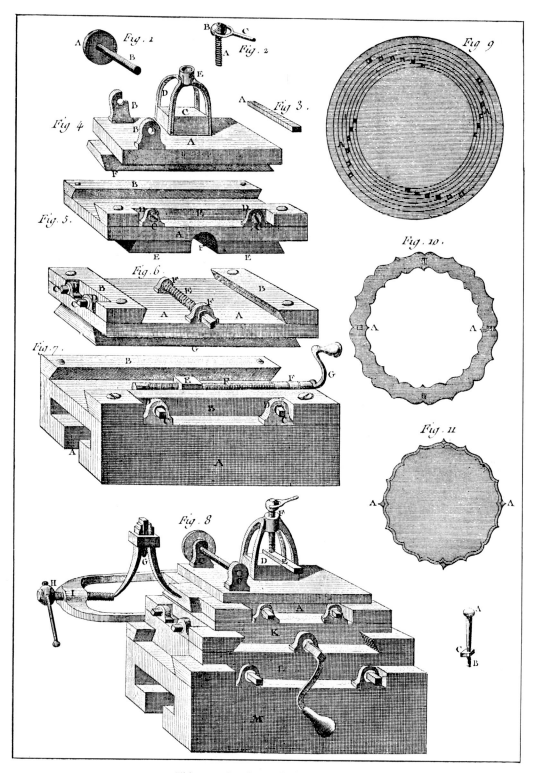

Slide rest of early copying-lathe. Diderot

PLATE 13

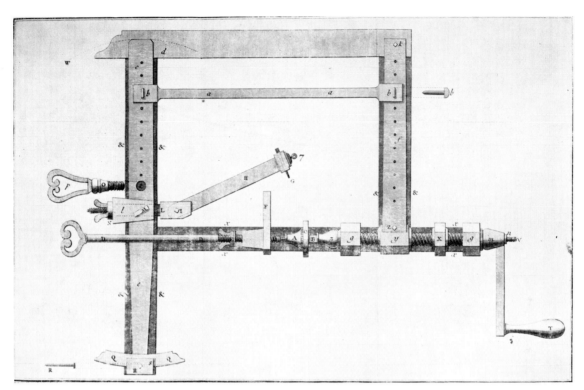

a. Fusee machine of Regnaud de Chaalon. Thiot

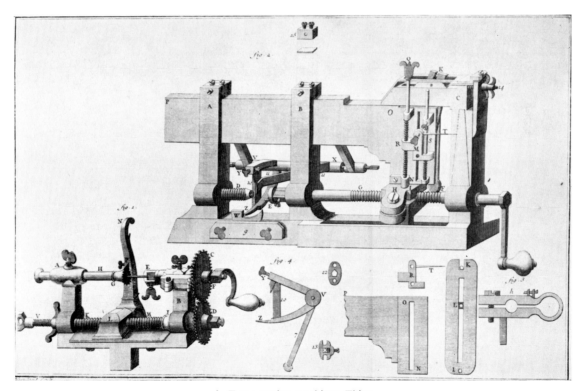

b. Fusee-cutting machines. Thiot

PLATE 14

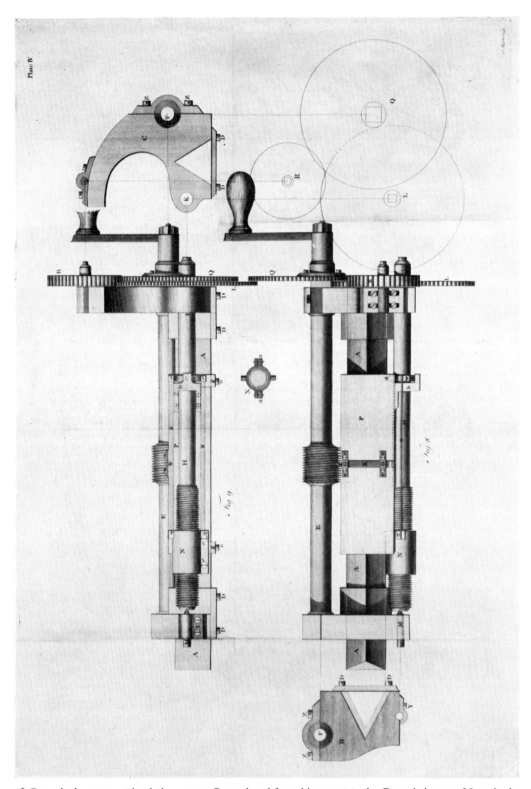

J. Ramsden's screw-cutting lathe *c.* 1777. Reproduced from his report to the Commissioners of Longitude

PLATE 15

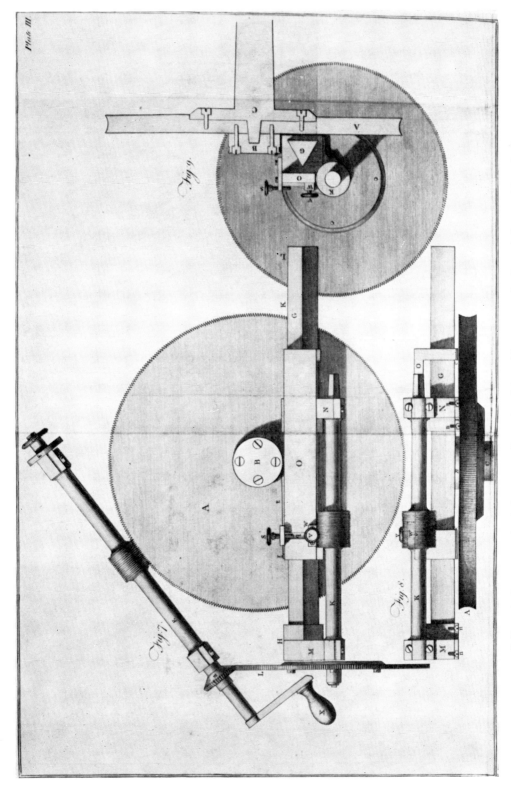

J. Ramsden's screw-cutting lathe c. 1779. Reproduced from his report to the Commissioners of Longitude

PLATE 16

a. Tour à charioter de Vaucanson 1770–80. Conservatoire National des Arts et Métiers, Paris

b. Tour à tailler les vis de Senot 1795. Conservatoire National des Arts et Métiers, Paris

PLATE 17

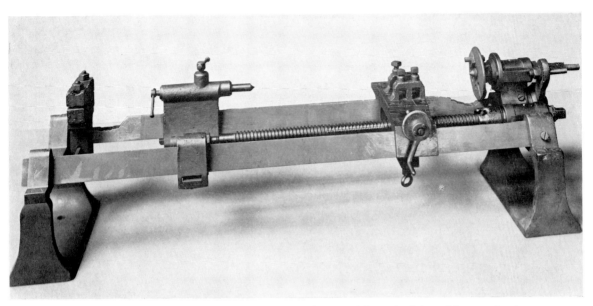

a. Maudslay's original screw-cutting lathe *c.* 1800. Photograph from the Science Museum, London
(Crown copyright reserved)

b. Maudslay's screw-cutting lathe *c.* 1800. Photograph from the Science Museum, London
(Crown copyright reserved)

PLATE 18

Joseph Bramah's metal-sawing machine *c.* 1790. Photograph from the Science Museum, London
(Crown copyright reserved)

PLATE 19

Musket-barrel milling-machine, eighteenth century. Diderot

PLATE 20

a. Clock-wheel cutting machine by M. Gutierrez 1789. Photograph from the Science Museum, London (Crown copyright reserved)

b. Lathe by G. von Reichenbach *c.* 1800. Deutsches Museum, Munich

PLATE 21

a. English *Leitspindel* lathe *c*. 1810. Deutsches Museum, Munich

b. Early English lathe *c*. 1810. Bridewell Museum, Norwich

PLATE 22

a. Heavy lathe by Maudslay *c.* 1810. *Engineering, Lond.* 18 January 1901

b. Holtzapffel ornamental lathe 1815. Photograph from the Science Museum, London
(Crown copyright reserved)

PLATE 23

Maudslay £200 lathe 1810. Photograph from the Science Museum, London (Crown copyright reserved)

PLATE 24

a. Richard Roberts's back-geared lathe 1817. Photograph from the Science Museum, London
(Crown copyright reserved)

b. Richard Roberts's screw-cutting lathe *c*. 1820. *Engineer, Lond.* 21 October 1910

PLATE 25

a

b

Lathe by James Fox 1817–27. Birmingham Museum
a Rear view, *b* Front view

PLATE 26

a. Lathe by James Fox *c.* 1830. Conservatoire National des Arts et Métiers, Paris

b. Joseph Clement's multi-purpose lathe *c.* 1820. Photograph from the Science Museum, London
(Crown copyright reserved)

PLATE 27

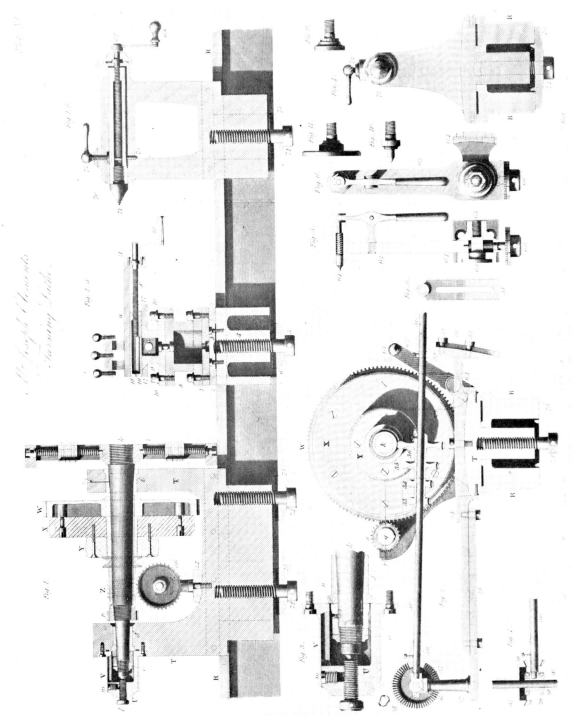

Clement's facing lathe with constant cutting-speed gear 1825. *Trans. R. Soc. Arts*, Vol. 46, 1828

PLATE 28

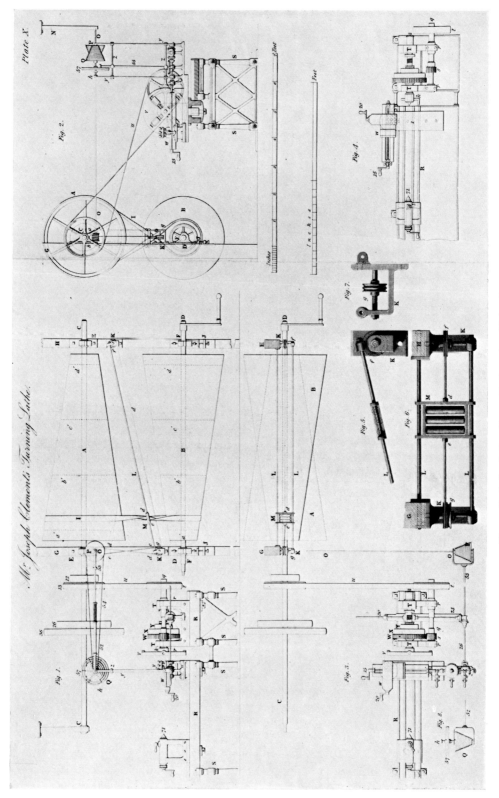

Clement's facing lathe. *Trans. R. Soc. Arts*, Vol. 46, 1828

PLATE 29

a. Lathe by Henry Gambey *c.* 1830. Conservatoire National
des Arts et Métiers, Paris

b. Heavy German lathe *c.* 1830. Deutsches Museum, Munich

PLATE 30

a. Heavy German lathe *c.* 1830. Deutsches Museum, Munich

b. Roberts's planing machine 1817. Photograph from the Science Museum, London
(Crown copyright reserved)

PLATE 31

Soho Foundry boring machine. *Engineer, Lond.* 27 October 1895

PLATE 32

Drilling and boring machines, Soho Foundry. *Engineer, Lond.* 1 November 1895

PLATE 33

James Fox's planing machine 1820–5. Birmingham Museum

PLATE 34

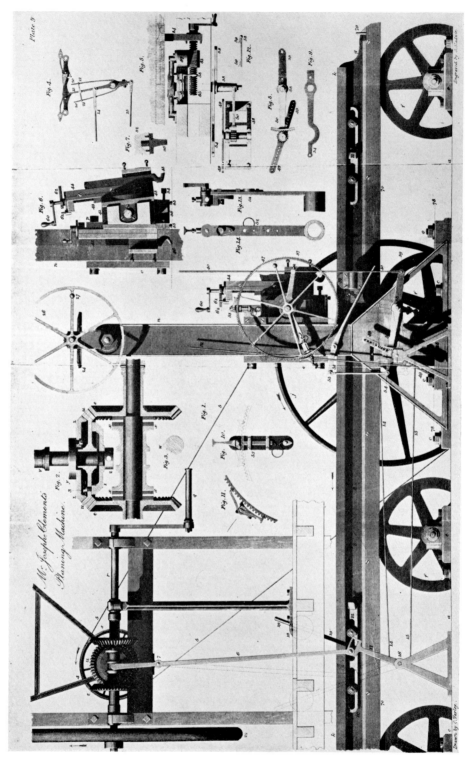

Clement's planing machine *c. 1825. Trans. R. Soc. Arts*, Vol. 49, 1832

PLATE 35

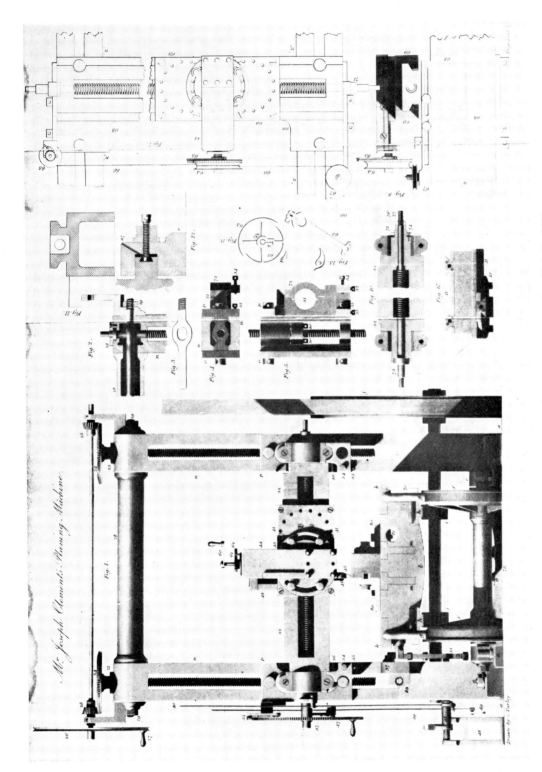

Clement's planing machine, end view. *Trans. R. Soc. Arts,* Vol. 49, 1832

PLATE 36

a. Roberts's gear-cutting machine c. 1821.
Proc. Instn Mech. Engrs 1908

b and c. Bevel gear-cutting machines, Maudslay Sons &
Field works. Engineering, Lond. 1 February 1901

PLATE 37

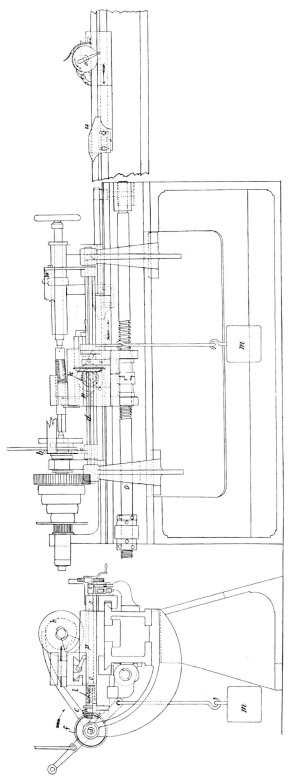

Bodmer's relieving lathe 1841. Patent specification No. 8912

PLATE 38

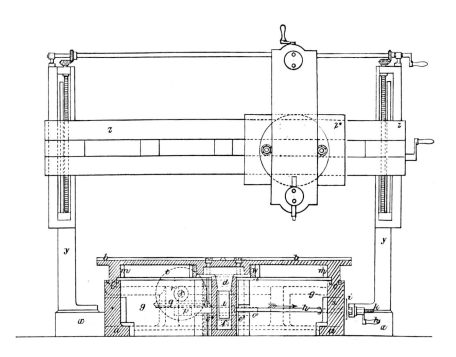

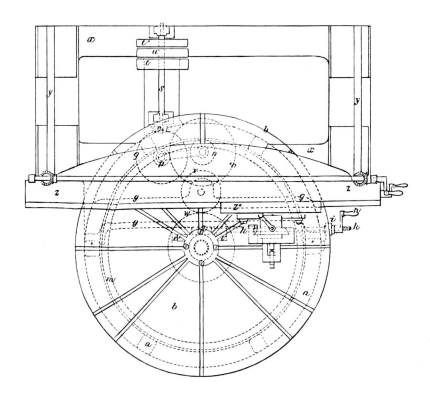

Scale

Bodmer's circular planer 1839. Patent specification No. 8070

PLATE 39

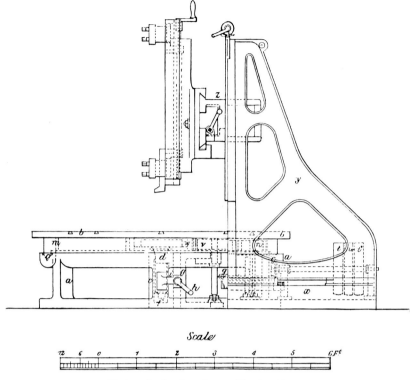

Scale

a. Bodmer's circular planer, side elevation

b. Baxter D. Whitney's lathe *c.* 1854. *Am. Mach.*, *Lond.* (also *N.Y.*) 14 March 1908

PLATE 40

a. Heavy faceplate lathe, Soho Foundry. *Engineer, Lond.* 18 October 1895

b. Large faceplate lathe, Soho Foundry. *Engineer, Lond.* 4 October 1895

PLATE 41

Large faceplate lathe, Soho Foundry. *Engineer, Lond.* 4 October 1895

PLATE 42

a. Whitworth lathe 1843. Photograph from the Science Museum, London.
(Crown copyright reserved)

b. Whitworth lathe *c.* 1850. Birmingham Museum

PLATE 43

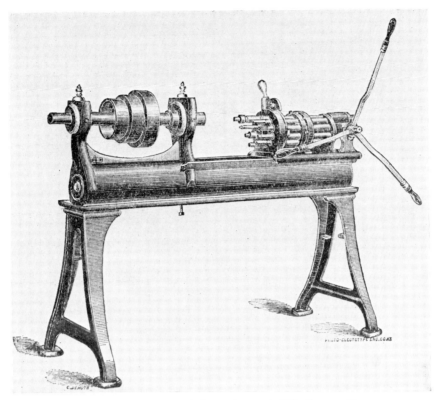

a. Stephen Fitch's turret lathe *c.* 1850. 10th U.S. Census 1880

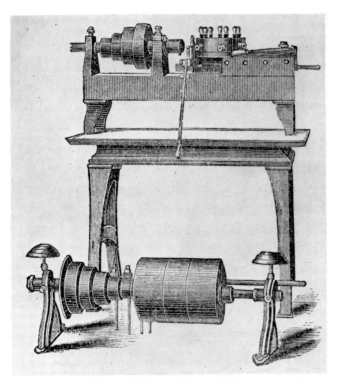

b. H. D. Stone's turret lathe *c.* 1858. 10th U.S. Census 1880

PLATE 44

Boring machine, Maudslay Sons & Field works. *Engineering*, *Lond.* 1 February 1901

PLATE 45

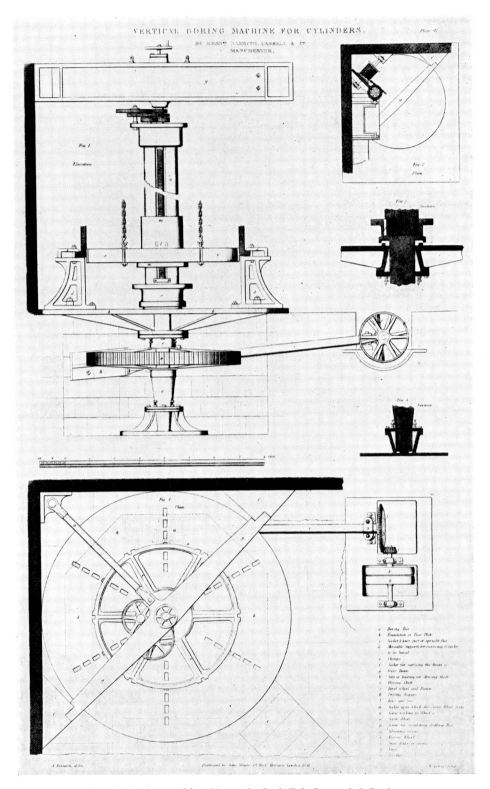

Cylinder boring-machine, Nasmyth, Gaskell & Co. *c.* 1838. Buchanan

PLATE 46

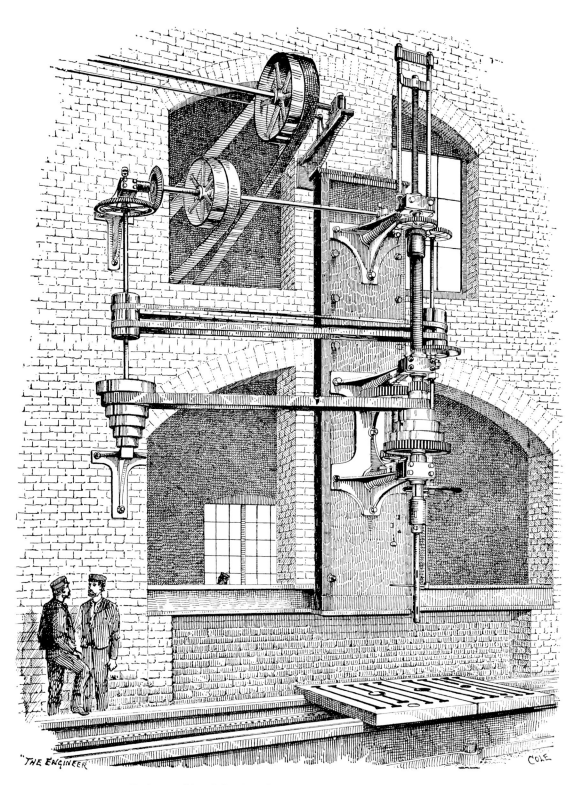

Boring machine, Soho Foundry. *Engineer, Lond.* 27 September 1895

PLATE 47

a. Drilling machine by Whitworth *c.* 1850.
Birmingham Museum

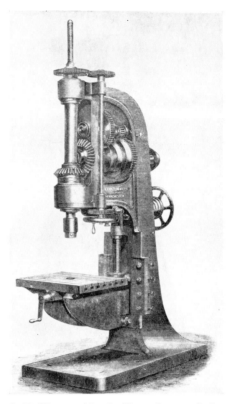

b. Drilling machine by Sharp, Stewart & Co.
c. 1860. Clark

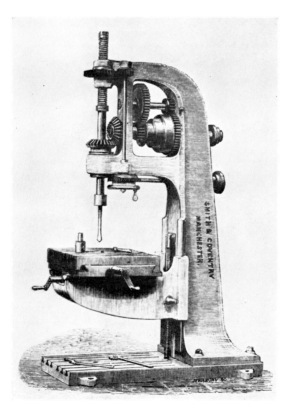

c. Drilling machine by Smith & Coventry *c.* 1860.
Clark

PLATE 48

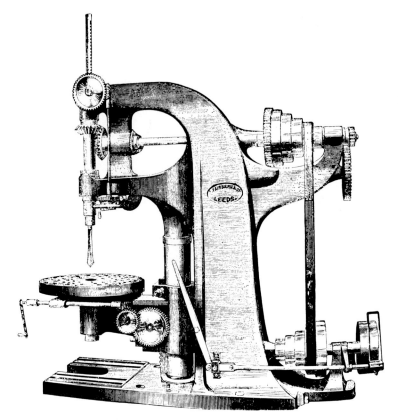

a. Drilling machine by P. Fairbairn & Co. *c.* 1860. Clark

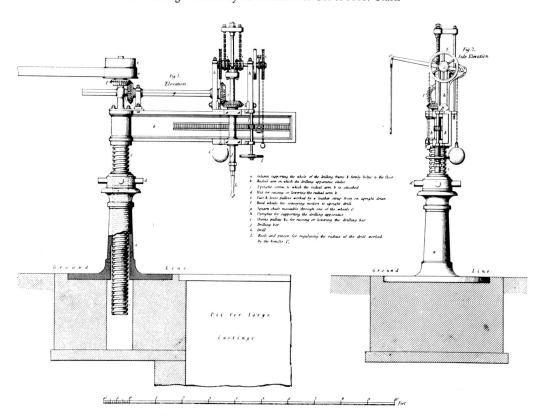

b. Radial drilling-machine by Benjamin Hick & Son *c.* 1838. Buchanan

PLATE 49

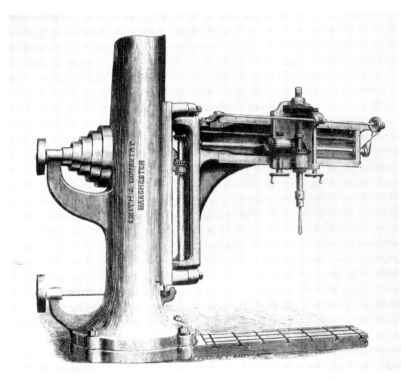

a. Radial drilling-machine by Smith & Coventry *c.* 1860. Clark

b. Planing machine by James Fox *c.* 1833. Conservatoire National des Arts et Métiers, Paris

PLATE 50

a. Morinière's travelling standards planing-machine *c.* 1834. Conservatoire National des Arts et Métiers, Paris

b. Wall planing-machine, Soho Foundry *c.* 1830? Birmingham Museum

PLATE 51

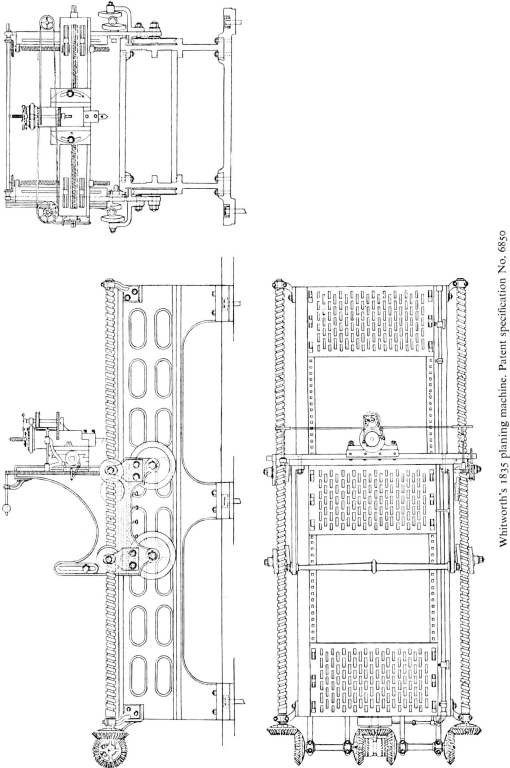

Whitworth's 1835 planing machine. Patent specification No. 6850

Whitworth's 1842 planing machine. Photograph from the Science Museum, London (Crown copyright reserved)

PLATE 53

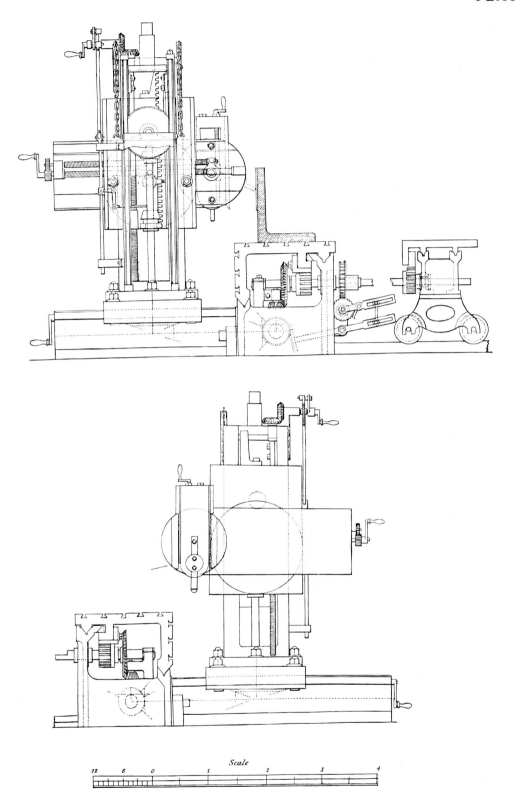

Scale
12   6   0   1   2   3   4

Bodmer's 'open-side' planing machine 1839. Patent specification No. 8070

PLATE 54

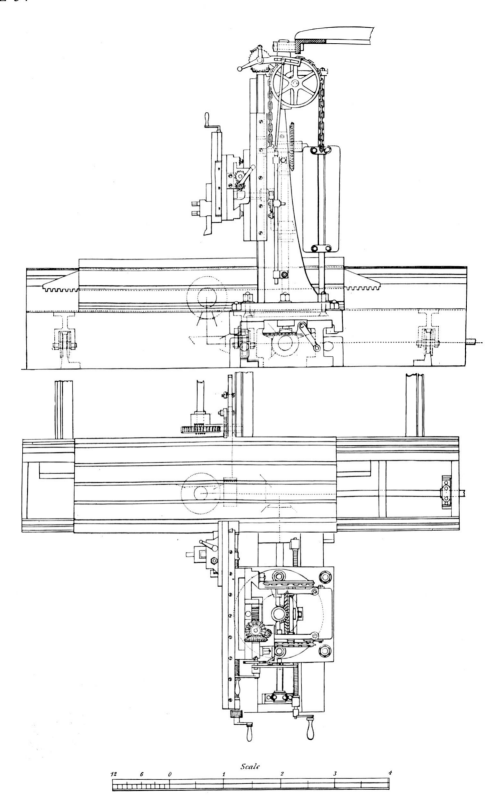

Scale

12   6   0   1   2   3   4

Bodmer's 'open-side' planing machine

PLATE 55

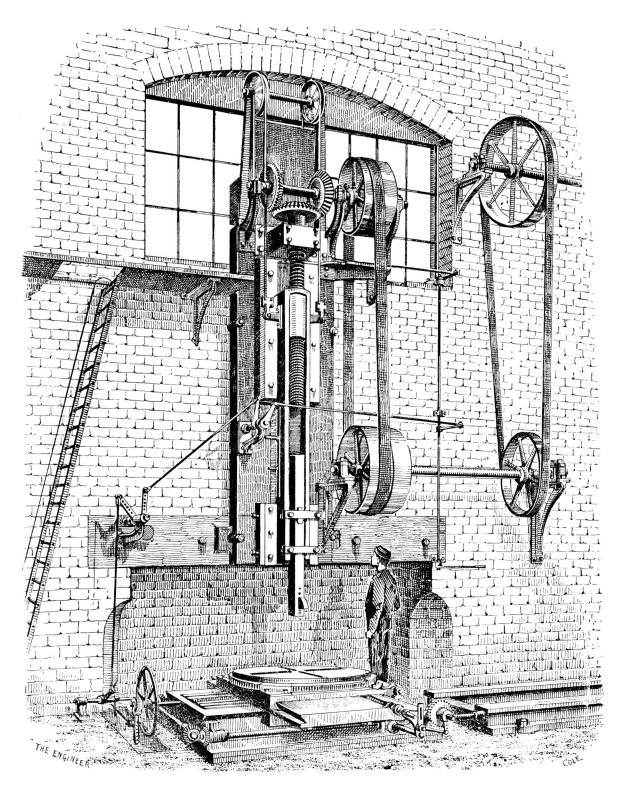

Wall-mounted slotting machine, Soho Foundry. *Engineer, Lond.* 1 November 1895

PLATE 56

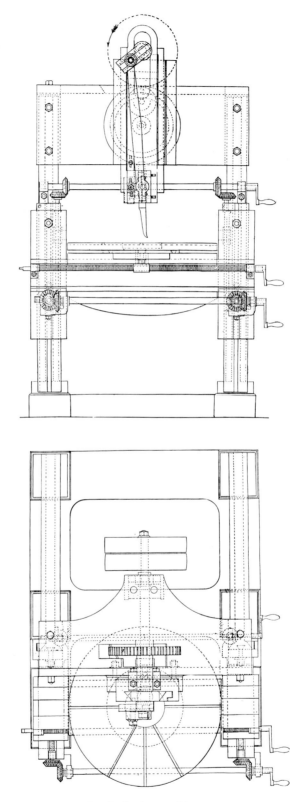

Bodmer's slotting machine 1841.
Patent specification No. 8912

PLATE 57

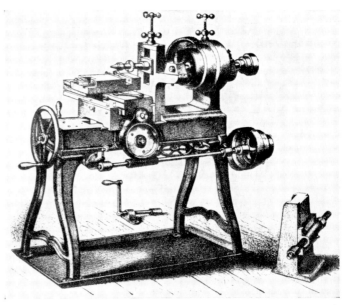

a. Gay & Silver milling machine *c.* 1835. *Am.Mach., Lond.* (also *N.Y.*) 31 October 1908

b. Lincoln-type milling machine *c.* 1854. *Am. Mach., Lond.* (also *N.Y.*) 14 July 1900

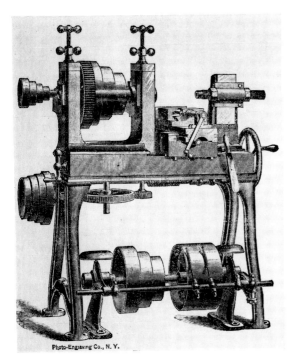

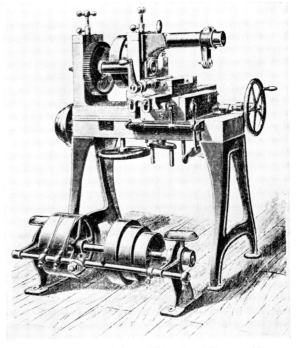

c. Lincoln-type milling machine. Hutton, 1885

d. Elisha Root's design of Lincoln milling machine. Hutton, 1885

PLATE 58

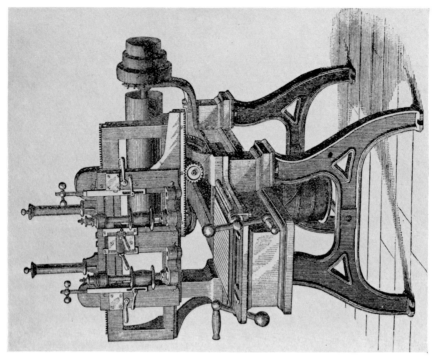

b. Howe's profile milling-machine c. 1848. 10th U.S. Census 1880

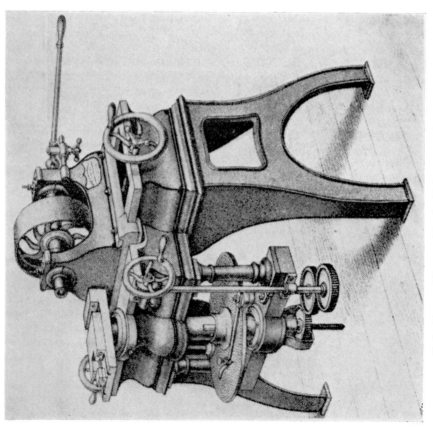

a. 'Index'-type milling machine by F. Howe. Taylor & Fenn Co.

PLATE 59

b. Sharp, Stewart & Co.'s 'marine slotting drill'. *Engineer, Lond.* 2 May 1862

a. Sharp, Stewart & Co.'s vertical milling-machine *c.* 1857. Conservatoire National des Arts et Métiers, Paris

PLATE 60

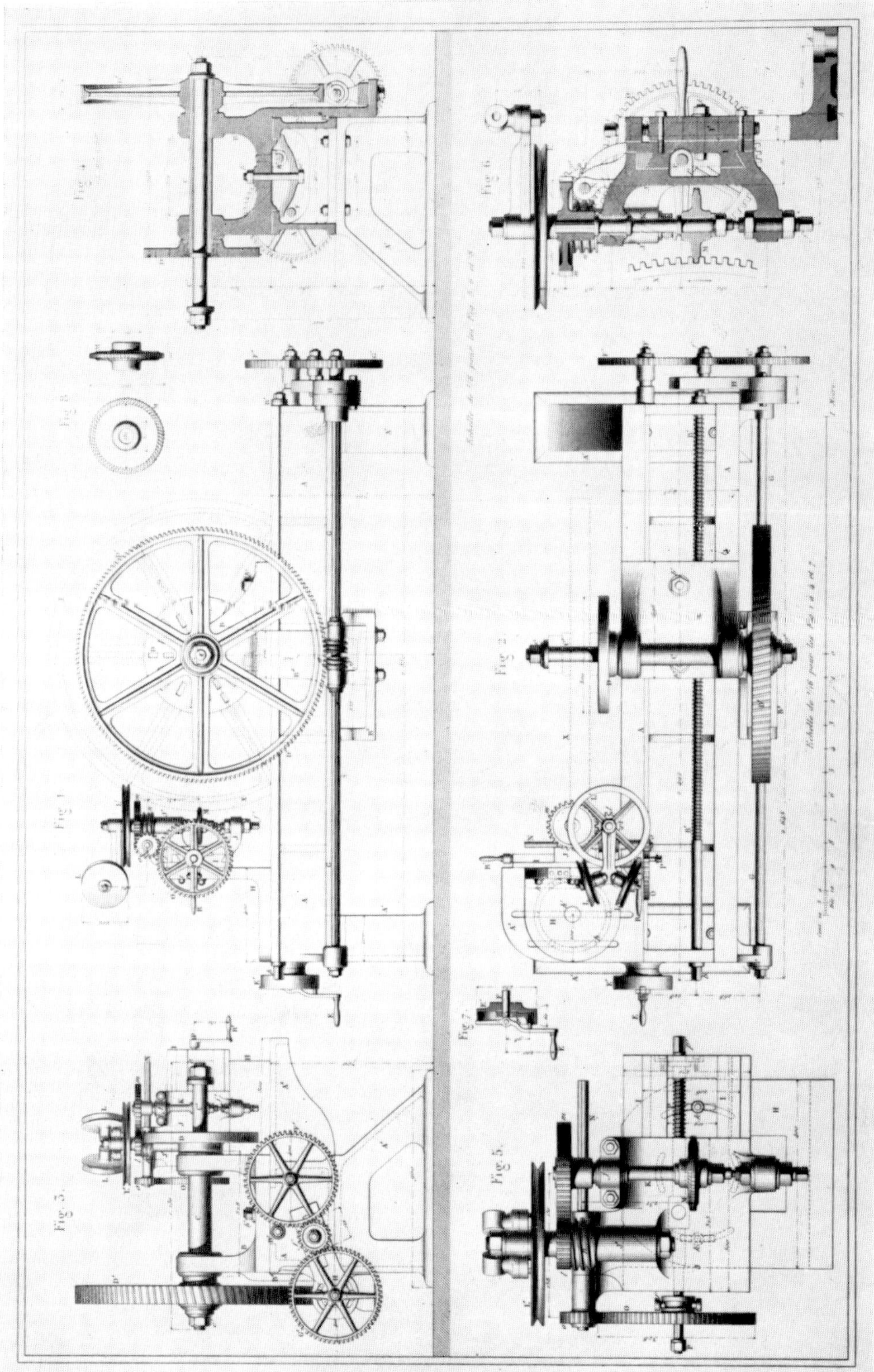

Whitworth gear-cutting machine c. 1840. Armengaud

PLATE 61

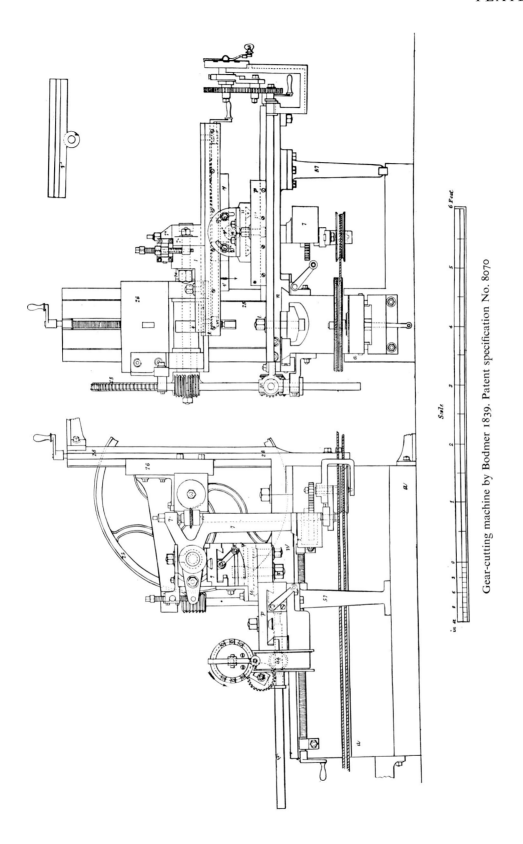

Gear-cutting machine by Bodmer 1839. Patent specification No. 8070

PLATE 62

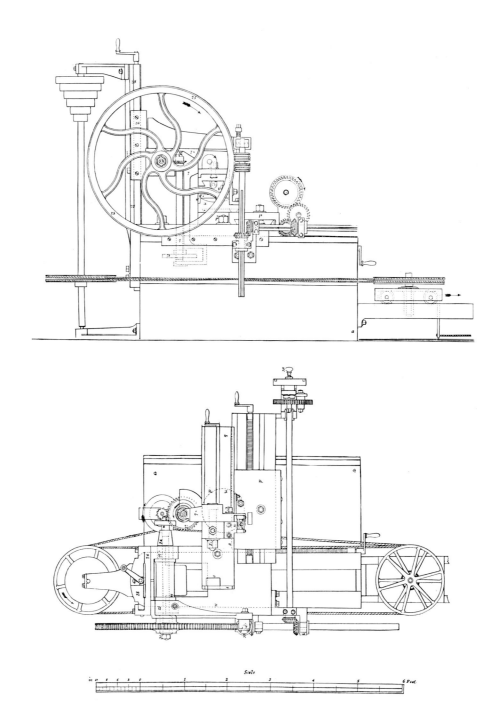

Gear-cutting machine by Bodmer 1839

PLATE 63

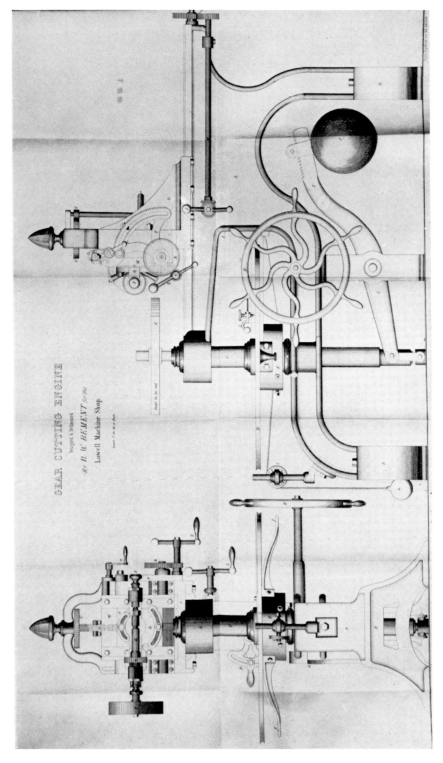

B. W. Bement's gear-cutting machine *c.* 1850. Byrne

PLATE 64

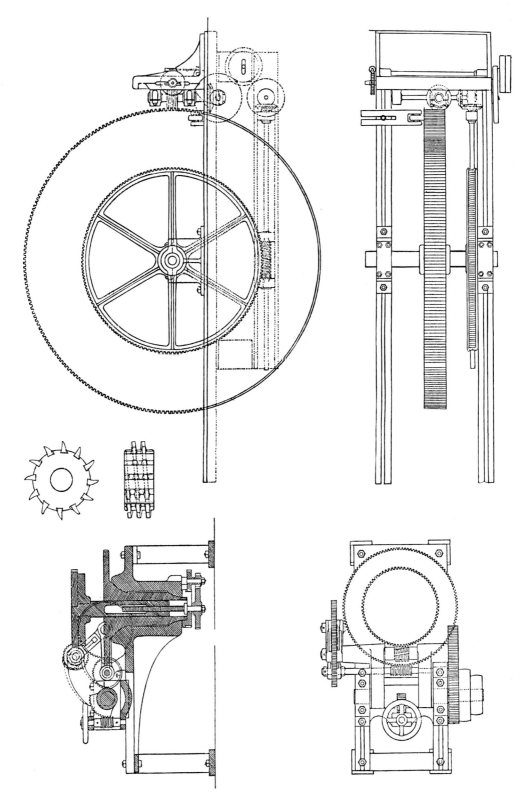

PLATE 65

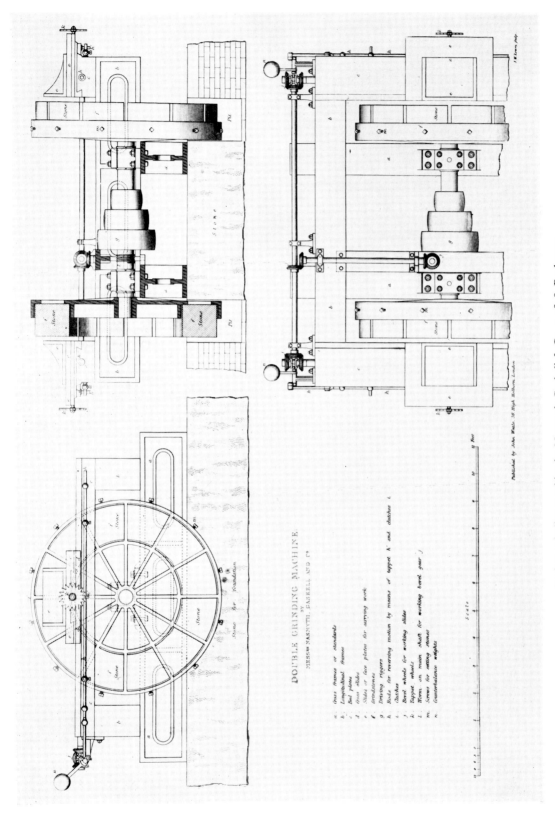

Surface grinding machine by Nasmyth Gaskell & Co. c. 1838. Buchanan

PLATE 66

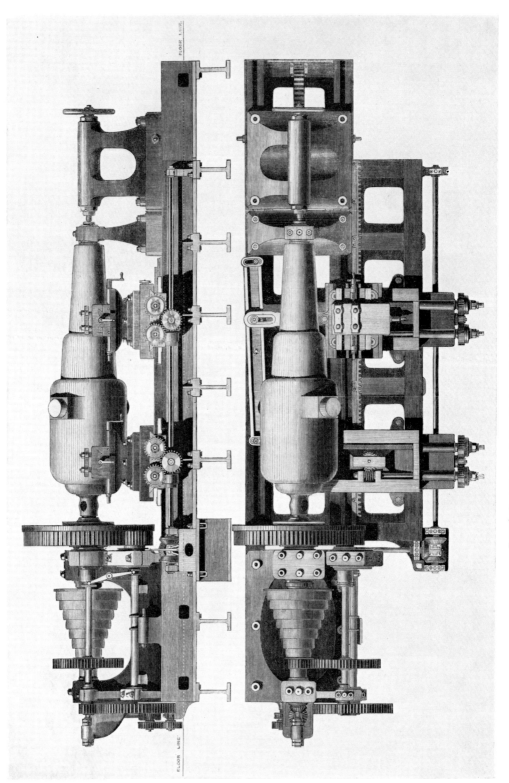

Royal Gun Factory lathe. *Engineer, Lond.* 8 February 1867

PLATE 67

Treble-geared facing lathe, Francis Berry & Sons. *Engineering*, *Lond.* 15 June 1888

PLATE 68

a. American facing lathe. Hutton, 1885

b. Pulley lathe by Niles Tool Works. Hutton, 1885

PLATE 69

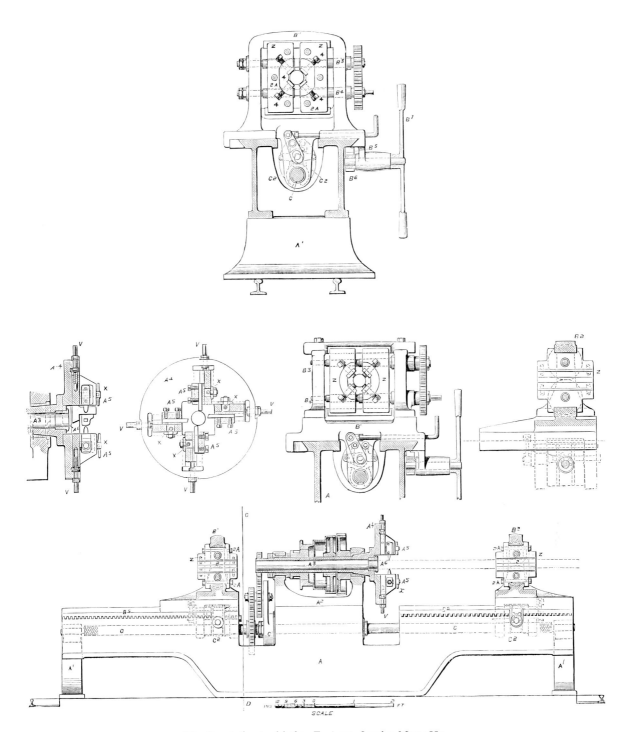

Hunt's rotating-tool lathe. *Engineer, Lond.* 3 May 1889

PLATE 70

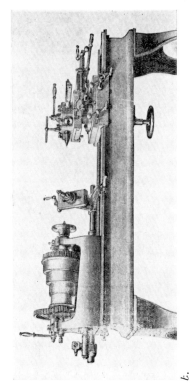

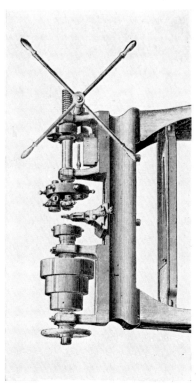

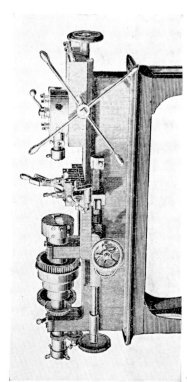

a. Rotating-tool lathe by Booth & Co. *Engineer, Lond.* 10 February 1893
b. 'Turret head' lathe. Hutton, 1885
c. American turret lathe. Hutton, 1885
d. Horizontal-axis turret lathe. Hutton, 1885

PLATE 71

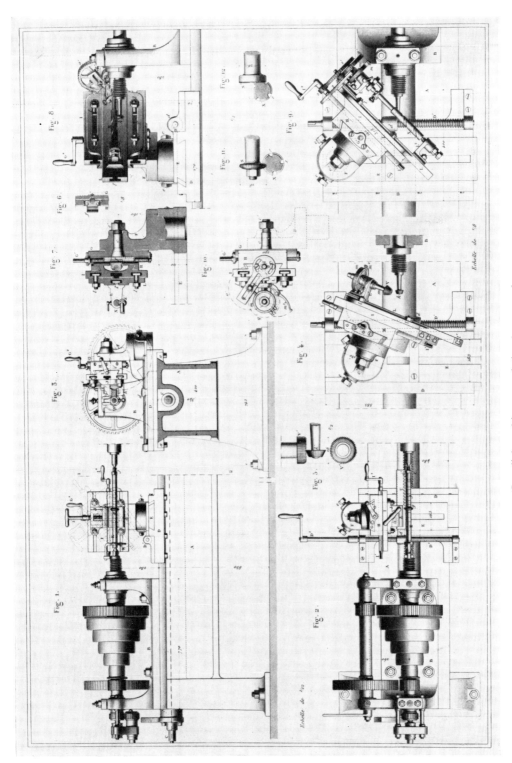

Jamelin's multi-purpose lathe. Armengaud

PLATE 72

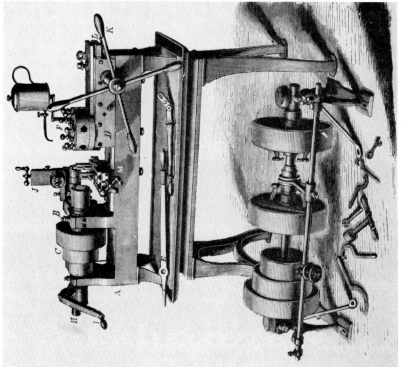

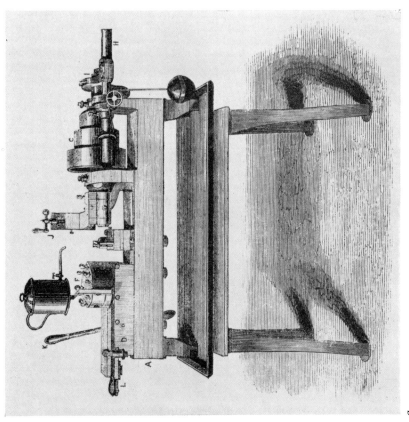

Brown & Sharpe turret lathe 1867. *Engineer, Lond.* 19 July 1867

PLATE 73

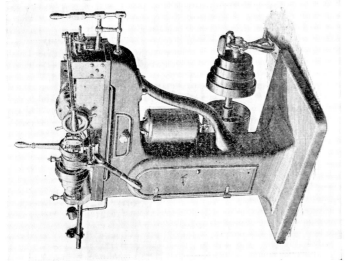

b. Turret lathe with transverse turret axis. Hutton, 1885

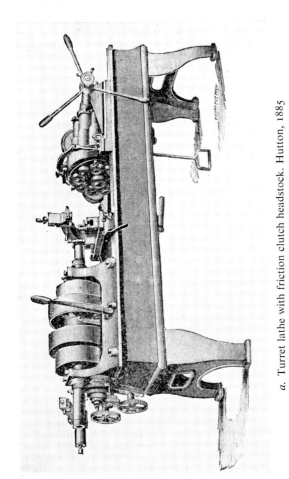

a. Turret lathe with friction clutch headstock. Hutton, 1885

c. Smith & Coventry capstan lathe. *Engineer, Lond.* 6 May 1887

PLATE 74

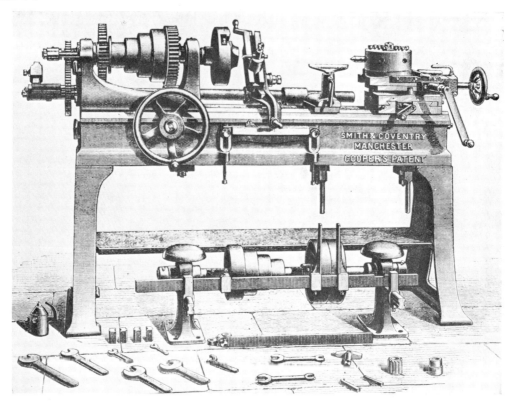

a. Smith & Coventry capstan lathe. *Engineer, Lond.* 6 May 1887

b. Nettlefold & Chamberlain wood-screw machine *c.* 1860. Birmingham Museum

a. Nettlefold & Chamberlain wood-screw machine

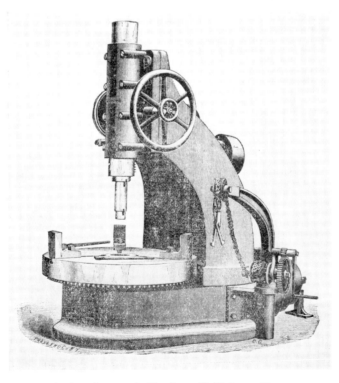

b. American vertical boring-mill. Hutton, 1885

PLATE 75

PLATE 76

Schweizer automatic lathe 1872. Alfred Herbert Ltd., Coventry

PLATE 77

'Hartford' auto-screw machine *c.* 1873. Birmingham Museum

PLATE 78

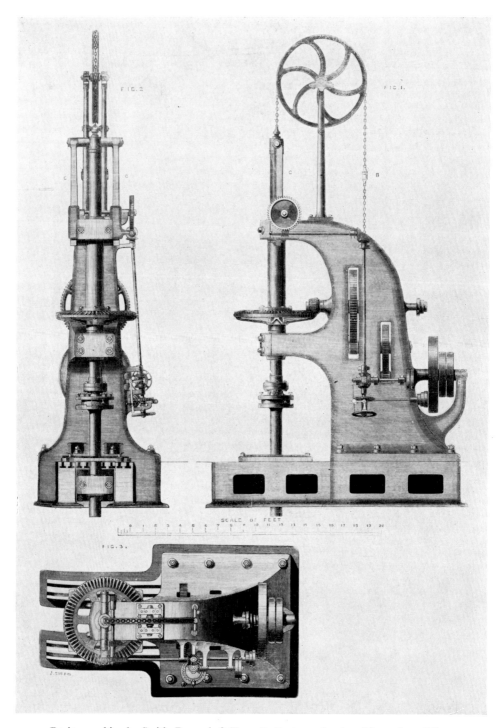

Boring machine by Smith, Beacock & Tannett. *Engineer, Lond.* 23 November 1866

PLATE 79

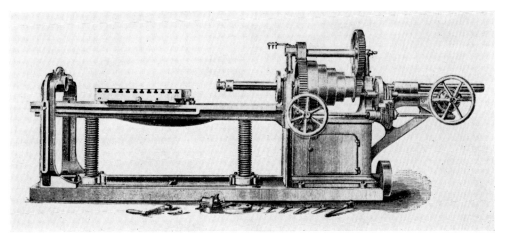

a. Elevating-table boring machine. Hutton, 1885

b. Elevating spindle-head boring machine by F. Pearn & Co. *Engineering*, *Lond.* 16 October 1908

PLATE 80

a. Floor type horizontal boring machine by Wm. Sellers & Co. Hutton, 1885

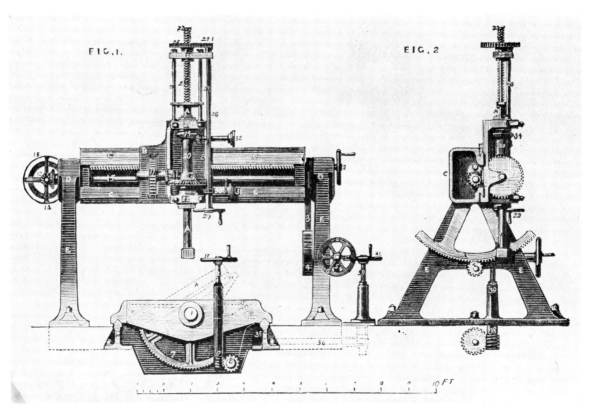

b. 'Universal' boring machine by G. & A. Harvey Ltd. *Engineer, Lond.* 22 May 1863

PLATE 81

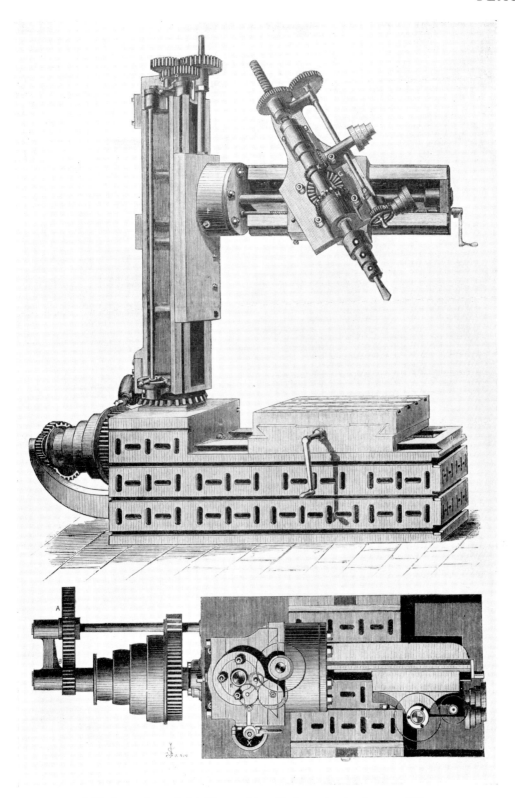

Miller's angular radial drilling-machine. *Engineer, Lond.* 3 January 1868

PLATE 82

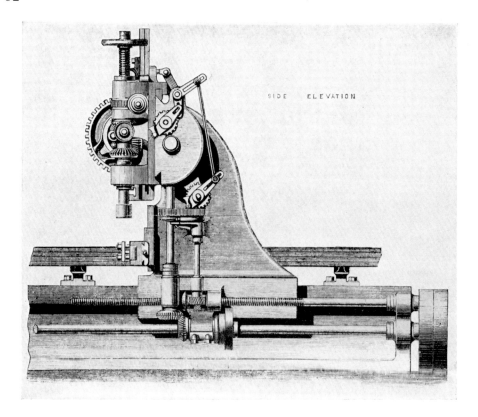

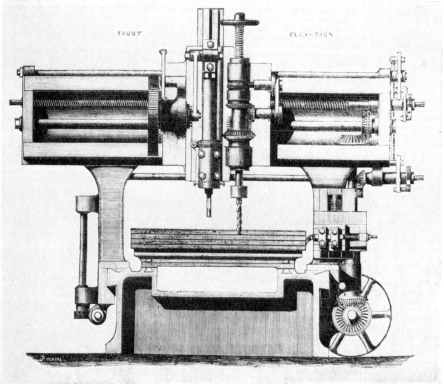

Drilling, slotting and planing machine, Sharp, Stewart & Co. *Engineer*, *Lond*. 9 August 1867

PLATE 83

Boiler drilling machine by Thos. Shanks. *Engineer, Lond.* 24 February 1888

PLATE 84

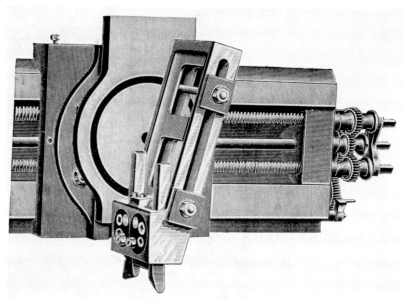

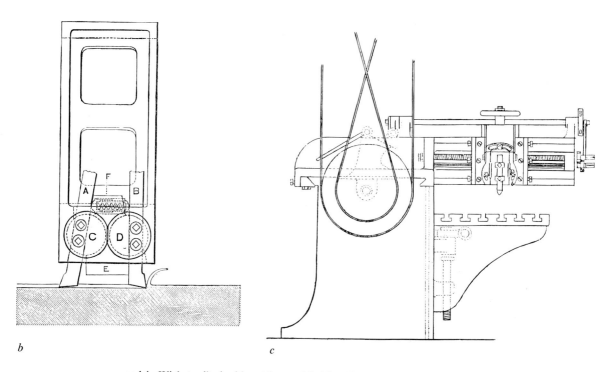

a and *b*. Wicksteed's double cutting tool-holder. *Engineer, Lond.* 8 April 1887.
c. Hulse's side-planing machine, 1865. Patent specification No. 1571

PLATE 85

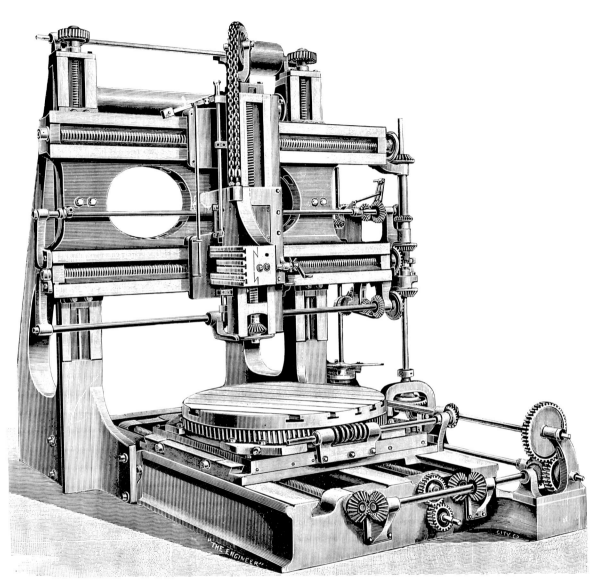

Hulse's planing and slotting machine. *Engineer, Lond.* 19 August 1892

PLATE 86

a. R. P. Doxford's propellor blade shaping-machine. *Engineering, Lond.* 27 January 1888

b. Cylinder face and port planing-machine by Craven Bros. *Engineer, Lond.* 18 December 1892

PLATE 87

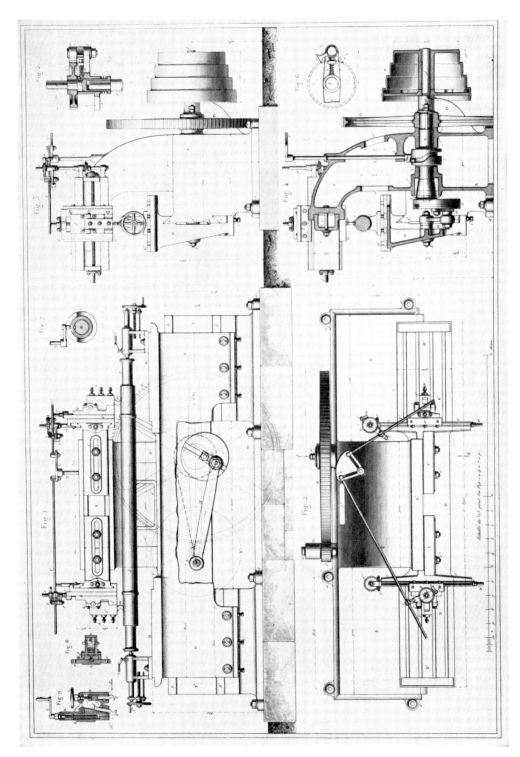

Key-way shaping machine by Ducommun et Dubied. Armengaud

PLATE 88

Universal milling machine *c.* 1862. Brown & Sharpe Manufacturing Co., N. Kingstown, Rhode Island, U.S.A.

PLATE 89

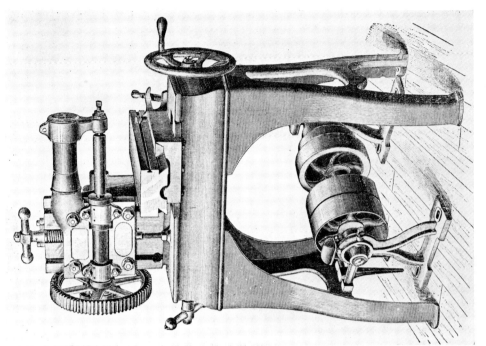

b. Elevating-head milling machine with integral overarm.
Hutton, 1885

a. Oscillating-head horizontal milling machine. Hutton, 1885

PLATE 90

a. Two-spindle milling machine by **P.** Huré *c.* 1874. Leon Huré et Cie

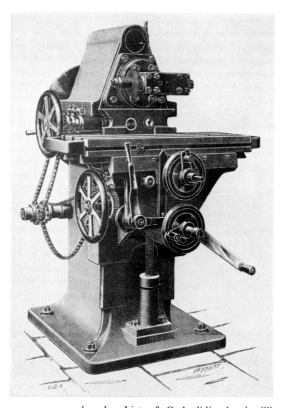

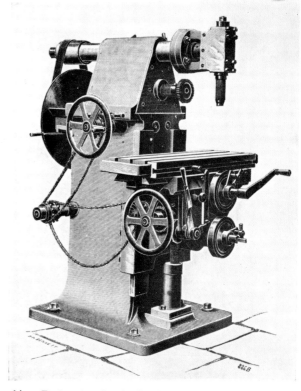

b and *c.* Lister & Co.'s sliding-head milling machine. *Engineering, Lond.* 26 February 1892

PLATE 91

a. Vertical milling attachment. Brown & Sharpe catalogue, 1895

b. Ludwig Loewe's circular milling machine. *Engineering, Lond.* 28 October 1892

PLATE 92

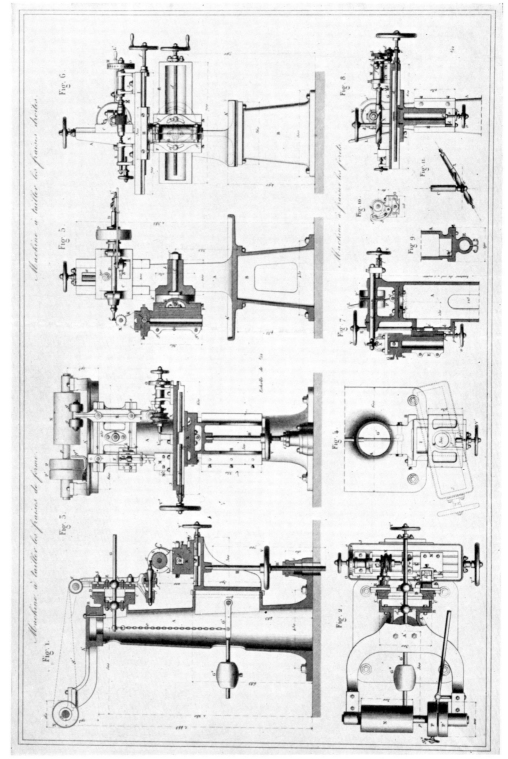

Cutter milling machine by Frey. Arrrengaud

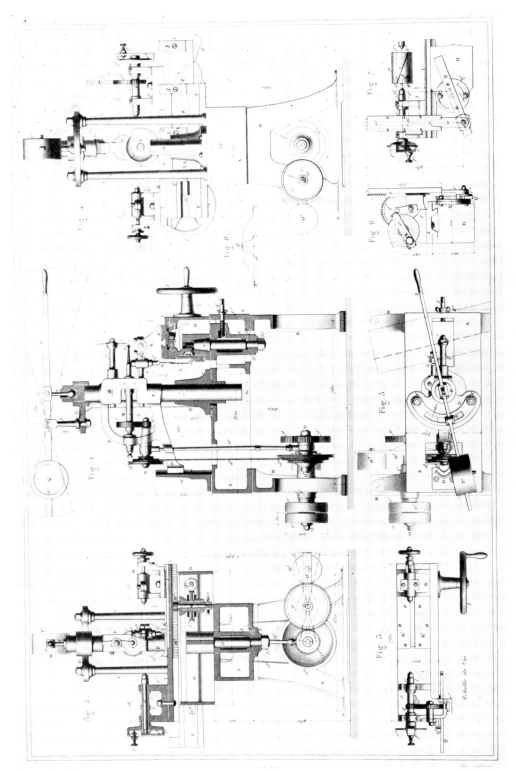

PLATE 93

Cutter milling machine by Kreutzberger. Armengaud

PLATE 94

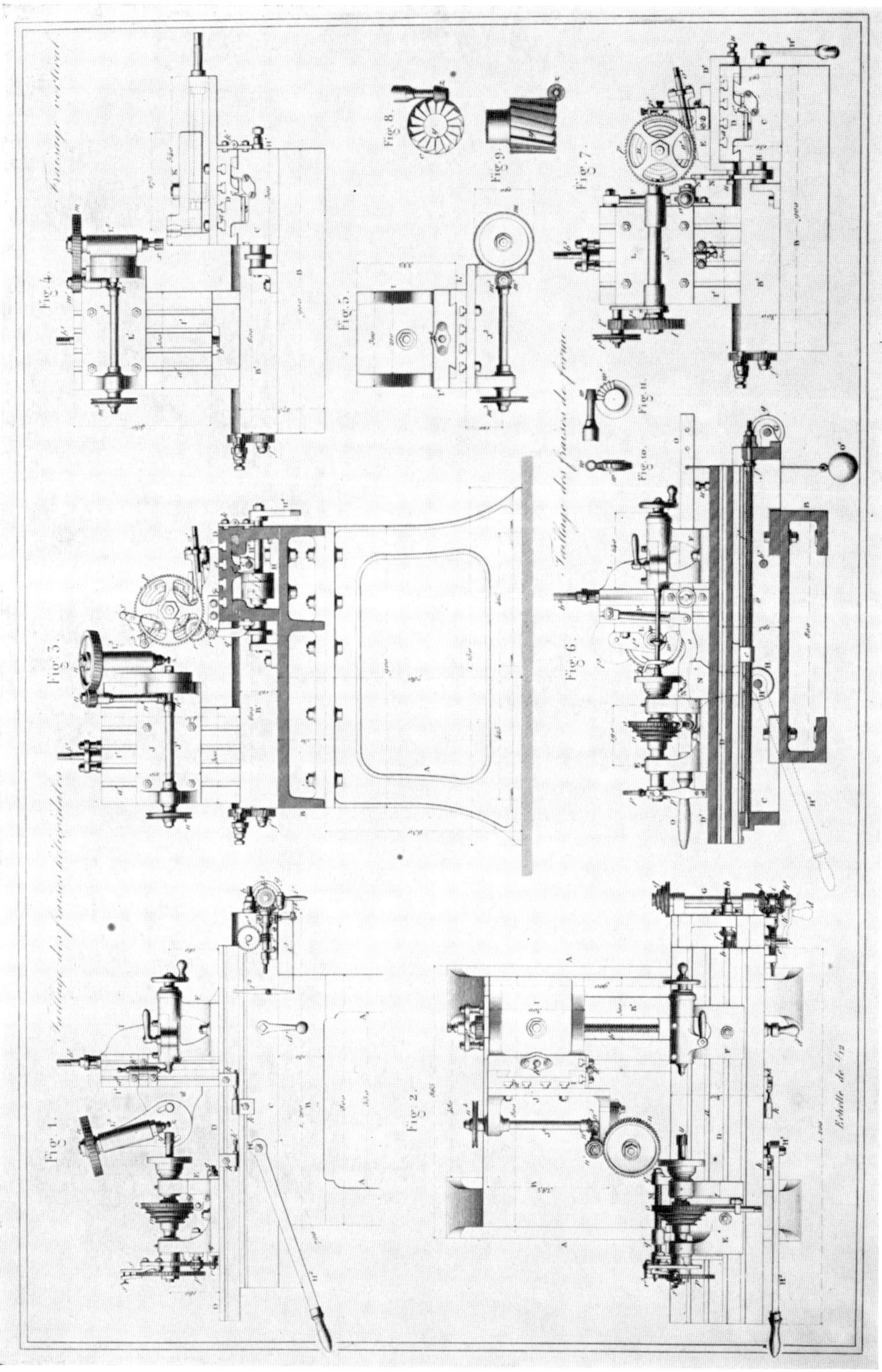

Cutter milling machine by Colmant. Armengaud

PLATE 95

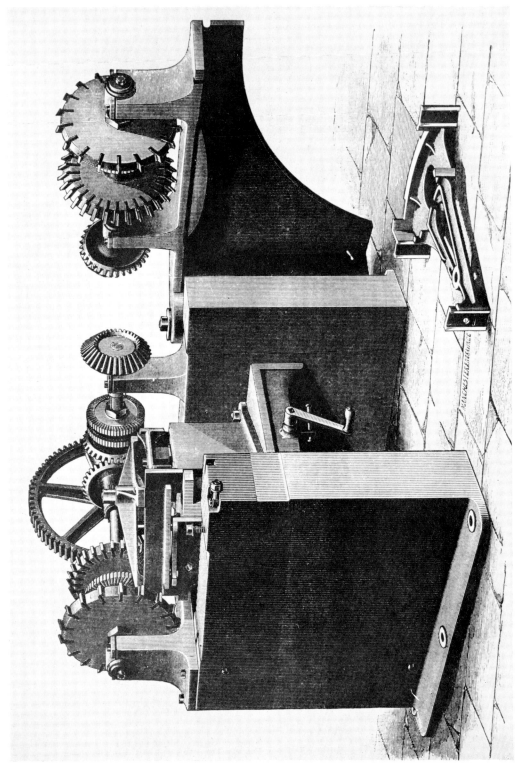

8-face milling machine by Hetherington & Co. *Engineer, Lond.* 30 December 1887

PLATE 96

a. Ingersoll plano-type milling machine. *Engineer, Lond.* 3 February 1895
b. Ingersoll milling cutters. *Engineer, Lond.* 3 February 1893
c. Addy's adjustable milling cutter. *Proc. Instn Mech. Engrs*, Vol. 41, 1890

PLATE 97

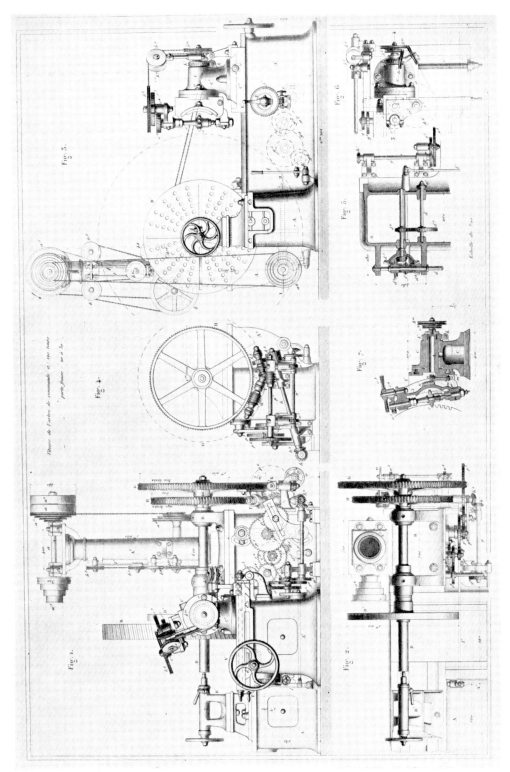

Piat's gear-cutting machine. Armengaud

PLATE 98

a. Kendall & Gent's automatic gear cutter. *Engineer, Lond.* 12 June 1868

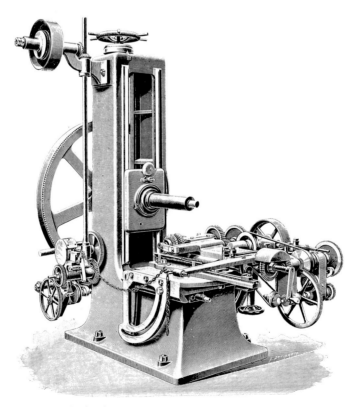

b. Lang–Eberhardt gear cutter. *Engineering, Lond.* 1 March 1889

PLATE 99

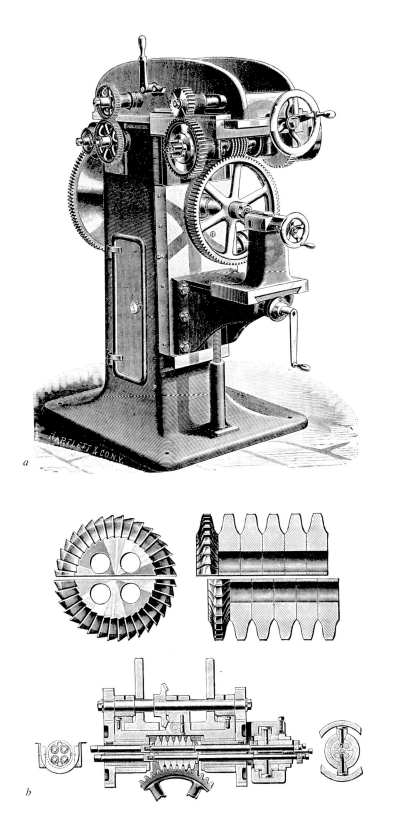

a and *b*. Swasey's gear-tooth generating machine. *Engineering, Lond.* 9 January 1891

PLATE 100

b. Pratt & Whitney weighted grinding lathe. Rose

a. Brown & Sharpe cylindrical grinding-machine c. 1875. Rose

PLATE 101

a

b

a and *b*. A. B. Landis grinding-machine *c*. 1883. Landis Tool Co., Waynesboro, Pennsylvania, U.S.A.

PLATE 102

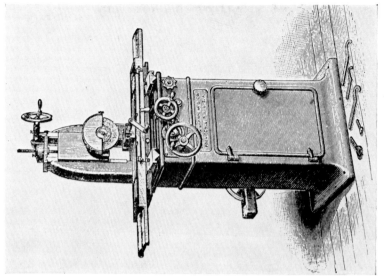

b. Pedestal surface grinding-machine *c.* 1880. Brown & Sharpe catalogue, 1895

a. Plano-type surface grinding-machine *c.* 1877. Brown & Sharpe catalogue, 1895

PLATE 103

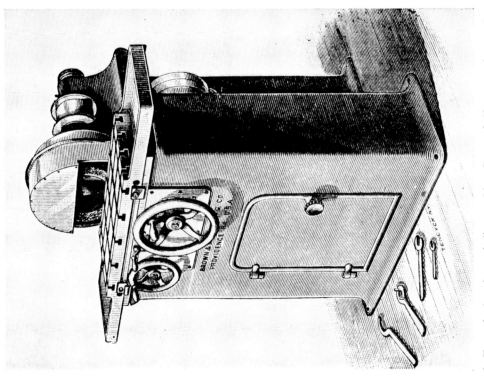

b. Face-wheel surface grinding-machine. Brown & Sharpe catalogue, 1895

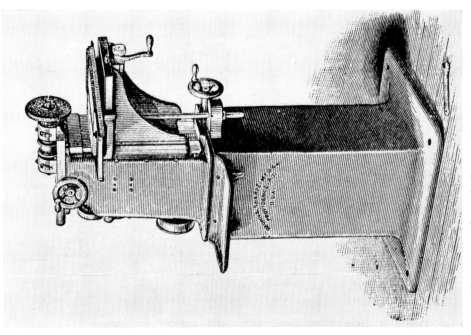

a. Knee-type surface grinding-machine. Brown & Sharpe catalogue, 1895

PLATE 104

a. Key-way broaching machine by Smith & Coventry. *Engineering, Lond.* 22 March 1889

b. Crankshaft lathe 1906. Thomas Ryder & Sons Ltd., Bolton

PLATE 105

Duplex wheel and tyre boring-machine by G & A. Harvey. *Engineering, Lond.* 27 January 1893

PLATE 106

Triple-geared lathe by Sharp, Stewart & Co. *Engineer, Lond.* 8 December 1893

PLATE 107

90-inch gun lathe by Niles Tool Works. *Engineering, Lond.* 6 October 1893

PLATE 108

Ingot-trepanning machine by Craven Bros. Ltd. *Engineer, Lond.* 29 December 1899

PLATE 109

Boiler-flue turning and drilling machine by Hulse & Co. *Engineer, Lond.* 28 July 1899

PLATE 110

a. Crankshaft lathe by L. Gardner & Sons. *Engineering, Lond.* 12 May 1911

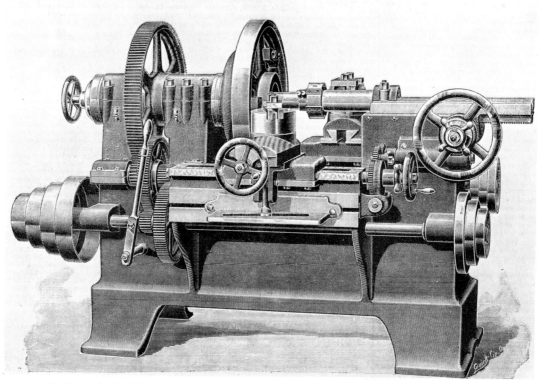

b. Gear wheel and pulley lathe by Ohio Machine Works Co. *Engineer, Lond.* 14 July 1893

PLATE 111

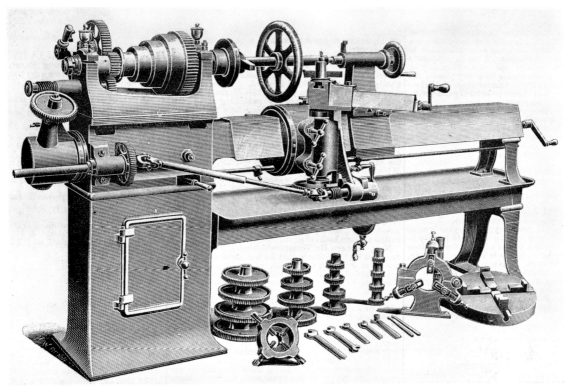

a. Pittler universal lathe. *Engineering, Lond.* 20 January 1893

b. Parkinson's screw-cutting lathe. *Engineering, Lond.* 18 July 1902

PLATE 112

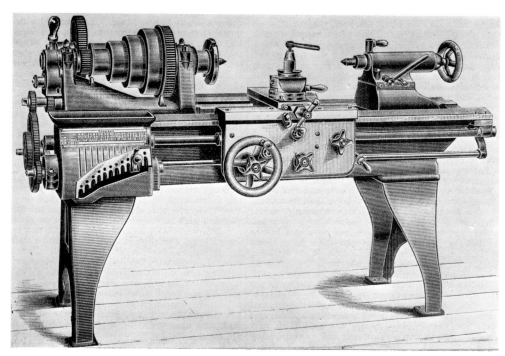

a. Hendey Machine Co.'s lathe. *Engineer, Lond.* 19 January 1894

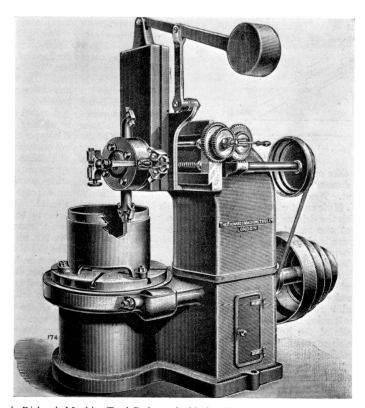

b. Richards Machine Tool Co.'s vertical lathe. *Engineer, Lond.* 12 April 1895

PLATE 113

b. G. Wilkinson & Sons vertical lathe. *Engineer, Lond.* 28 February 1902

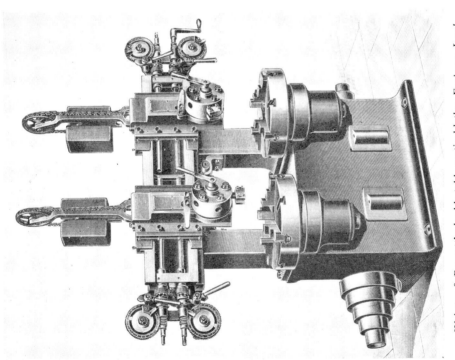

a. Webster & Bennett's double-table vertical lathe. *Engineer, Lond.*
4 October 1901

PLATE 114

a. Jones & Lamson flat-turret lathe. *Engineering, Lond.* 1 December 1893

b. Wolseley Machine Co.'s 'cross'-turret lathe. *Engineer, Lond.* 6 October 1899

PLATE 115

Gisholt turret lathe. *Engineering, Lond.* 22 September 1893

PLATE 116

a. Pittler turret lathe. *Engineering, Lond.* 5 October 1906

b. 'Ring' turret lathe. *Engineering, Lond.* 5 October 1906

PLATE 117

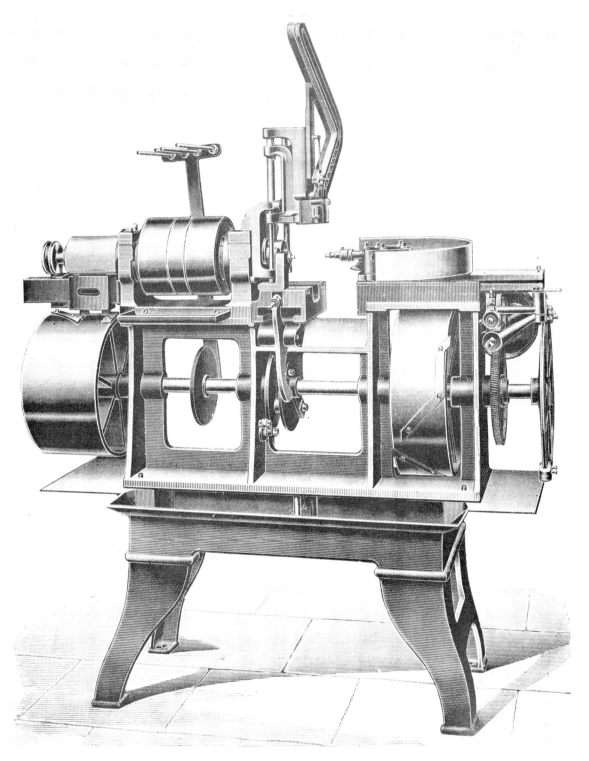

Pratt & Whitney auto with magazine loading. *Engineer, Lond.* 17 November 1899

PLATE 118

a. Wolseley Machine Co.'s automatic. *Engineer, Lond.* 17 November 1899

b. Brockie automatic. *Engineering, Lond.* 15 March 1901

PLATE 119

a. Dormer–Schmutz automatic. *Engineering, Lond.* 14 March 1902

b. Craven–Gridley automatic. *Engineer, Lond.* 4 November 1910

PLATE 120

Acme four-spindle automatic c. 1898. The National Acme Co.

PLATE 121

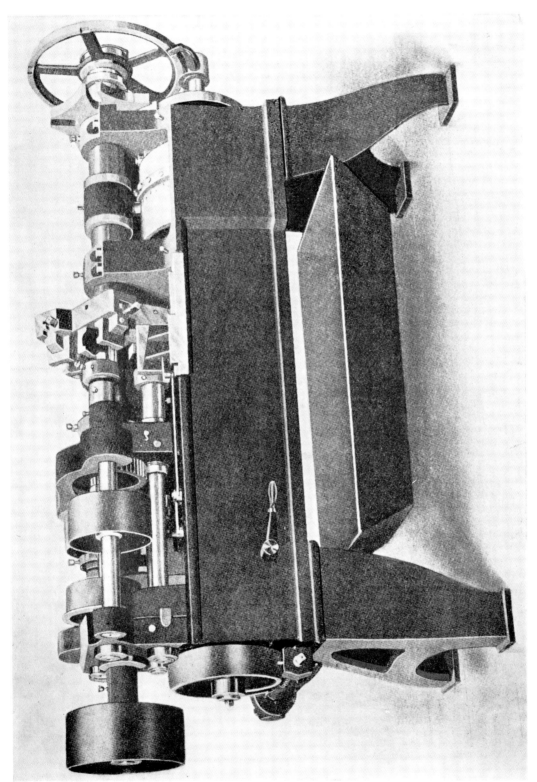

Prentice automatic *Engineer, Lond.* 11 May 1906

PLATE 122

b. Two-spindle boring machine by Cuncliffe and Croom. *Engineer, Lond.*
6 March 1891

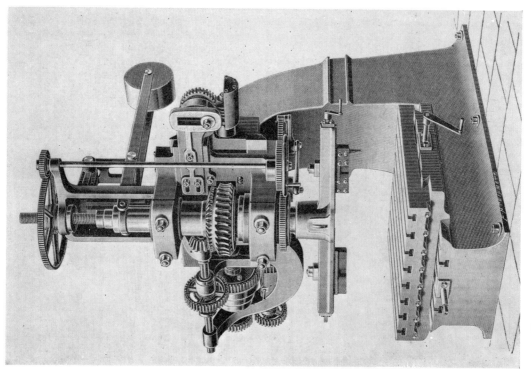

a. Elliptical boring-machine by G. & A. Harvey. *Engineering, Lond.*
16 December 1892

PLATE 123

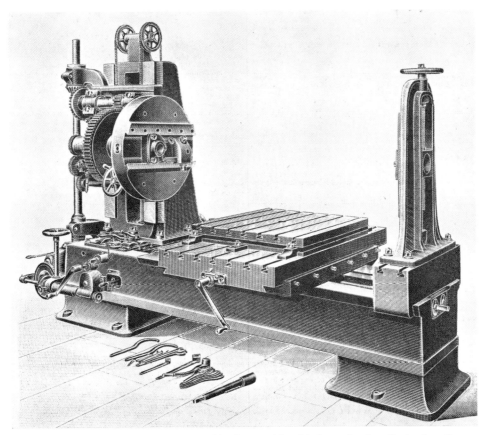

a. G. Richards & Co.'s pipe-facing and boring machine. *Engineer, Lond.* 15 September 1899

b. 'Snout'-type boring machine by J. Buckton & Co. *Engineer, Lond.* 24 March 1899

PLATE 124

a. Four-spindle boring machine by Newton Machine Tool Works. *Engineering, Lond.* 5 February 1899

b. Double-ended boring machine by Ward, Haggas & Smith. *Engineering, Lond.* 21 August 1903

PLATE 125

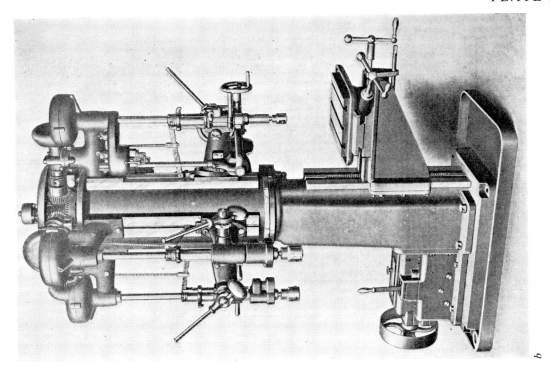

a. Twelve-spindle drilling machine by G. Richards & Co. *Engineering, Lond.*
11 January 1895

b. Schuchardt & Schutte five-spindle drilling machine. *Engineering, Lond.*
4 October 1907

PLATE 126

a. Geo. Richards & Co.'s side-planing machine. *Engineering, Lond.* 6 March 1891

b. Typical pillar-type shaping machine

PLATE 127

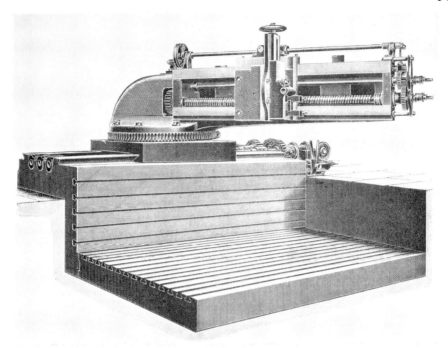

a. Hulse & Co.'s radial side-planing machine. *Engineer*, *Lond.* 28 August 1896

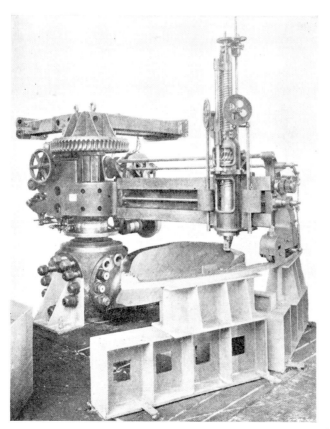

b. Propeller-blade shaping machine by Stettiner Maschinenbau A.G.
Engineering, *Lond.* 9 October 1903

PLATE 128

Slotting machine by Thos. Shanks & Co. *Engineering*, *Lond.* 15 July 1892

PLATE 129

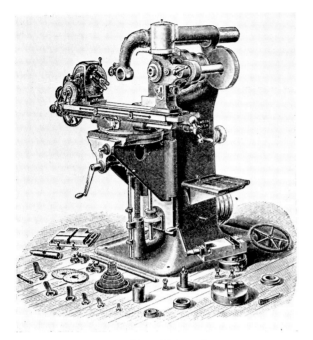

a. No. 3 Universal

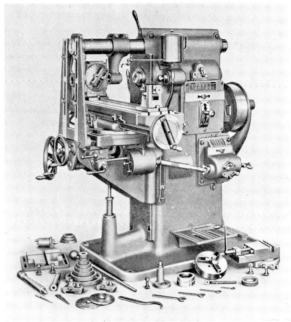

b. No. 3A Universal

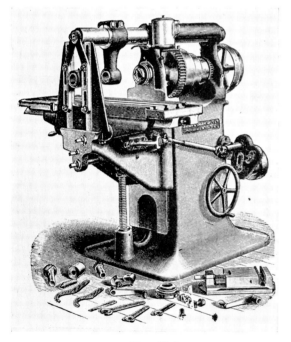

c. No. 5 Plain

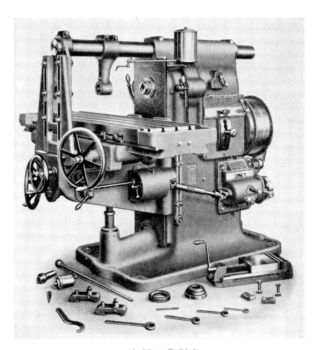

d. No. 5B Plain

Brown & Sharp milling-machines
Brown & Sharp catalogues: *a* and *c* 1895, *b* and *d* 1913

PLATE 130

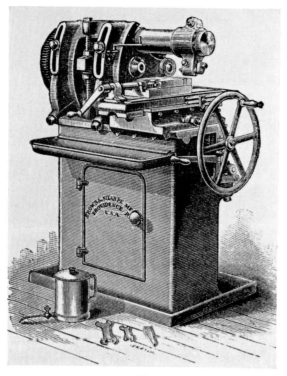

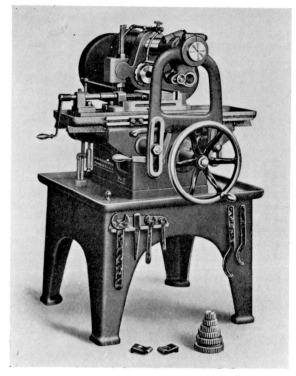

a. No. 13

b. No. 12

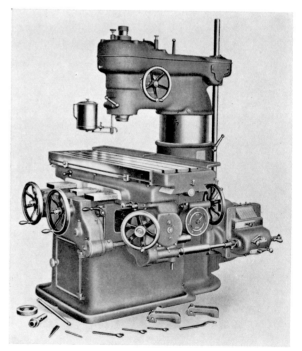

c. No. 2 Vertical

d. No. 5 Vertical

Brown & Sharp milling-machines
Brown & Sharpe catalogues: *a* and *c* 1895, *b* and *d* 1913

PLATE 131

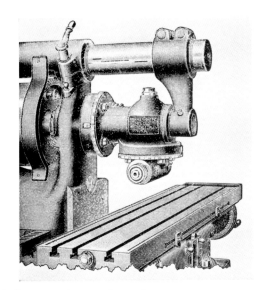

Vertical-spindle milling attachments Brown & Sharpe catalogues, 1895 and 1903

b. Kendall & Gent vertical milling-machine. *Engineer, Lond.* 17 August 1896

PLATE 132

b. Knee-type vertical milling-machine by Alfred Herbert. *Engineering, Lond.*
11 October 1907

a. Vertical milling-machine by Alfred Herbert. *Engineering, Lond.*
16 June 1900

PLATE 133

b. Plano-type milling-machine by W. Muir & Co. *Engineer, Lond.* 15 December 1894

a. Milling-machine by H. W. Ward & Co. *Engineering, Lond.* 19 April 1901

PLATE 134

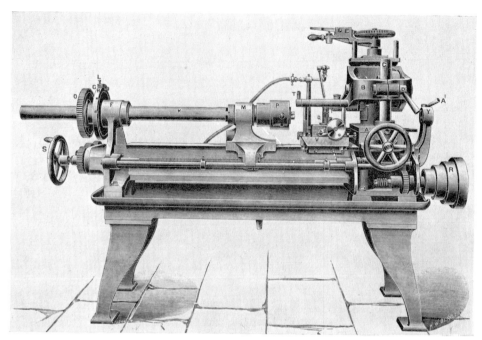

a. 'Liebert' thread milling-machine by J. Holroyd & Co. *Engineering, Lond.* 9 February 1900

b. Reinecker worm and thread milling-machine *c.* 1898. Reinecker & Co., Chemnitz, E. Germany

PLATE 135

b. Reinecker universal gear-hobbing machine *c.* 1900.
Reinecker & Co., Chemnitz, E. Germany

a. Reinecker gear-hobbing machine *c.* 1894. Reinecker & Co., Chemnitz, E. Germany

PLATE 136

a. Holroyd gear-hobbing machine. *Engineer, Lond.* 23 November 1906

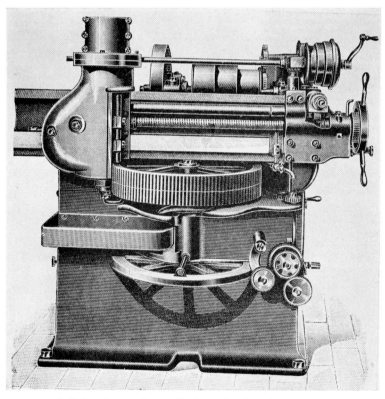

b. Fellows's gear shaper. *Engineer, Lond.* 31 August 1900

PLATE 137

a. Reinecker generating-gear planer. Reinecker & Co., Chemnitz, E. Germany

b. 'Sunderland' generating-gear planer *c.* 1909. J. Parkinson & Son, Shipley, Yorks.

PLATE 138

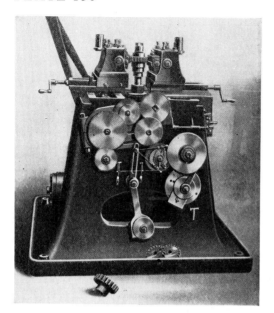
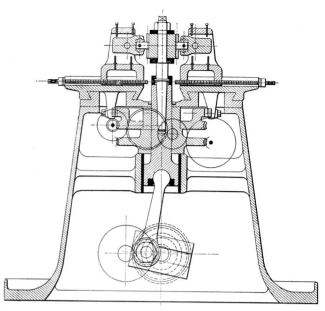

a. Spencer & Speir's gear-cutting machine. *Am. Mach., N.Y.* 22 August 1908

b. Pedersen gear-cutting machine. *Engineering, Lond.* 5 June 1908

PLATE 139

b. Warren's bevel-gear cutting machine. *Engineer, Lond.*
20 November 1906

a. Reinecker–Bilgram bevel-gear cutting machine *c.* 1904. Reinecker & Co., Chemnitz,
E. Germany

PLATE 140

a

b

a and *b*. Gleason straight-bevel generating machine. Catalogue of the Gleason Works,
Rochester, New York, U.S.A., 1914

PLATE 141

a. Smith & Coventry bevel-gear planer. *Engineer, Lond.* 24 August 1900

b. Dubosc bevel-gear machine. *Engineer, Lond.* 23 November 1906

PLATE 142

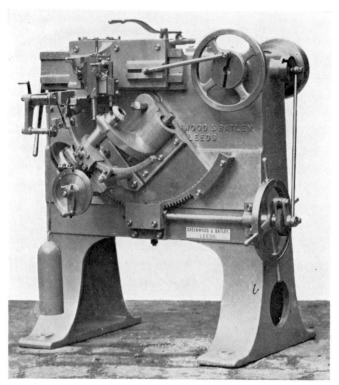

a. Bevel-gear shaping machine. Greenwood & Batley Ltd., Leeds

b. Spiral bevel-gear machine by Monneret. *Engineer, Lond.* 23 November 1900

PLATE 143

a

b

a and *b*. Greenwood & Batley's spiral-gear machines. *Engineer, Lond.* 7 December 1906

PLATE 144

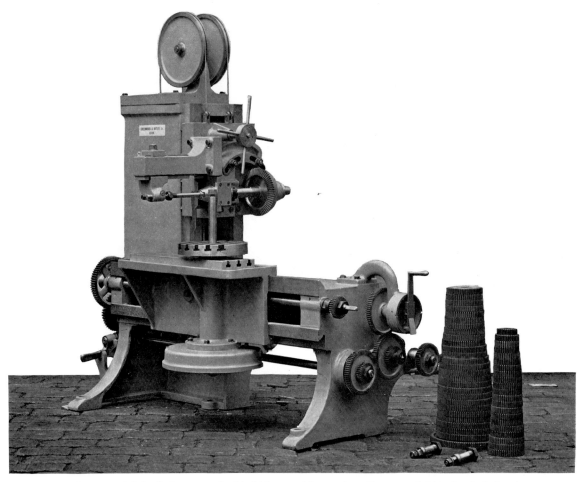

a. Greenwood & Batley's worm-wheel hobbing machine *c.* 1894. Greenwood & Batley Ltd., Leeds

b. Niles Tool Works Co.'s worm-wheel hobbing machine. *Engineering, Lond.* 20 January 1899

PLATE 145

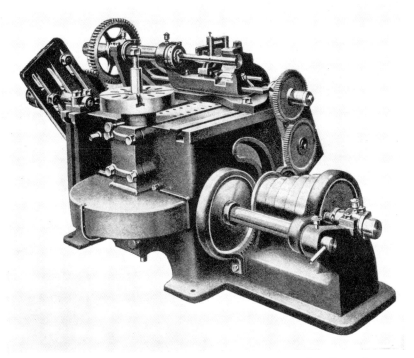

a. Wallwork worm-wheel hobbing machine. *Engineering, Lond.* 27 September 1907

b. Lanchester worm hobbing machine. Associated Iliffe Press photograph

PLATE 146

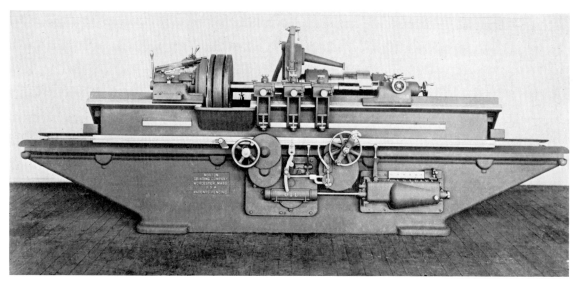

a. Norton heavy grinding machine *c.* 1900. Norton Company, Worcester, Massachusetts, U.S.A.

b. Landis Tool Co.'s plain grinding-machine. *Engineering*, *Lond.* 4 September 1903

PLATE 147

a. Traversing wheel-head internal grinding-machine by Heald. *Am. Mach., Lond.* (and *N.Y.*) 18 April 1908

b. Traversing work-table internal grinding-machine *c.* 1910. Churchill Machine Tool Co., Broadheath, Cheshire

PLATE 148

a. Planetary spindle 'link' grinding-machine by Beyer Peacock & Co. *Engineering, Lond.* 16 January 1903

b. Pratt & Whitney profile grinding-machine. *Engineering, Lond.* 3 April 1903

c. Double-wheel surface grinding-machine by O. S. Walker & Co. *Engineering, Lond.* 7 November 1902

PLATE 149

b. Vertical-axis face-wheel surface grinder *c.* 1912. Churchill Machine Tool Co., Broadheath, Cheshire

a. Circular table grinding-machine *c.* 1910. Churchill Machine Tool Co., Broadheath, Cheshire

PLATE 150

b. Sellers tool-grinding machine. *Engineering, Lond.* 19 August 1904

a. Gisholt tool-grinding machine. *Engineer, Lond.* 24 November 1899

PLATE 151

b. Cutter grinder by American Watch-Tool Co. *Engineer, Lond.*
28 November 1902

a. Cutter grinder by London Emery Works Co. *Engineer, Lond.*
7 August 1896

PLATE 152

a. Spur-gear grinding machine *c*. 1909. Reinecker & Co.,
Chemnitz, E. Germany

b. Broaching machine *c*. 1902. The Lapointe Machine Tool Co., Watford

PLATE 153